THE MICROSCOPIC ANATOMY OF THE WHITE RAT

A Photographic Atlas

THE MICROSCOPIC ANATOMY OF THE WHITE RAT ❧ *A Photographic Atlas*

ESTHER M. SMITH M. LOIS CALHOUN

THE IOWA STATE UNIVERSITY PRESS, AMES, IOWA

ESTHER M. SMITH is Associate Professor in the Department of Anatomy and Director of the School of Medical Technology at Michigan State University, where she also received her B.S., M.S., and Ph.D. degrees. She co-authored (with M. Lois Calhoun) a chapter on Hematology and Hematopoietic Organs in *Diseases of Swine* (Iowa State University Press, 1964), and has written numerous journal articles.

M. LOIS CALHOUN, Professor and Chairman of the Department of Anatomy at Michigan State University, received four degrees from Iowa State University—B.S., M.S., D.V.M., and Ph.D. Her previous publications include *The Microscopic Anatomy of the Digestive System of the Chicken* (Iowa State University Press, 1961), a chapter (with Esther M. Smith) in *Diseases of Swine,* and many articles in professional journals.

© 1968 The Iowa State University Press
Ames, Iowa, U.S.A. All rights reserved

Printed in the U.S.A.

Stock # 0763

FIRST EDITION, 1968

Library of Congress Catalog Card Number: 67–20167

QL
739
.S6
c.3

SPECIAL ACKNOWLEDGMENT

THE CONTRIBUTIONS made by the following individuals proved invaluable to the compilation of this atlas. Their special knowledge, esteemed efforts, and unfailing interest in this work while on the staff of the Anatomy Department at Michigan State University merit a special commendation.

MADAN BHARADWAJ, D.V.M., Ph.D.
Professor and Chairman of Anatomy
College of Veterinary Science
Mathura, U. P., India

RAY T. JACOBS, D.V.M.
Medical Research Laboratory
Chas. Pfizer Laboratories
Groton, Connecticut

PREFACE

This atlas is an outgrowth of a project on the histology of the white rat originally supported by the Upjohn Company, Kalamazoo, Michigan. For several years our friends and colleagues at the Upjohn Company, namely Dr. Ernest A. Feenstra and his staff, were aware of the need for a well-documented photographic atlas of normal tissues and organs of the laboratory rat. They sought the counsel of one of us (Dr. M. Lois Calhoun) to plan such an atlas. As the work progressed and interest in the plates grew, we began to search for means to make the material available to other investigators using the rat as an experimental animal.

As an atlas of this sort is assembled, the problems of what to include and what to omit mount. We hope our choices of omission do not prove unfortunate. We have not included much detail on the hemopoietic organs, for without color much of this is useless. We purposely have omitted ultrastructure because of our original agreement with the Upjohn Company and because we believe the kinds of illustrations presented here will be helpful to more scientists involved in a wide variety of research areas.

The Wistar strain rats supplied by the Upjohn Company of Kalamazoo were five to six weeks old and weighed approximately 120 grams. By the time the atlas was completed we had processed about 40 animals.

For the most part the technics followed were similar to those of the pathology department of the Upjohn Company. Fixation was in 10% buffered formalin followed by routine embedding methods and hematoxylin and eosin stain. In addition some special stains were utilized to facilitate interpretation of certain sections. The authors realize that other fixatives and stains are sometimes superior; however, since these routine technics are used most frequently by more people, it seemed wise to maintain this uniformity.

The drawings which precede each system are intentionally diagrammatic. They are anatomically correct in that all the organs are included, but in order to make the diagram more meaningful their positioning may not always be exact. The level of the sections taken is indicated by lines and numbers on each drawing, and this level number appears in each figure legend, giving the reader the relative location of each section illustrated; i.e. "Level 7," Figure 1, Plate 2.

A compilation such as this necessarily involves the efforts of many individuals. Certainly it would be virtually impossible to include all those who helped assemble this work, but the authors would like to recognize certain persons without whose efforts this atlas would never have been completed.

A very special thanks to Dr. R. A. Filkins who did all the original dissections, tissue procurement and processing while he was a veterinary student at Michigan State University. His careful and meticulous attention to details and records have made the final assembly a much easier task.

The authors are sincerely grateful to Mr. James Tucker who was responsible for most of the photomicrographs. His expertise and high standards for good print quality have added to the appeal and value of this work.

In addition to those mentioned above, the authors would like to express their sincere appreciation to the following people who contributed to this effort while they were students at Michigan State University: Dr. R. A. Holmes, for illustrations from his M.S. thesis on the integument; Dr. James Fox, photographer; Dr. Andrew Moore, (deceased) darkroom technician; Mrs. Mary Ellen Haggerty, artist; Mr. Robert Clark, tissue technician; Mrs. Linda Holmes, typist; and Mr. and Mrs. Gerald Kozlowski for their work on the bibliography.

We are especially appreciative to Drs. Ernest Feenstra, Richard Johnston and Russell Runnells of the Upjohn Company, and to Mr. Marshall Townsend, formerly of the Iowa State University Press, who encouraged us to develop this atlas. Finally, we are indebted to the Upjohn Company for the grant which provided a monetary support for this endeavor.

The authors sincerely hope that this collection of photographs will be especially helpful to those scientists who use this remarkable animal for research and yet may not be entirely familiar with histology. We also believe this may help students in histology become familiar with the major organ systems.

ESTHER M. SMITH
M. LOIS CALHOUN

CONTENTS

MUSCULO-SKELETAL SYSTEM
1. Reference drawing, 13
2. Intracartilaginous bone development; Epiphysis, 15
3. Intracartilaginous bone development; Area of calcified cartilage, 17
4. Adult bone, 19
5. Bone structure; Stifle joints, 21
6. Sternebrae; Vertebrae; Sternum, 23
7. Muscle; Tendon; Muscle spindle, 25

BLOOD VASCULAR SYSTEM
8. Reference drawing, Heart, 27
9. Atrial wall; Cardiac muscle fibers, 29
10. Trigonum fibrosum; Atrial wall; Ventricle; Chorda tendineae, 31
11. Reference drawing, Vessels, 33
12. Aorta, ascending and thoracic, 35
13. Femoral artery and vein; Brachial artery, 37
14. Carotid artery with carotid body; Ascending aorta and posterior vena cava, 39
15. Common iliac artery and vein, 41
16. Coronary vein; Spermatic artery and vein, 43
17. Leucocytes, 45

LYMPHOID SYSTEM
18. Lymph node, 47
19. Spleen, 49

INTEGUMENTARY SYSTEM
20. Reference drawing, 51
21. Skin: Metacarpal pad; Sweat glands; Tail region, 53
22. Skin: Abdominal wall; Pinna; Teat, 55
23. Skin: Hair follicle and associated structures, 57
24. Skin: Eyelid; Conjunctiva, 59

DIGESTIVE SYSTEM
25. Reference drawing, Oral cavity, 61
26. Lip; Buccal mucosa; Soft and hard palate, 63
27. Tooth, 65
28. Tongue, 67
29. Taste buds, 69
30. Pharyngo-esophageal junction, 71
31. Reference drawing, Digestive tube and glands, 73
32. Esophagus, various levels, 75
33. Forestomach; Fundic stomach, 77
34. Pyloric stomach; Duodenum, 79
35. Ileum, 81
36. Ileocecal junction, 83
37. Cecum; Colon, 85
38. Rectum; Anus, 87
39. Salivary glands: Parotid; Submaxillary; Sublingual, 89
40. Parotid salivary gland; Exorbital lacrimal gland; Liver, 91
41. Liver; Pancreas, 93

RESPIRATORY SYSTEM
42. Reference drawing, 95
43. Nasal Cavity; Trachea, 97
44. Trachea, 99
45. Lung, 101

URINARY SYSTEM
46. Reference drawing, 103
47. Kidney, 105
48. Kidney; Ureter, 107
49. Bladder; Urethra, 109

MALE UROGENITAL SYSTEM
50. Reference drawing, 111
51. Bladder and accessory sex glands, 113
52. Prostate gland; Seminal vesicle, 115
53. Coagulating gland; Bulbourethral gland, 117
54. Bulbourethral gland, 119
55. Testis; Ductus deferens, 121
56. Testis; Epididymis, 123
57. Epididymis; Ductus efferens, 125
58. Penis, 127

FEMALE UROGENITAL SYSTEM
59. Reference drawing, 129
60. Ovary; Oviduct; Uterus, 131
61. Ovarian follicles; Oöcyte, 133
62. Ovarian follicles; Vestigial structures, 135
63. Corpus luteum; Oviduct, 137
64. Uterine horn, 139
65. Vagina, 141
66. Vagina; Preputial gland; Clitoris; Urethra, 143

ENDOCRINE SYSTEM
67. Reference drawing, 145
68. Pituitary gland, 147
69. Thyroid; Parathyroid; Thymus, 149
70. Thymus, 151
71. Adrenal gland, 153

NERVOUS SYSTEM
72. Reference drawing, 155
73. Olfactory bulb, 157
74. Cerebrum; Cerebellum, 159
75. Cerebellum; Choroid plexus, 161
76. Spinal cord, 163
77. Spinal cord, 165
78. Spinal ganglion; Autonomic ganglion, 167

EYE
79. Cornea; Sclera, 169
80. Nictitating membrane; Ciliary processes, 171
81. Iris and lens; Retina, 173

SELECTED REFERENCES, 175

INDEX, 185

THE MICROSCOPIC ANATOMY OF THE WHITE RAT

A Photographic Atlas

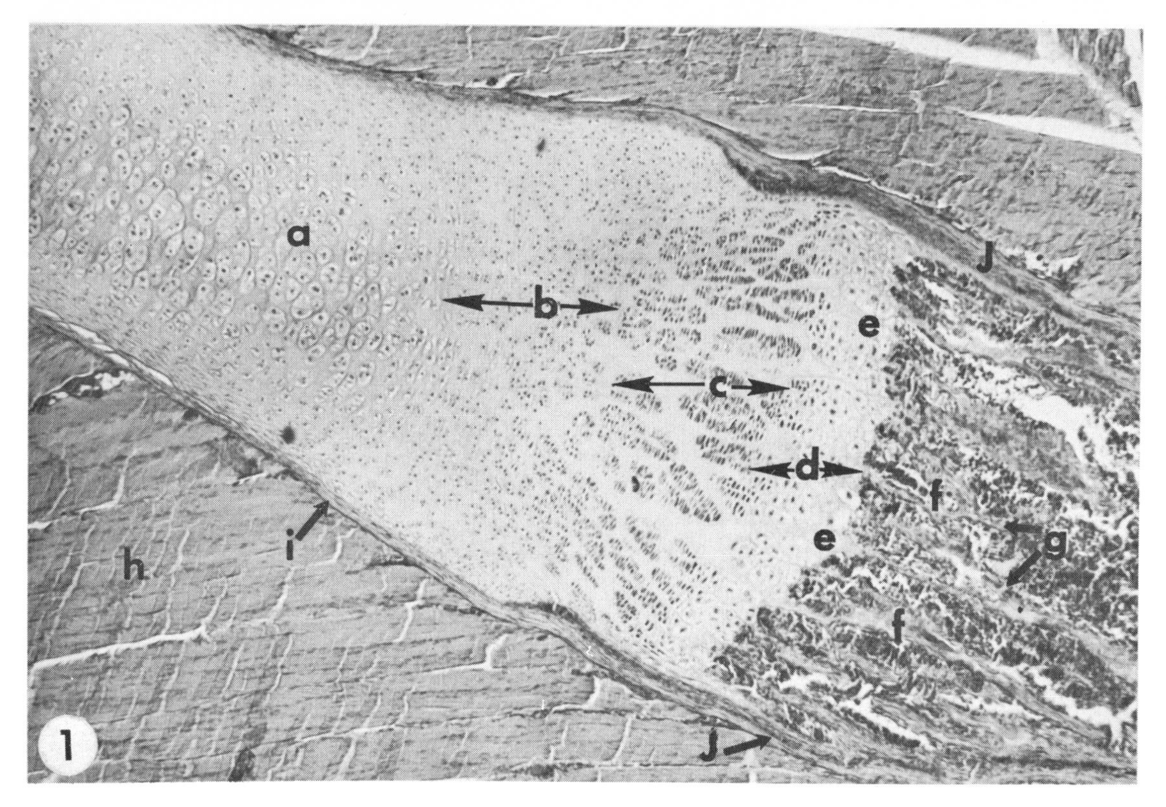

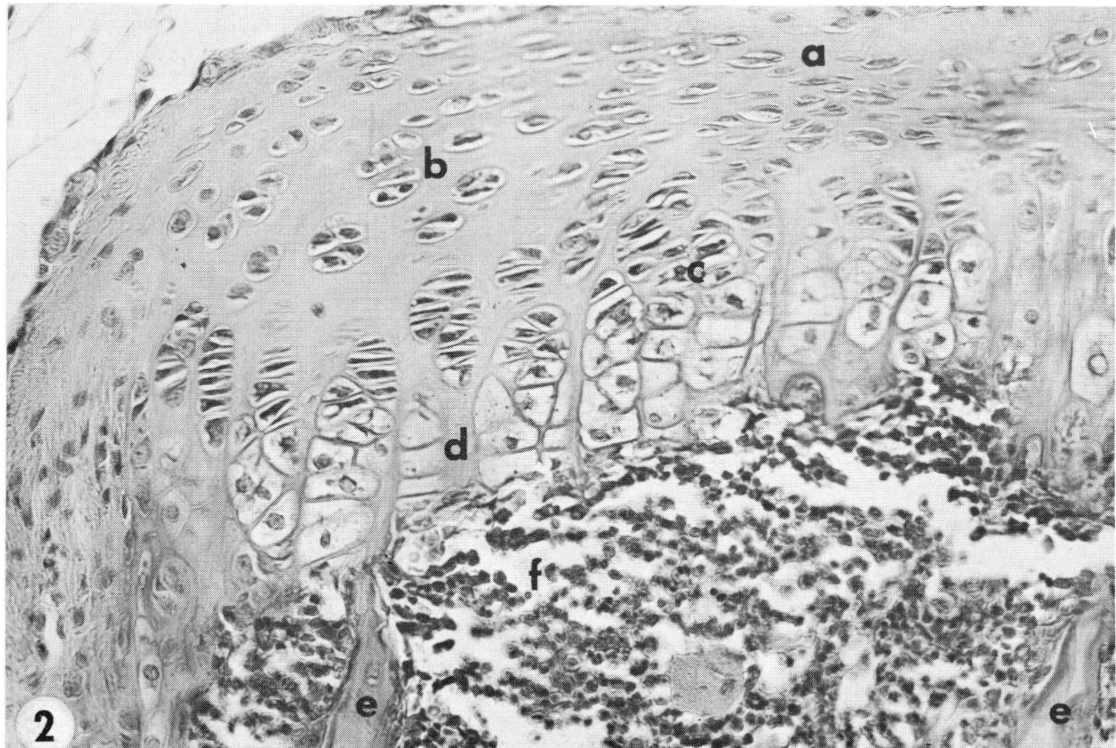

PLATE 2
Musculo-Skeletal System

FIG. 1. Intracartilaginous bone development (rib). Longitudinal section. Level 7. (H&E, × 70)

a. Hyaline cartilage
b. Zone of resting cartilage
c. Zone of chondrocyte multiplication
d. Zone of lacunar enlargement
e. Zone of cartilage calcification
f. Zone of bone deposition
g. Trabecular bone
h. Skeletal muscle
i. Perichondrium
j. Periosteum

FIG. 2. Epiphysis. Longitudinal section. Level 5. (H&E, × 340)

a. Zone of resting cartilage
b. Zone of chondrocyte multiplication
c. Zone of lacunar enlargement
d. Zone of cartilage calcification
e. Trabecular bone
f. Bone marrow

PLATE 3

Musculo-Skeletal System

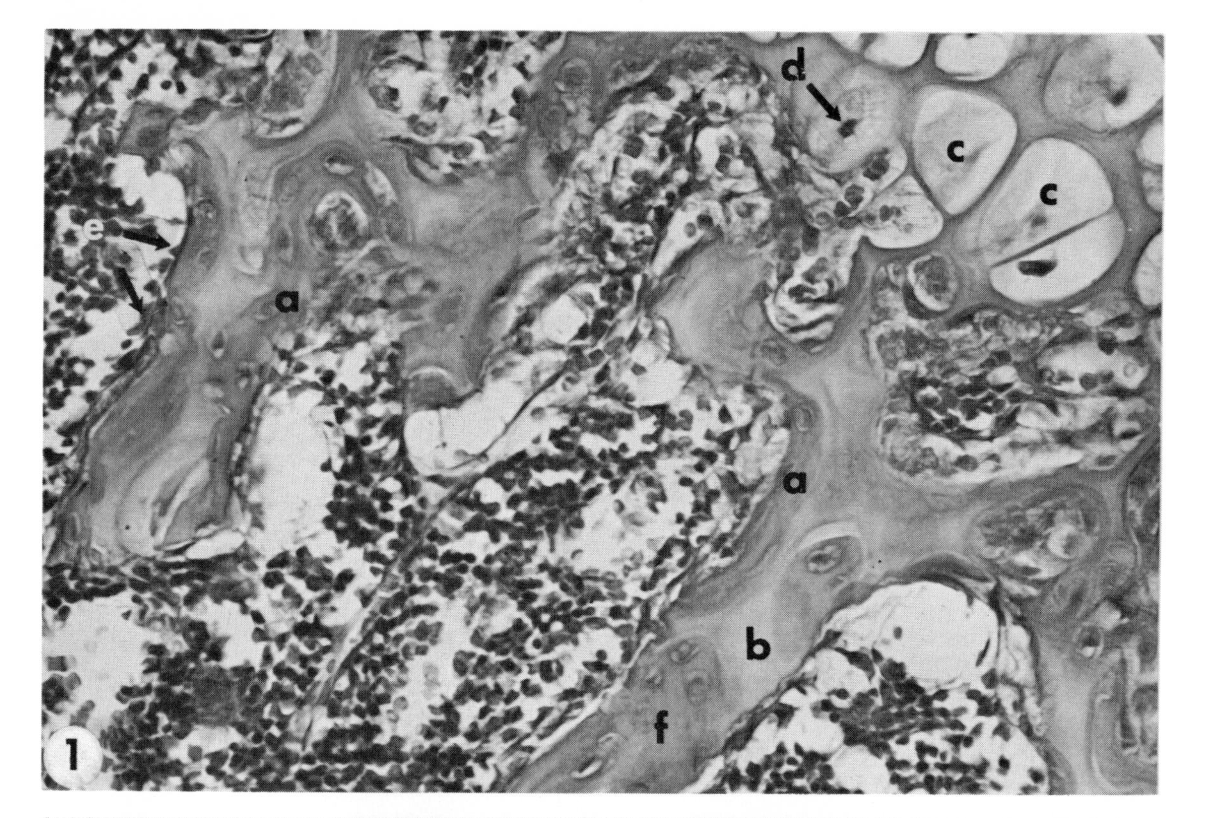

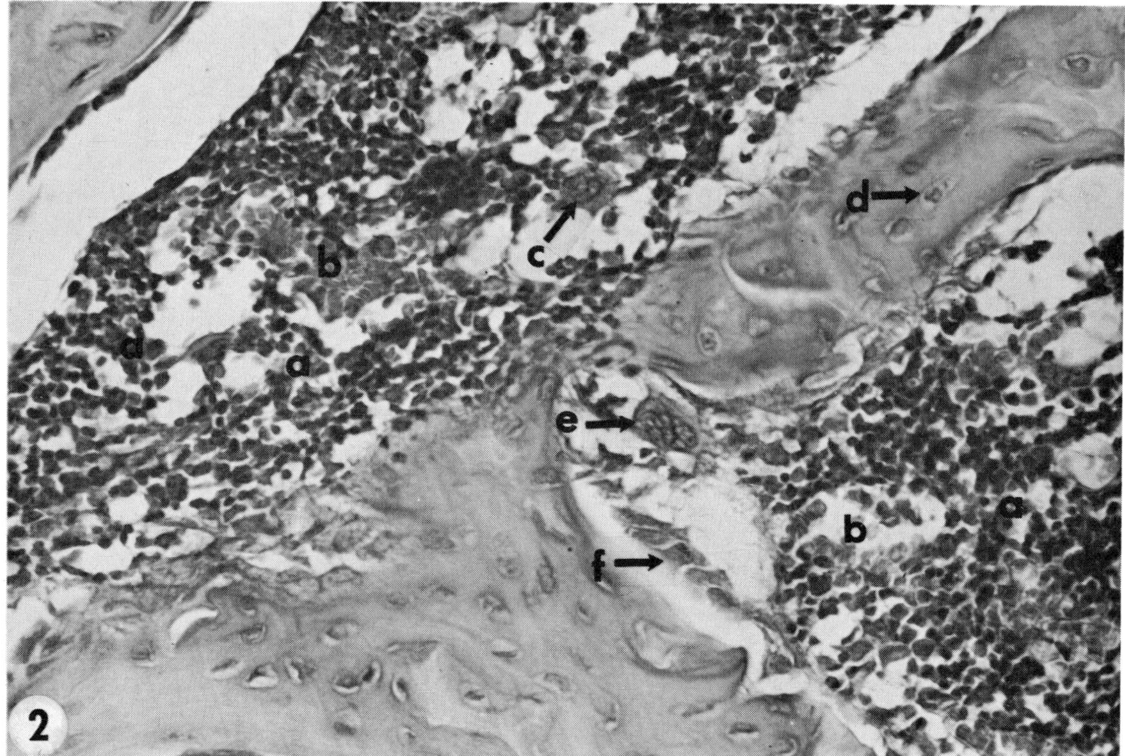

FIG. 1. Area of calcified cartilage and bone deposition. Longitudinal section. Level 5. (H&E, × 405)

a. Trabecular bone
b. Calcified cartilage
c. Enlarged cartilage lacunae
d. Chondrocyte within a lacuna
e. Osteoblasts
f. Osteoid tissue

FIG. 2. Bone development. Longitudinal section. Level 5. (H&E, × 405)

a. Bone marrow
b. Blood sinusoid
c. Megakaryocyte
d. Osteocyte
e. Osteoclast
f. Osteoblasts

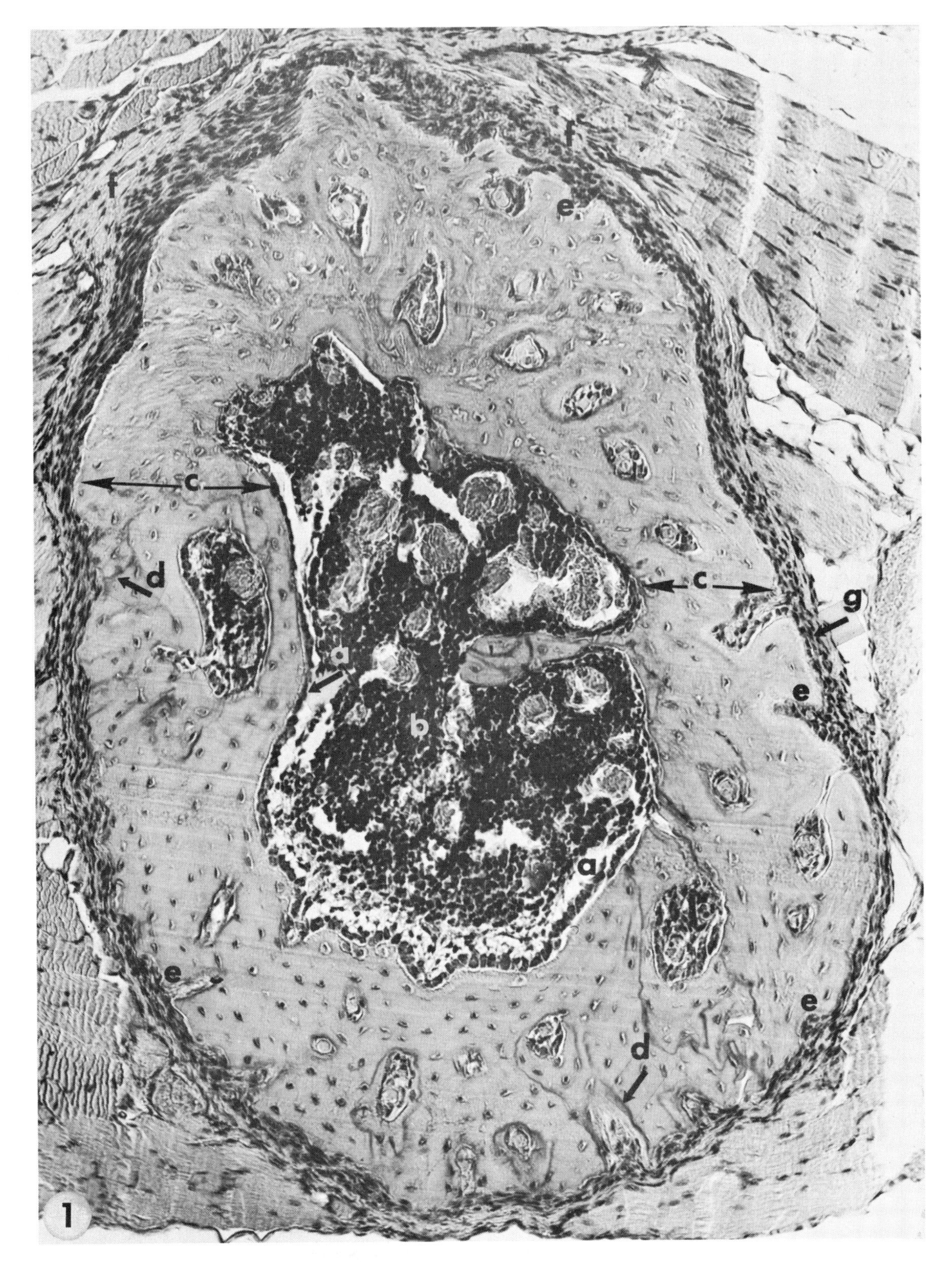

PLATE 4

Musculo-Skeletal System

FIG. 1. Adult bone (rib). Cross section. Level 8. (H&E, × 198)

a. Endosteum
b. Marrow cavity
c. Cortical bone
d. Cement lines
e. New lamellar bone at the periphery
f. Tendinous attachment of muscle to bone
g. Periosteum illustrating an active cellular layer covered by a fibrous layer

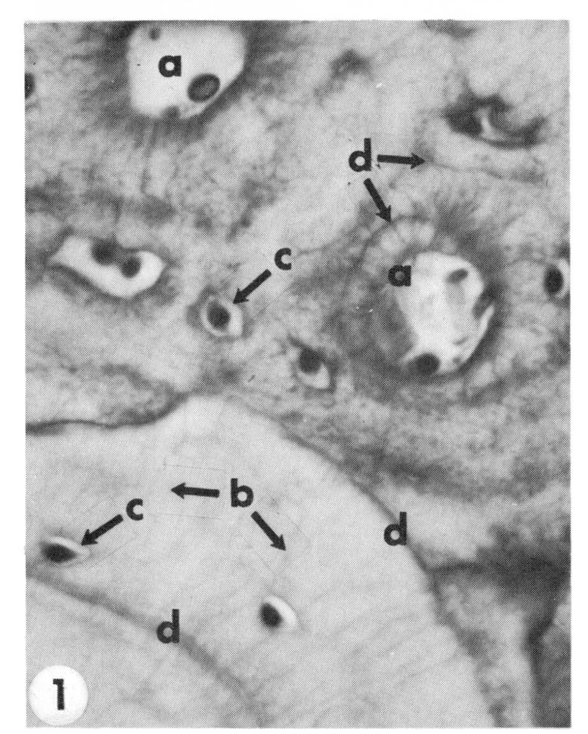

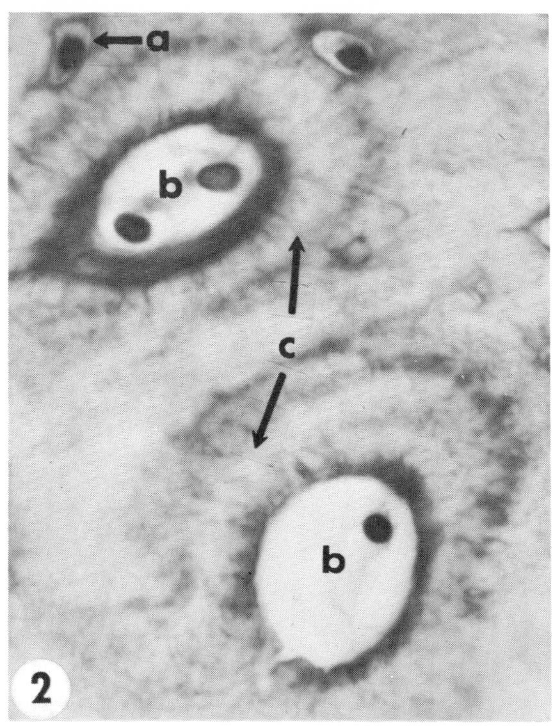

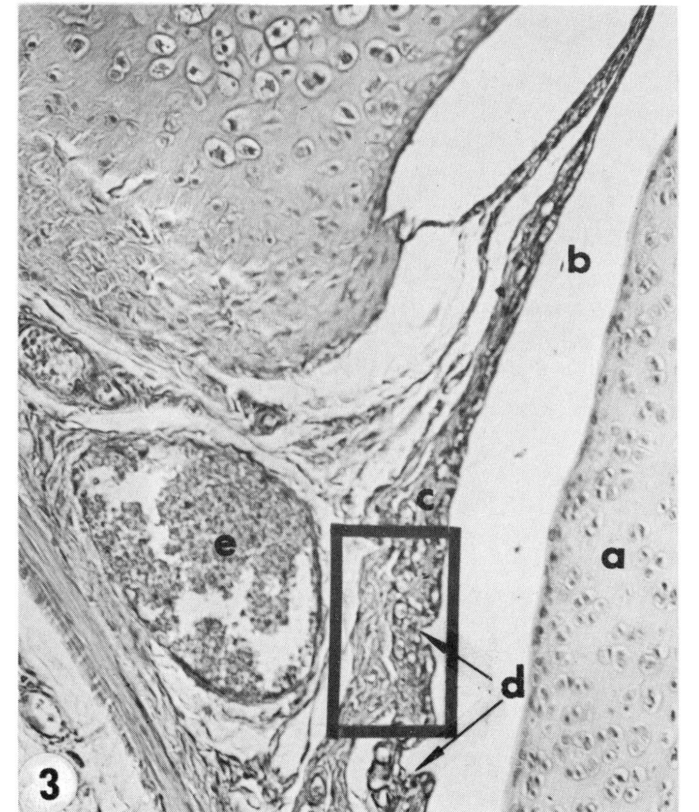

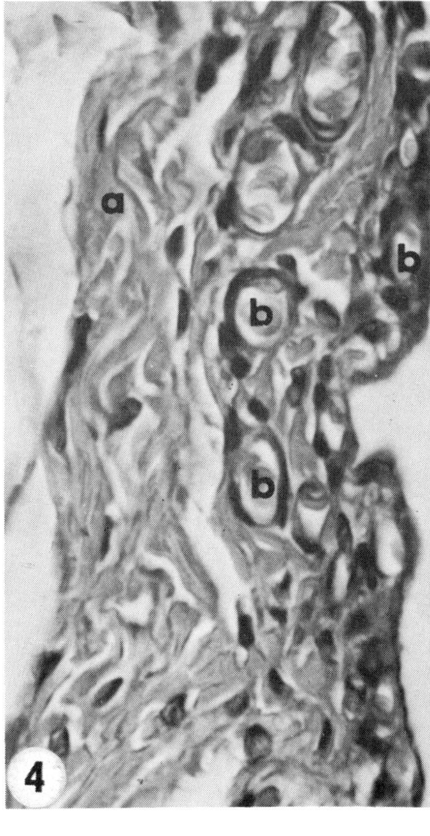

PLATE 5

Musculo-Skeletal System

FIG. 1. Lamellar structure of bone. Cross section. Level 10. (H&E, × 680)
- a. Haversian system
- b. Canaliculi
- c. Lacunae
- d. Cement lines

FIG. 2. Haversian system. Cross section. Level 10. (H&E, × 680)
- a. Lacuna containing an osteocyte
- b. Haversian canals with osteocytes
- c. Canaliculi

FIG. 3. Stifle joint with the synovial membrane. Longitudinal section. Level 3. (H&E, × 225)
- a. Articular cartilage
- b. Joint cavity
- c. Synovial membrane
- d. Synovial folds
- e. Blood vessel

FIG. 4. Synovial membrane (high power of area indicated in Fig. 3). Level 3. (H&E, × 1030)
- a. Dense fibrous connective tissue
- b. Capillary network

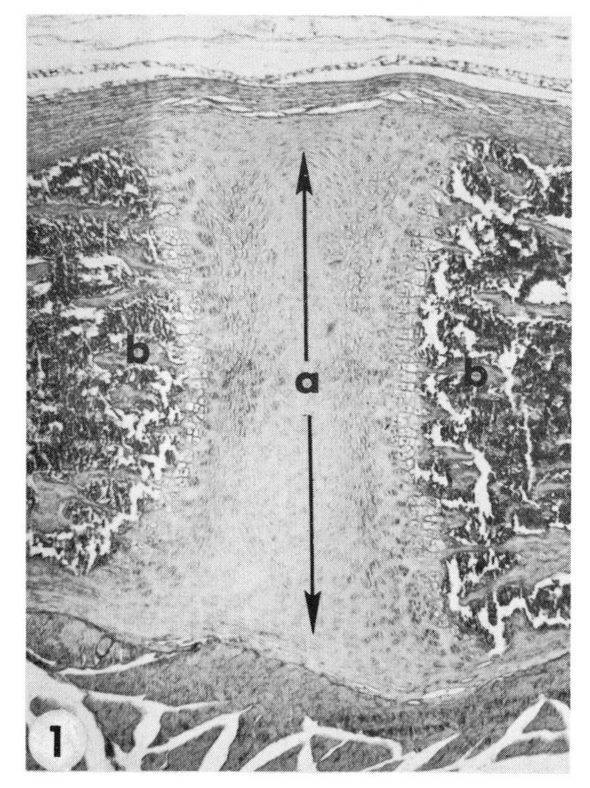

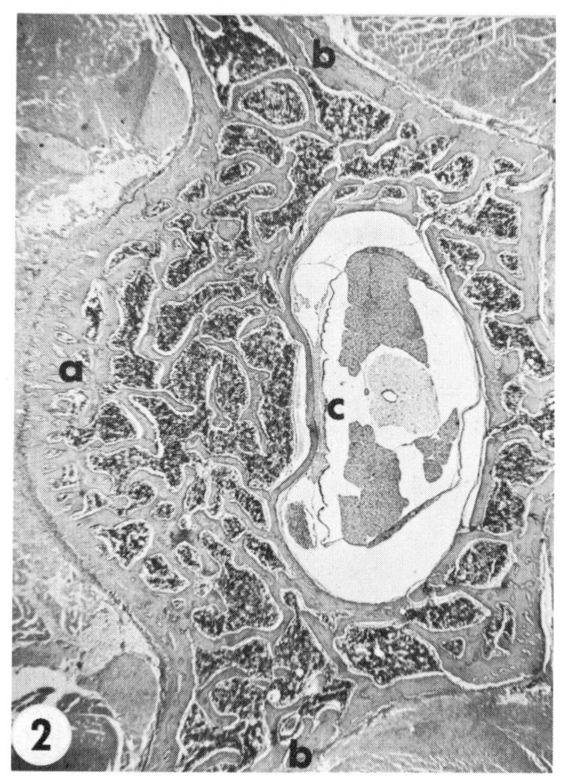

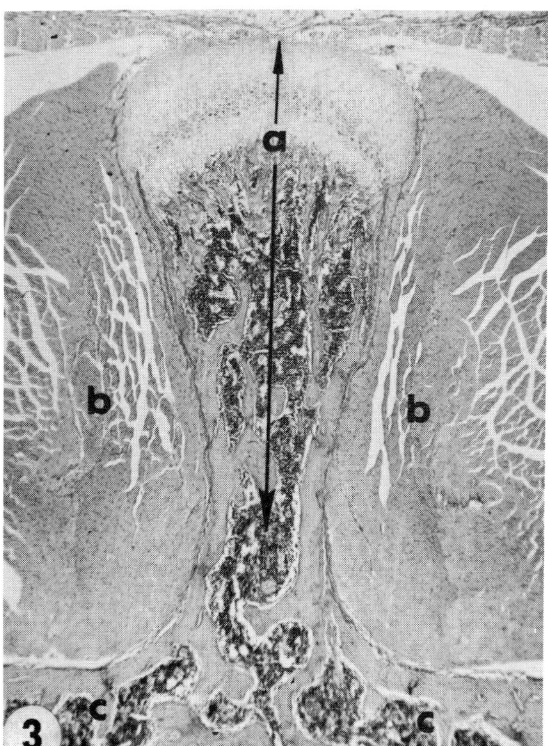

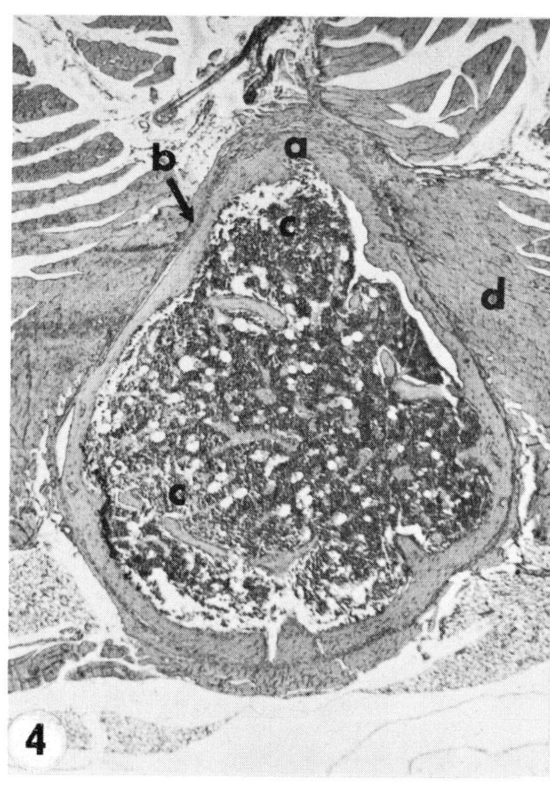

PLATE 6
Musculo-Skeletal System

FIG. 1. Fusion of two sternebrae. Longitudinal section. Level 5. (H&E, × 55)
- a. Fusion line
- b. Developing bone

FIG. 2. Cervical vertebrae with transverse processes. Cross section. (H&E, × 23)
- a. Body of vertebrae with cancellous bone and bone marrow
- b. Transverse processes
- c. Vertebral canal

FIG. 3. Developing spinous process of the cervical vertebrae. Cross section. (H&E, × 25)
- a. Spinous process with developing bone and cartilaginous tip
- b. Skeletal muscle
- c. Vertebral arch

FIG. 4. Sternum. Cross section. Level 4. (H&E, × 45)
- a. Sternal bone
- b. Periosteum
- c. Bone marrow
- d. Skeletal muscle

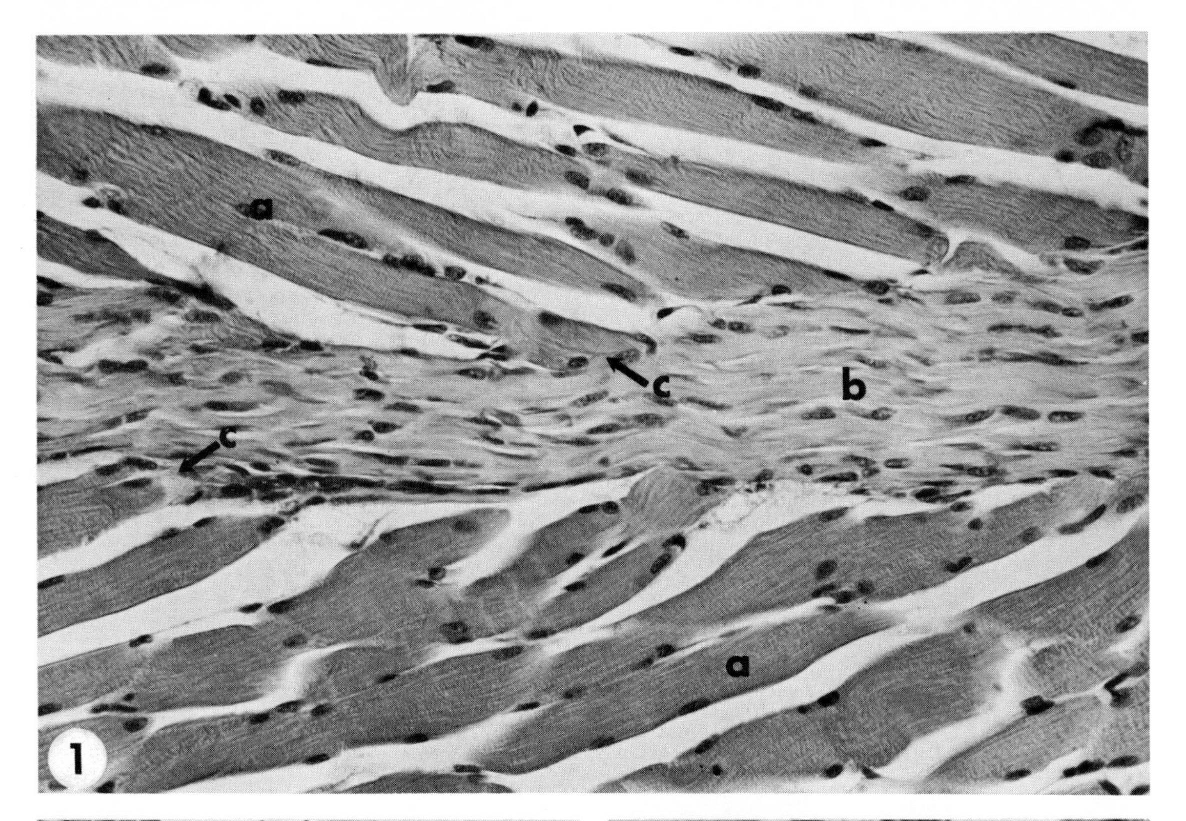

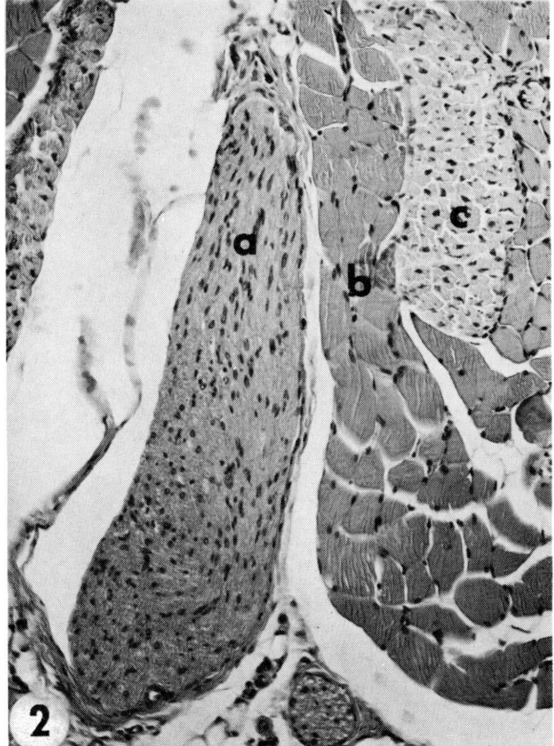

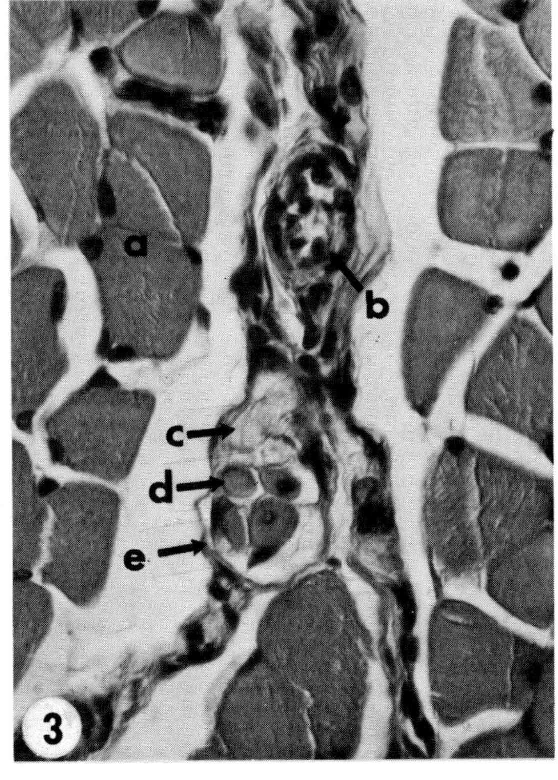

PLATE 7
Musculo-Skeletal System

FIG. 1. Relationship of muscle to tendon. Longitudinal section. Level 3. (H&E, × 210)

a. Skeletal muscle
b. White fibrous connective tissue of the tendon
c. Muscle and tendon anastomosis

FIG. 2. Relationship of nerve, tendon, and muscle. Cross section. Level 10. (H&E, × 170)

a. Nerve trunk
b. Skeletal muscle
c. Tendon

FIG. 3. Skeletal muscle with muscle spindle. Cross section. Level 2. (H&E, × 730)

a. Skeletal muscle fiber
b. Blood vessel
c. Nerve fibers
d. Intrafusal muscle fibers of the spindle
e. Connective tissue sheath of the spindle

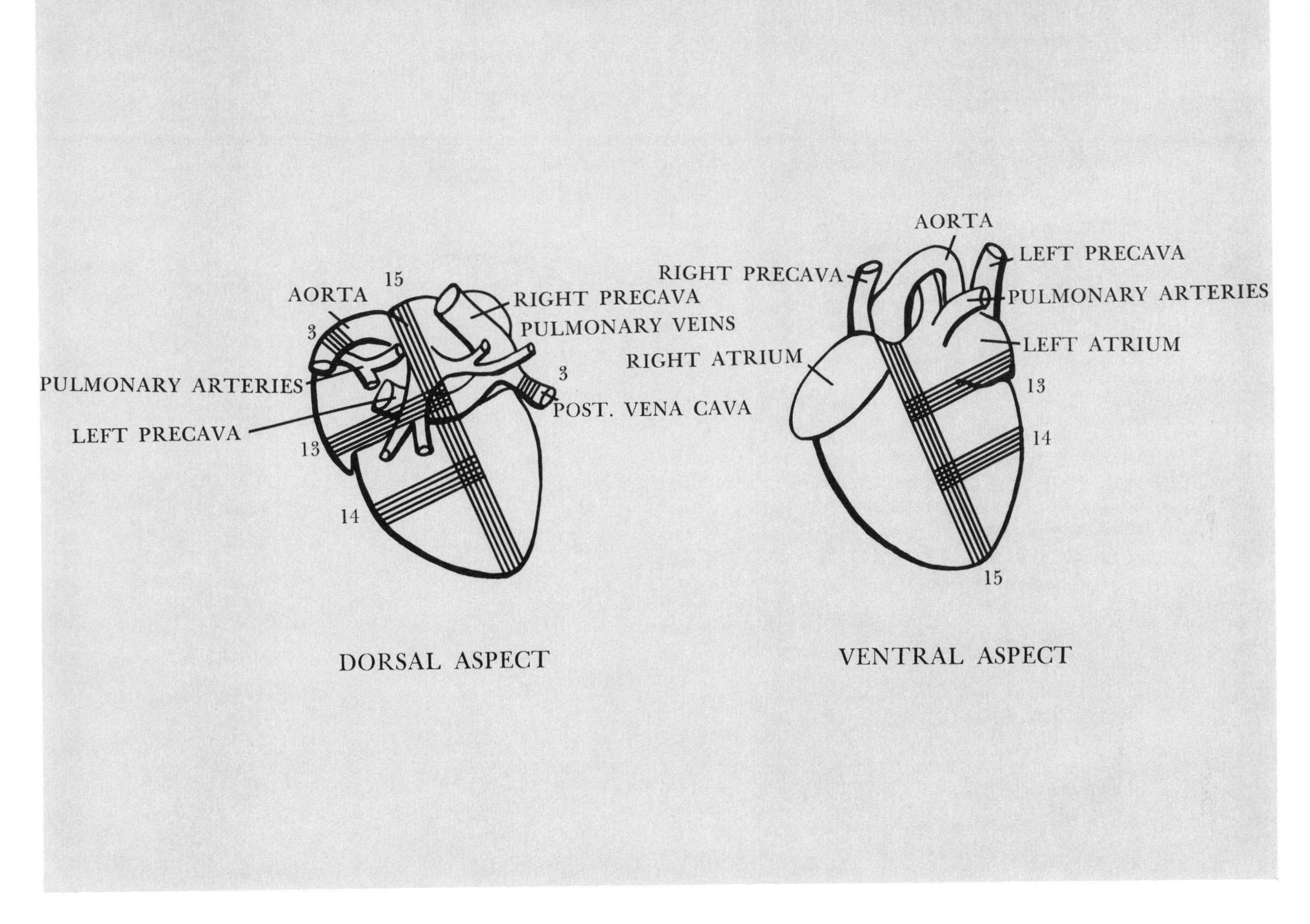

PLATE 8
Blood Vascular System

FIG. 1. The heart.

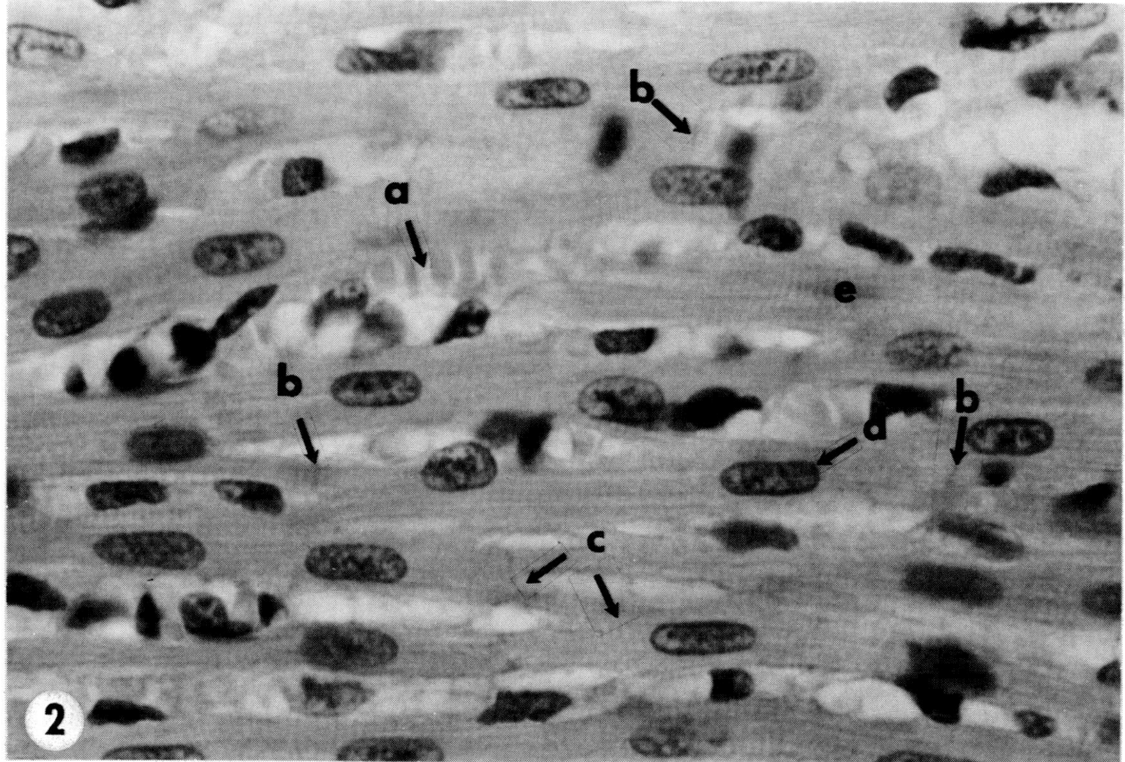

Plate 9
Blood Vascular System

Fig. 1. Atrial wall. Level 15. (H&E, × 325)
a. Epicardium
b. Myocardium in cross section
c. Myocardium cut longitudinally
d. Myocardium cut obliquely
e. Endocardium

Fig. 2. Cardiac muscle fibers. Level 14. (H&E, × 1100)
a. Capillary containing red blood cells
b. Intercalated discs
c. Cardiac muscle fibers branching and anastomosing
d. Nucleus of cardiac muscle (note central location and oval shape)
e. Cross striations

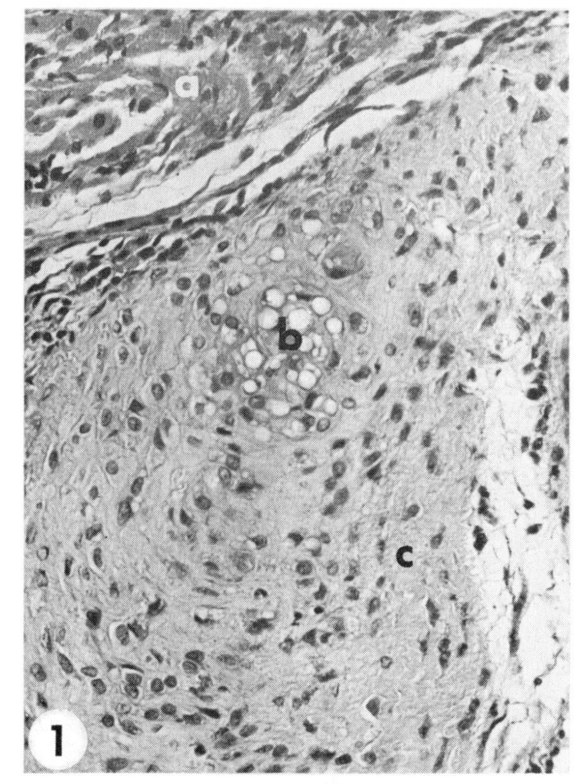

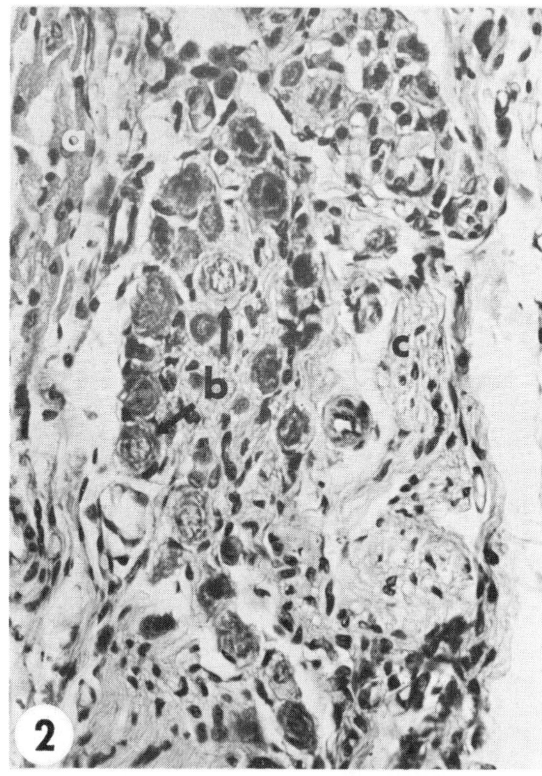

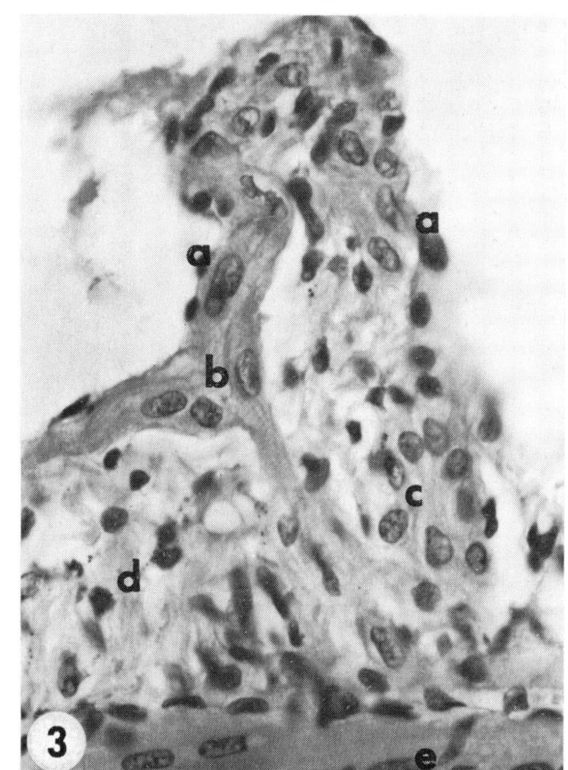

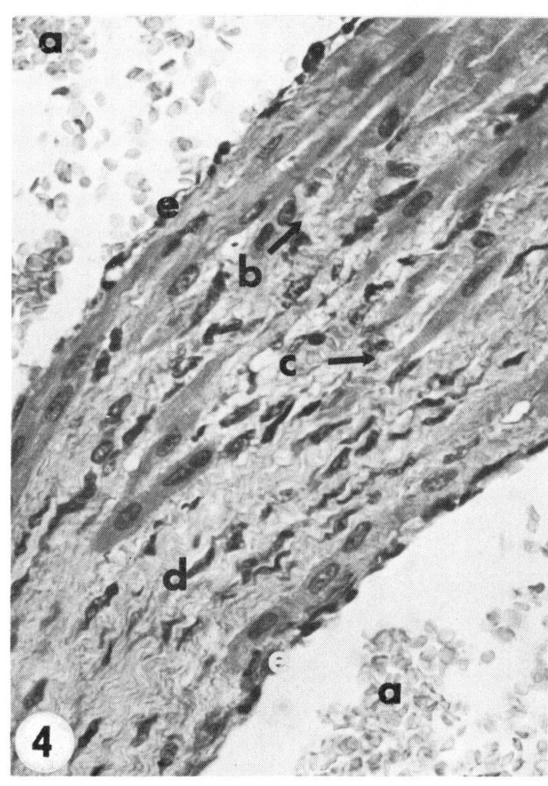

PLATE 10

Blood Vascular System

FIG. 1. Trigonum fibrosum. Level 13. (H&E, × 310)
- a. Cardiac muscle
- b. Hyaline cartilage
- c. White fibrous connective tissue

FIG. 2. Atrial wall with a surface ganglion. Level 15. (H&E, × 350)
- a. Cardiac muscle
- b. Ganglion cells
- c. Nerve fibers

FIG. 3. Ventricular subendocardium with Purkinje fibers. Level 15. (H&E, × 640)
- a. Endocardium
- b. Purkinje fibers cut longitudinally
- c. Purkinje fibers cut obliquely
- d. Subendocardium
- e. Myocardium

FIG. 4. Chorda tendineae at level of termination of papillary muscle. Longitudinal section. Level 15. (H&E, × 475)
- a. Blood cells in the ventricular chamber
- b. Arrow pointing in the direction of the ventricular wall
- c. Termination of the cardiac muscle fibers
- d. White fibrous connective tissue
- e. Endocardium

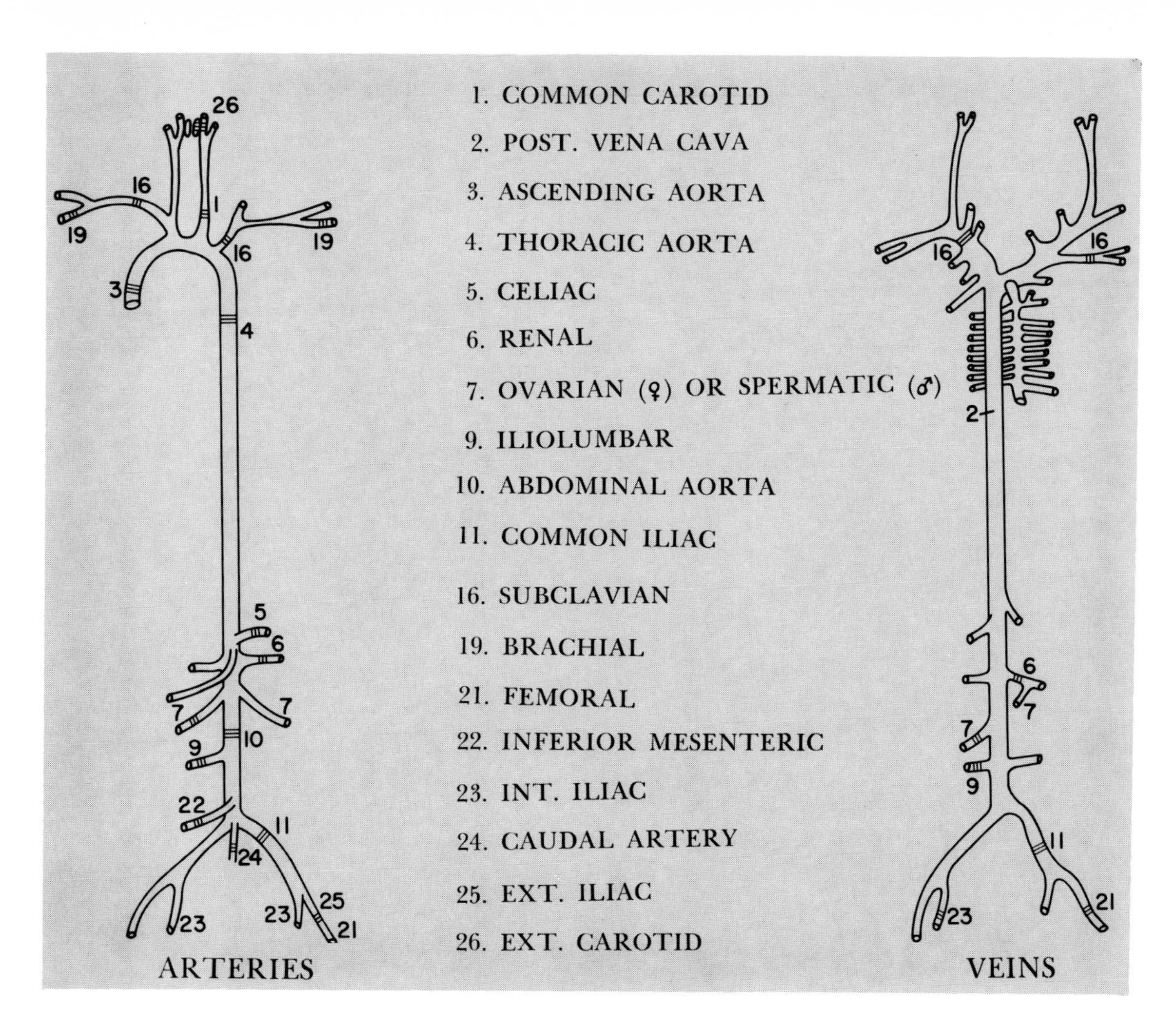

PLATE 11
Blood Vascular System

FIG. 1. Arteries and veins.

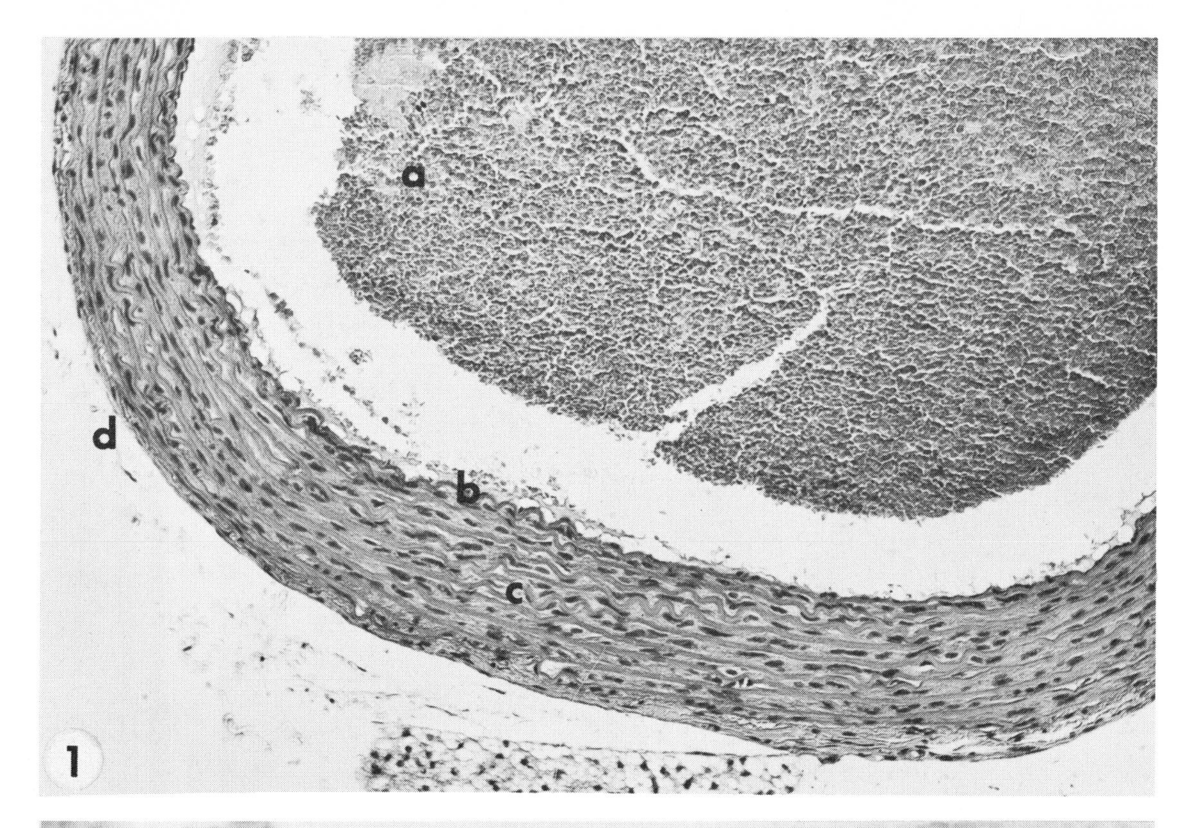

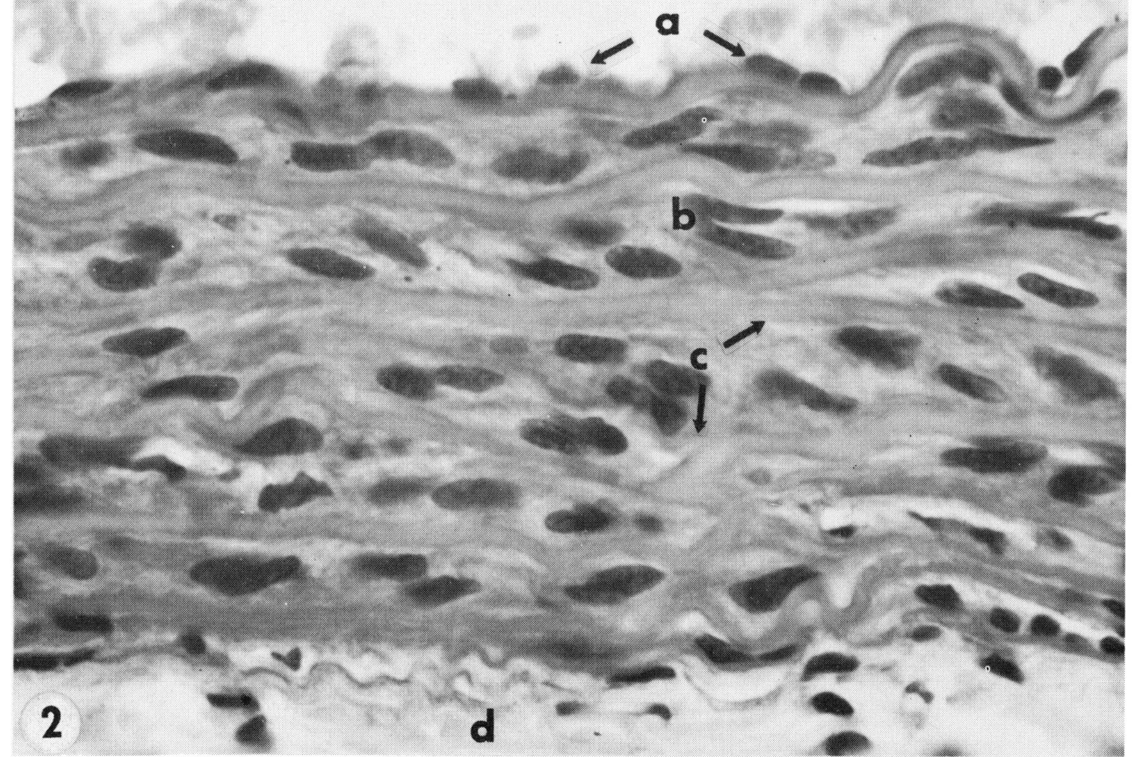

PLATE 12
Blood Vascular System

FIG. 1. Ascending aorta. Cross section, Level 3. (H&E, × 180)
a. Blood
b. Tunica intima
c. Tunica media composed chiefly of elastic fibers
d. Tunica adventitia

FIG. 2. Thoracic aorta. Cross section. Level 4. (H&E, × 1150)
a. Endothelium resting on the internal elastic membrane
b. Smooth muscle cells in the tunica media
c. Elastic fibers in the tunica media (note branching)
d. Tunica adventitia

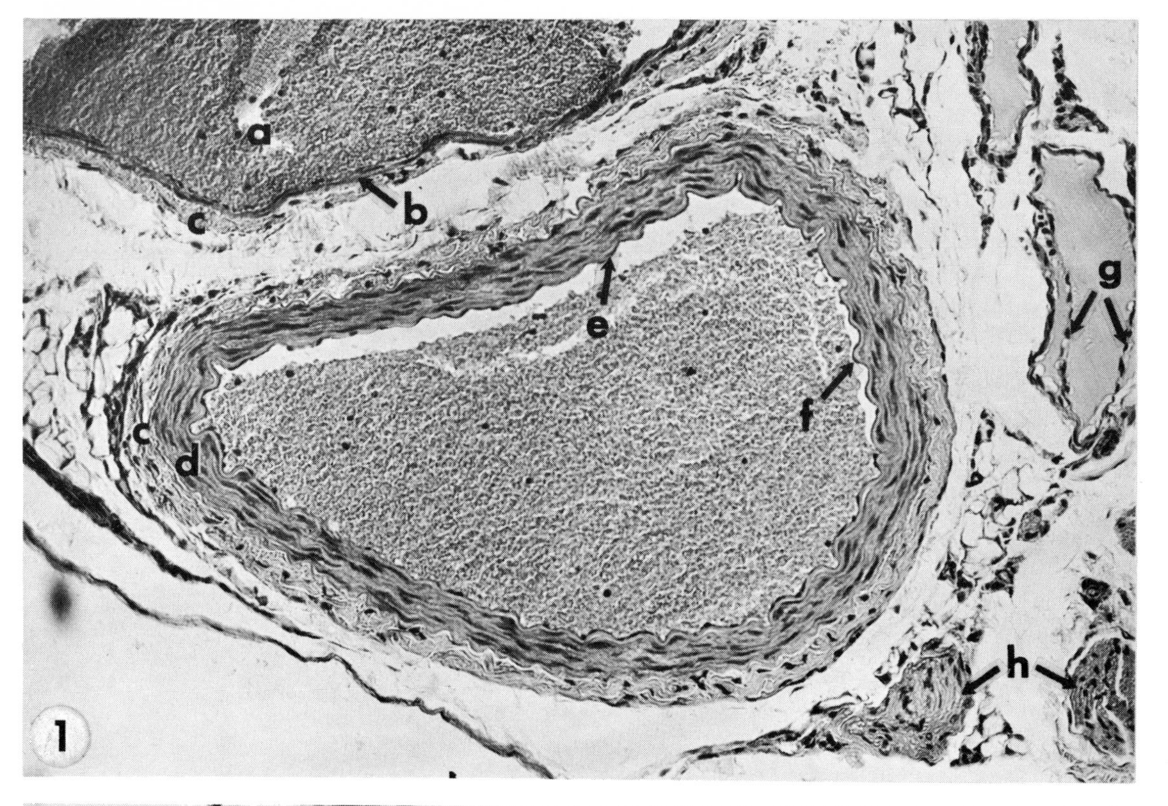

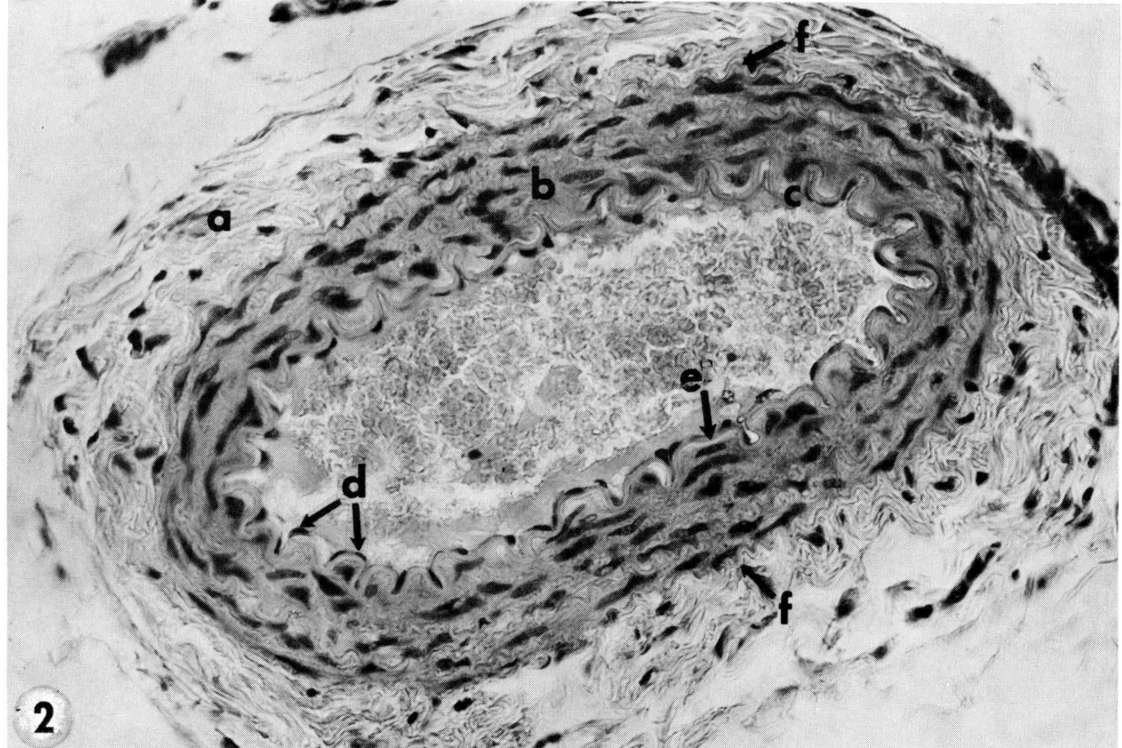

PLATE 13
Blood Vascular System

FIG. 1. Femoral artery and vein. Cross section. Level 21. (H&E, × 190)
- a. Vein filled with blood
- b. Tunica media of the vein
- c. Tunica adventitia of the vein
- d. Tunica media of the artery composed primarily of smooth muscle
- e. Tunica intima of the artery
- f. Endothelial lining resting on the internal elastic membrane
- g. Valves in a lymph vessel
- h. Nerve trunks

FIG. 2. Brachial artery. Cross section. Level 19. (H&E, × 375)
- a. Tunica adventitia
- b. Tunica media composed primarily of smooth muscle
- c. Tunica intima
- d. Endothelium
- e. Internal elastic membrane
- f. External elastic membrane

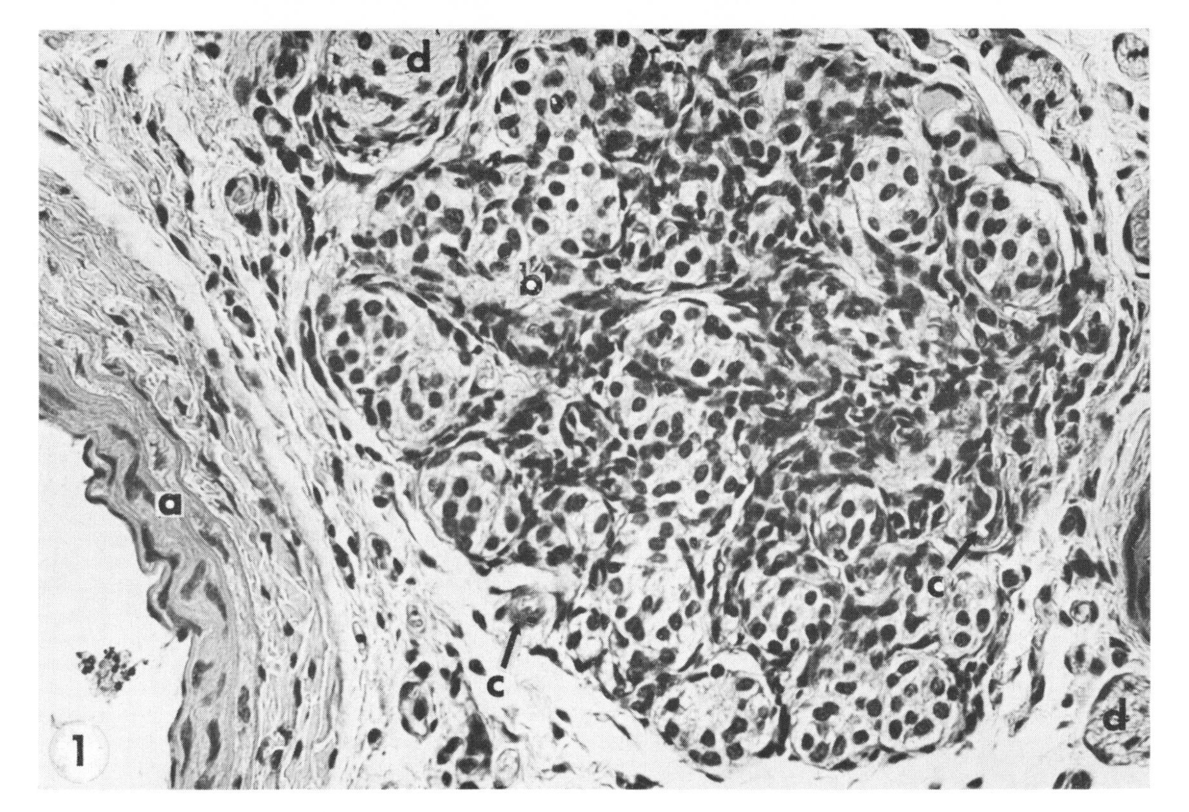

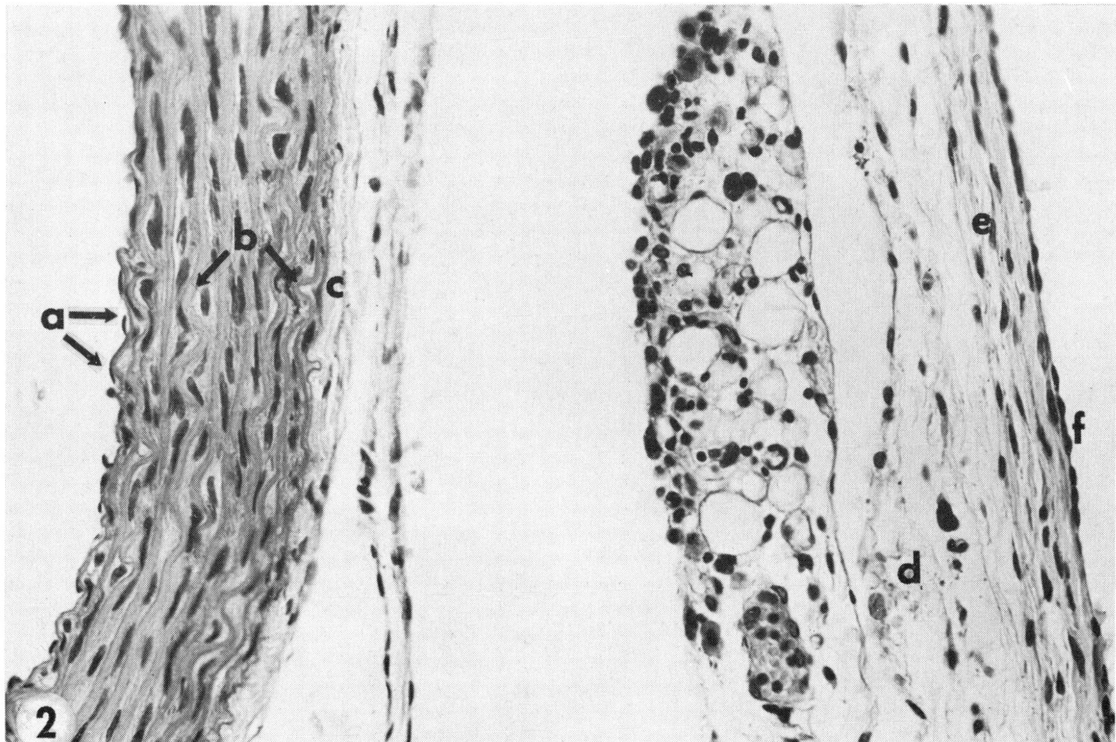

PLATE 14
Blood Vascular System

FIG. 1. External carotid artery and carotid body. Cross section. Level 26. (H&E, × 420)
- a. Carotid artery
- b. Carotid body parenchyma
- c. Capillaries
- d. Nerve trunks

FIG. 2. Ascending aorta and posterior vena cava. Cross section. Levels 2 & 3. (H&E, × 360)
- a. Endothelial lining of the artery
- b. Elastic fibers in the tunica media
- c. Tunica adventitia of the artery
- d. Tunica adventitia of the vein
- e. Tunica media of the vein
- f. Endothelial lining of the vein

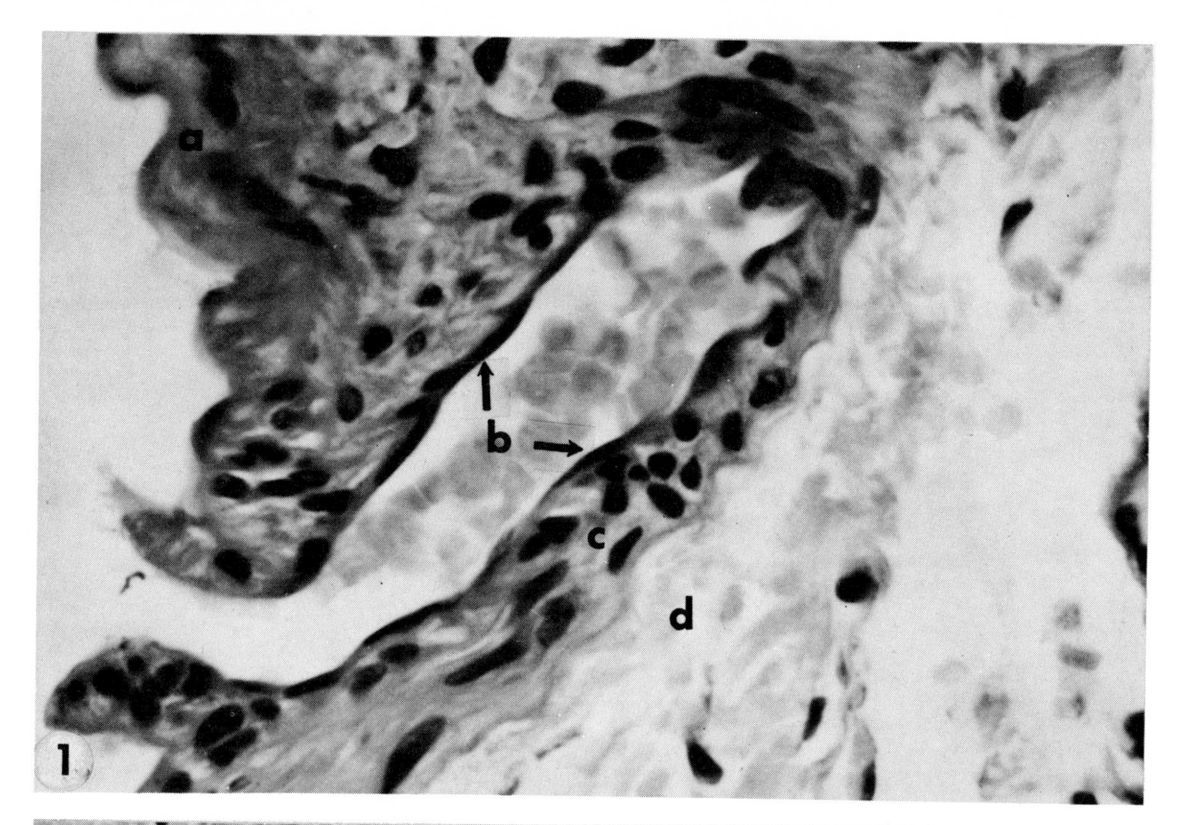

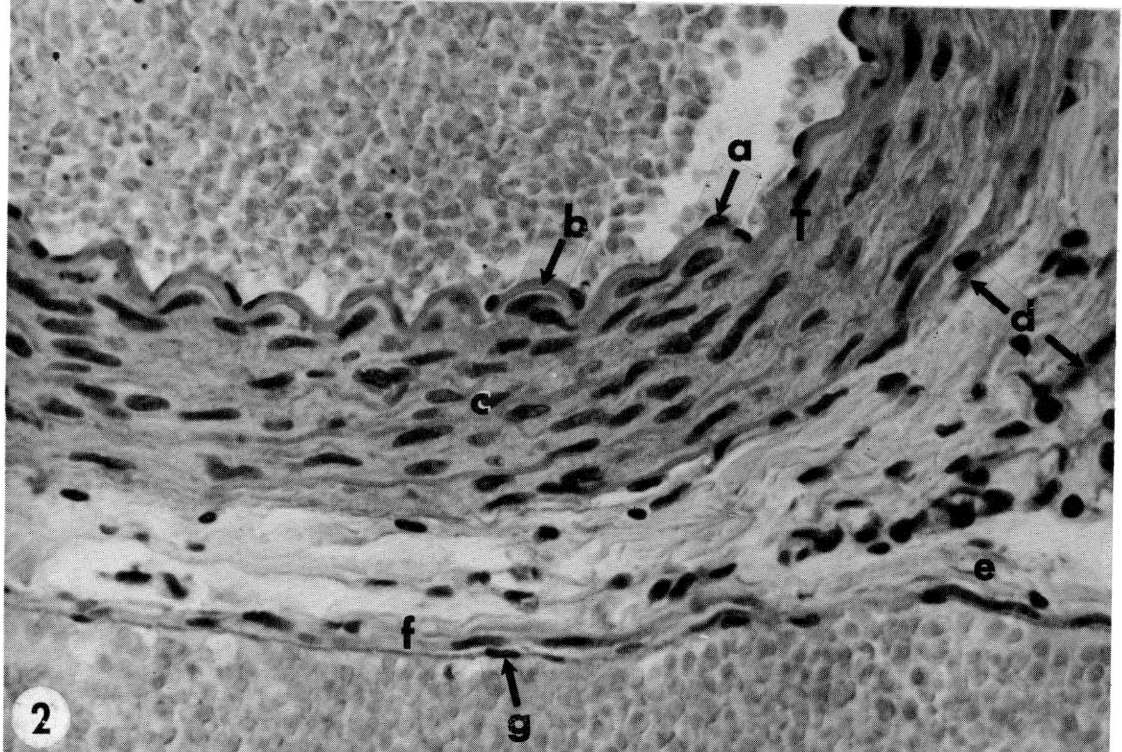

PLATE 15
Blood Vascular System

FIG. 1. Common iliac artery showing arterial branch. Longitudinal section. Level 11. (H&E, × 1310)

a. Tunica media of the artery
b. Endothelium of the arterial branch
c. Tunica media of the arterial branch
d. Adventitia of the arterial branch

FIG. 2. Common iliac artery and vein. Cross section. Level 11. (H&E, × 650)

a. Arterial endothelium
b. Internal elastic membrane of the artery
c. Tunica media of the artery
d. Tunica adventitia of the artery
e. Tunica adventitia of the vein
f. Tunica media of the vein
g. Venous endothelium

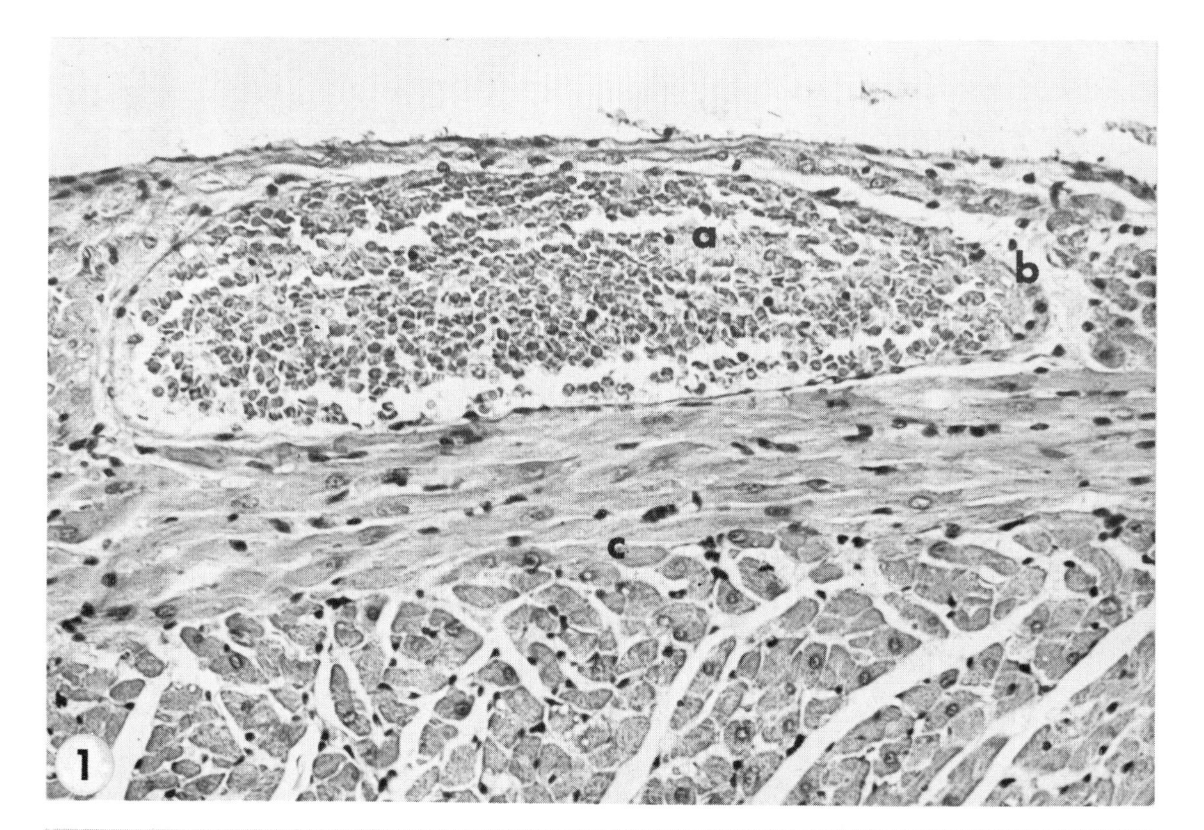

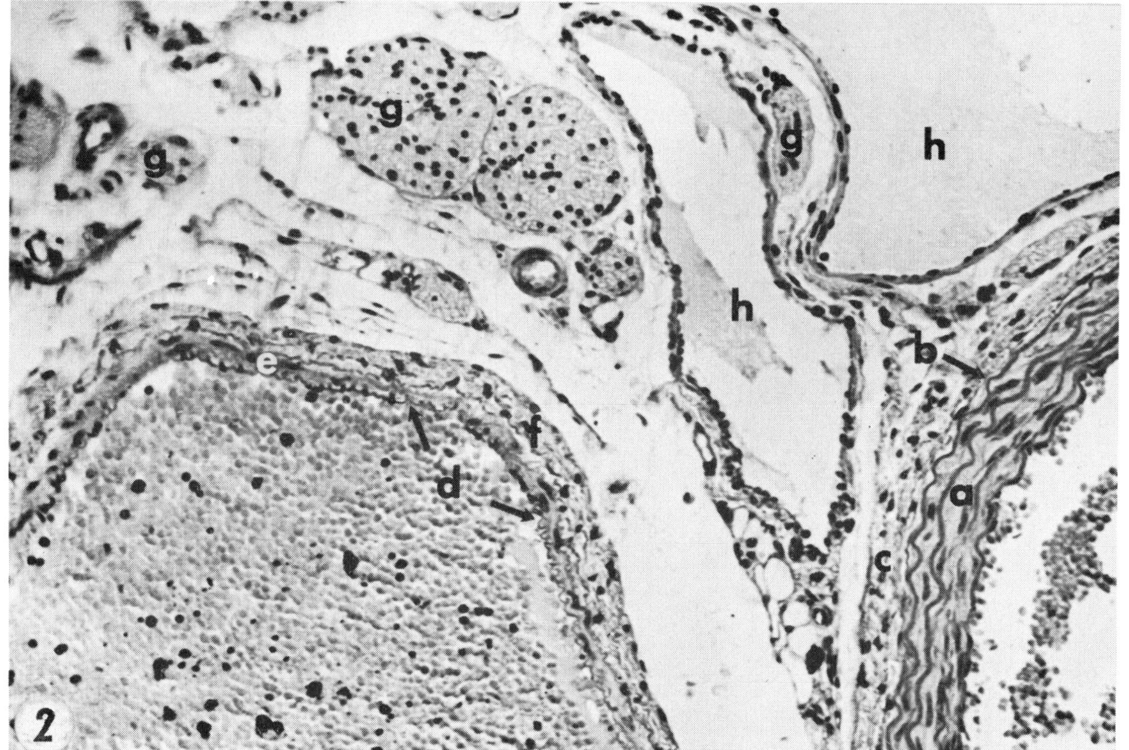

PLATE 16
Blood Vascular System

FIG. 1. Coronary vein in ventricular wall. Cross section. Level 15. (H&E, × 300)
- a. Coronary vein filled with blood
- b. Wall of the coronary vein
- c. Myocardium

FIG. 2. Spermatic artery and vein. Cross section. Level 7. (H&E, × 270)
- a. Tunica media of the artery
- b. External elastic membrane of the artery
- c. Tunica adventitia of the artery
- d. Internal elastic membrane of the vein
- e. Tunica media of the vein
- f. Tunica adventitia of the vein
- g. Nerve trunk
- h. Lymph vessels

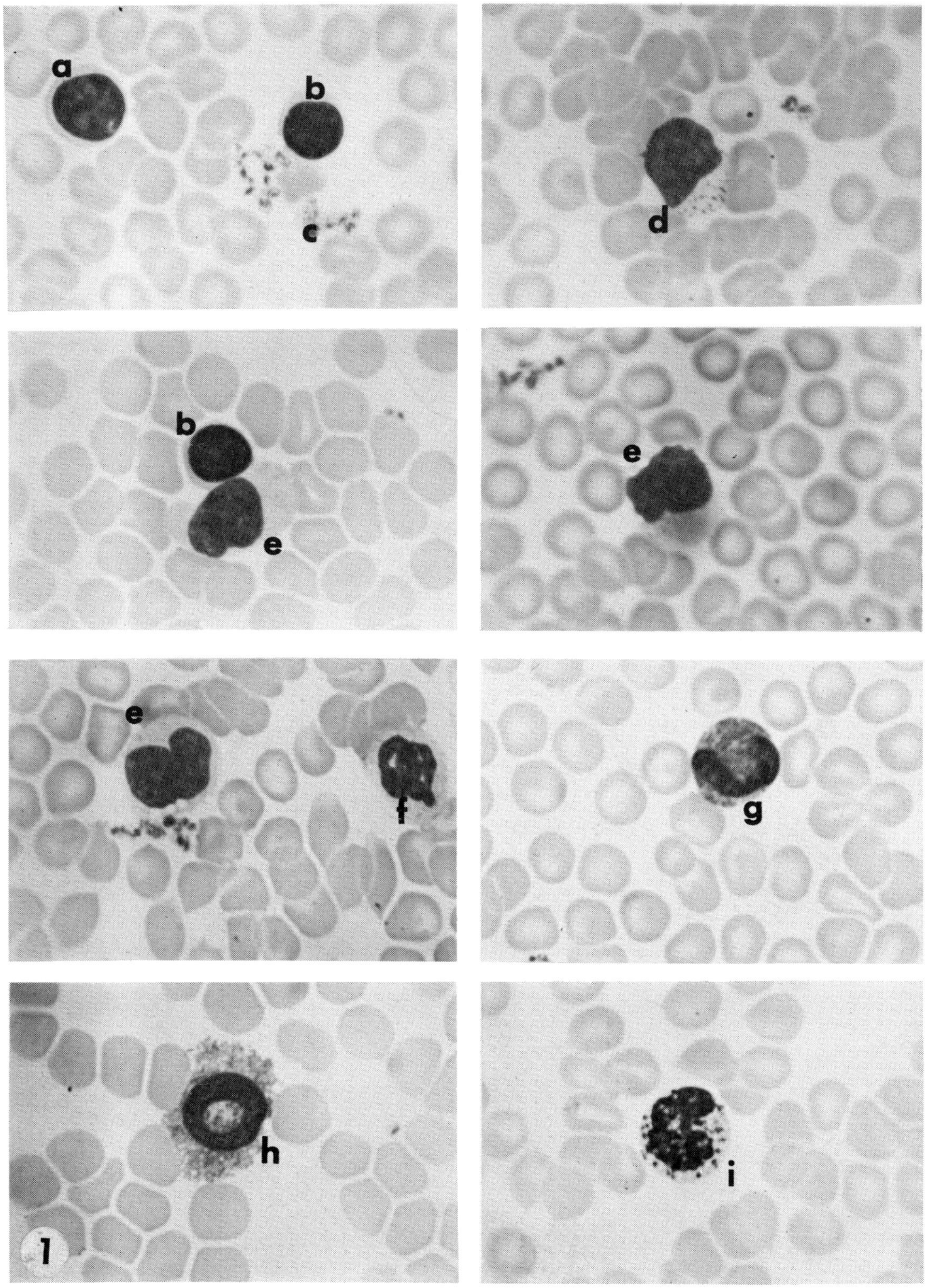

PLATE 17

Blood Vascular System

FIG. 1. Leucocytes of the peripheral blood. (Wright's stain, × 1780)

a. Large lymphocyte
b. Small lymphocyte
c. Platelets
d. Large lymphocyte with azurophilic granules
e. Monocyte (note fold in nucleus)
f. Neutrophil
g. Eosinophil (band)
h. Eosinophil with ring-shaped nucleus often seen in rat granular leucocytes
i. Basophil

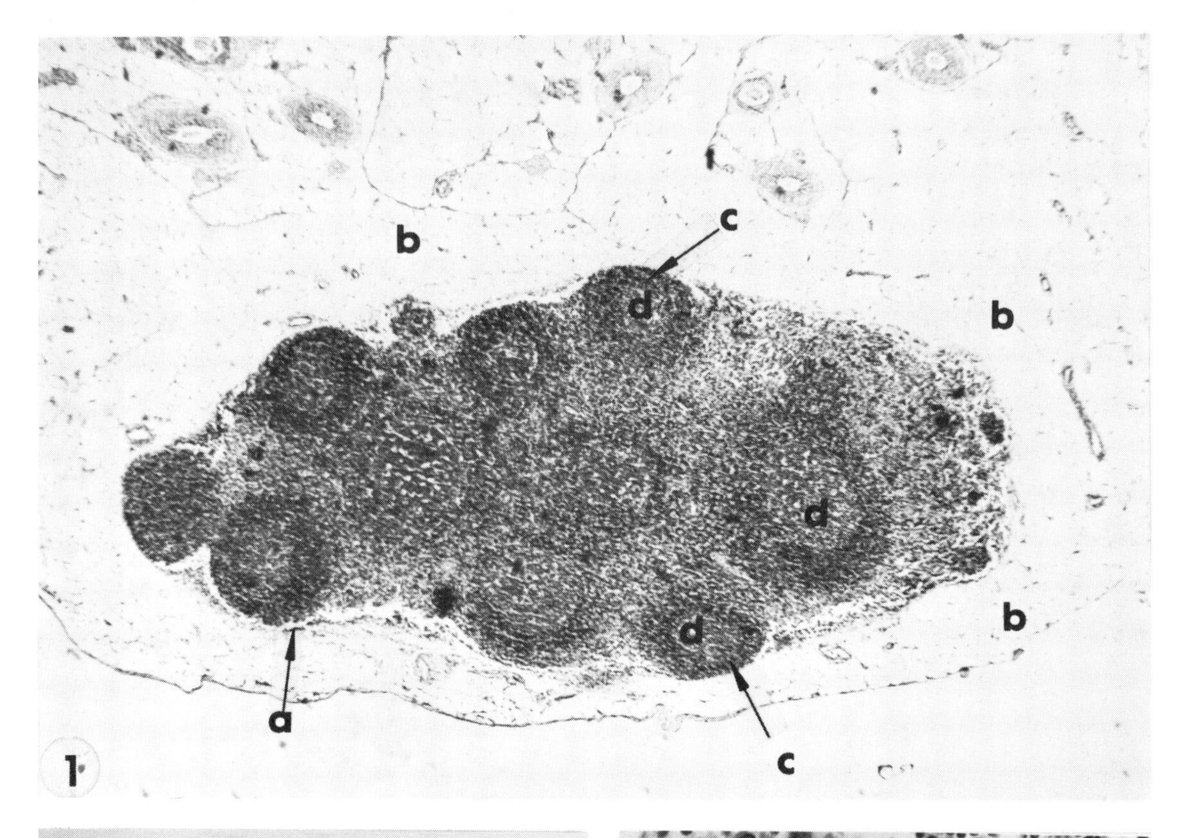

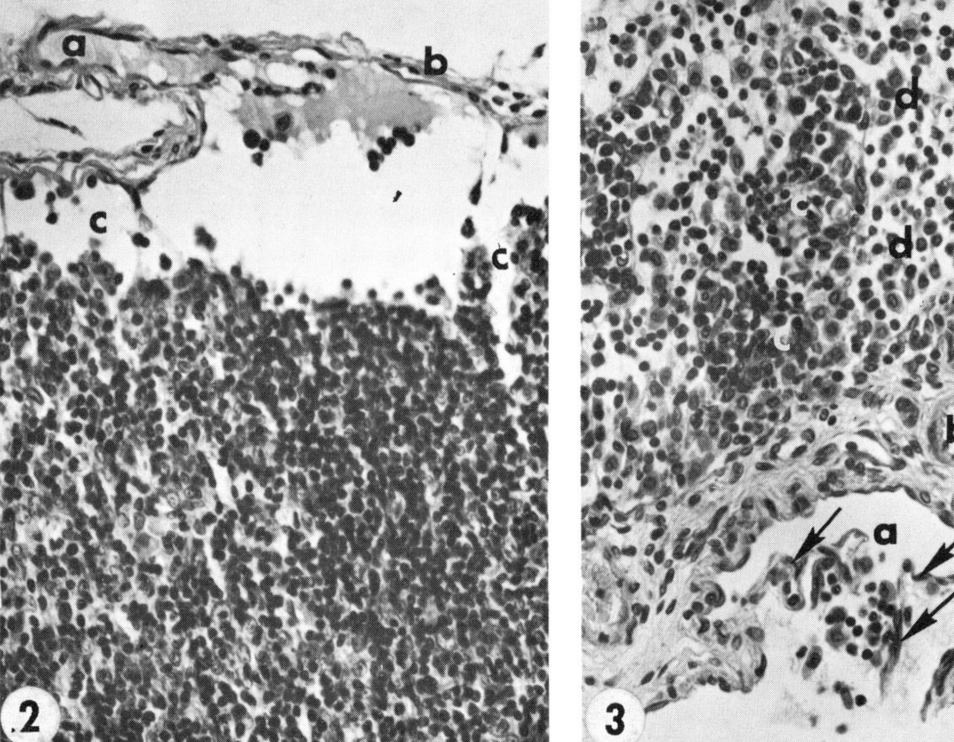

PLATE 18
Lymphoid System

FIG. 1. Lymph node. Longitudinal section. (H&E, × 40)
- a. Thin connective tissue capsule
- b. Adipose tissue completely surrounding the lymph node (note blood vessels)
- c. Primary lymph nodules
- d. Germinal center in the lymph nodules

FIG. 2. Cortex of the lymph node. Longitudinal section. (H&E, × 390)
- a. Afferent lymphatic entering the capsule (note precipitated lymph protein)
- b. Connective tissue capsule
- c. Subcapsular sinus

FIG. 3. Medulla of the lymph node at the hilum. Longitudinal section. (H&E, × 390)
- a. Efferent lymphatic at the hilum (note valve at arrows)
- b. Arteriole in the medulla
- c. Medullary cord
- d. Coarse mesh of the medulla containing reticuloendothelial cells

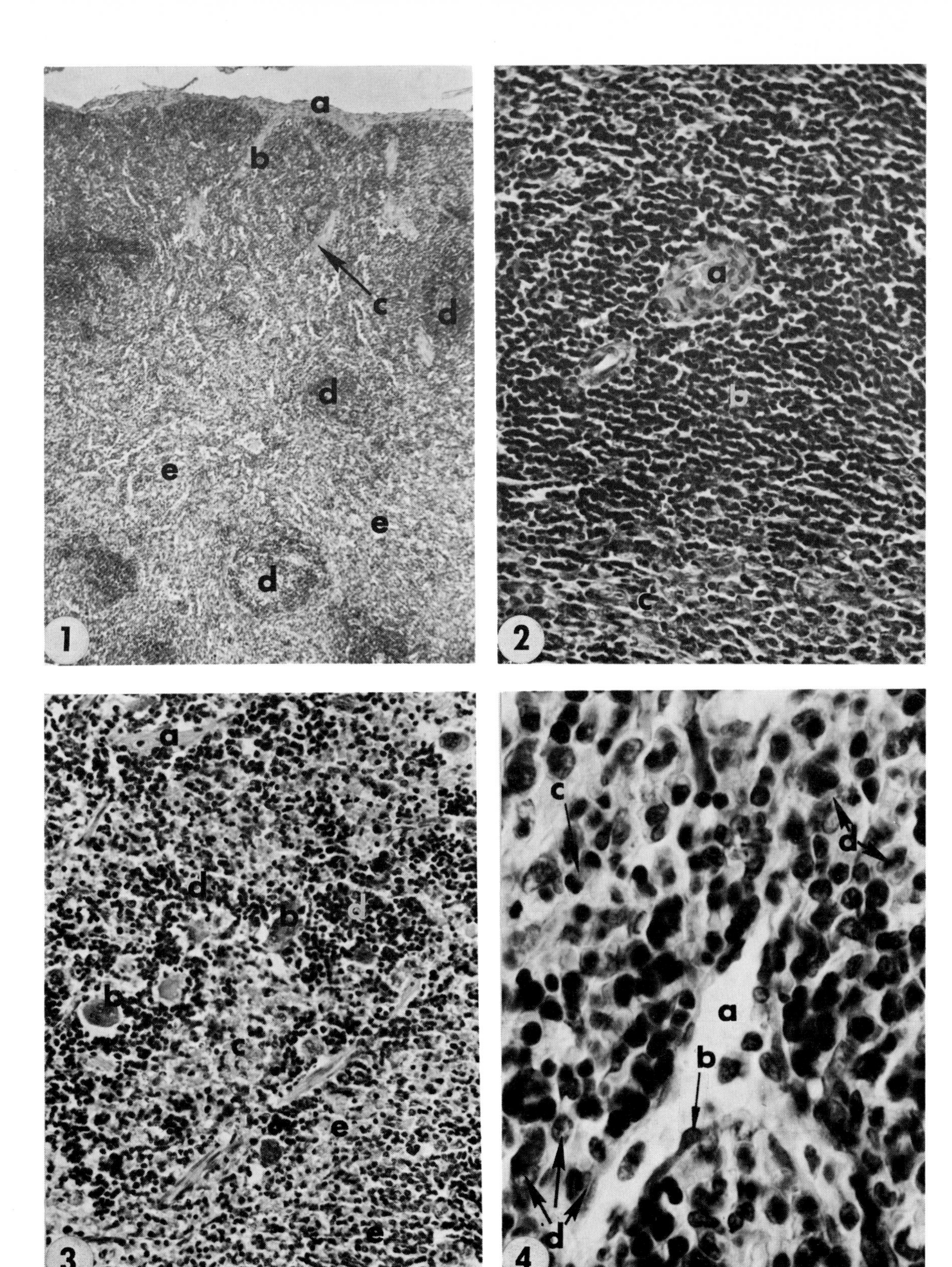

PLATE 19
Lymphoid System

FIG. 1. Spleen. (H&E, × 48)
- a. Capsule containing smooth muscle
- b. Trabecula
- c. Trabecular vein
- d. Splenic corpuscles
- e. Red pulp

FIG. 2. Splenic corpuscle. (H&E, × 325)
- a. Central artery
- b. Lymphocytes in the splenic corpuscle
- c. Adjacent red pulp

FIG. 3. Red pulp of the spleen. (H&E, × 325)
- a. Strands of trabecular smooth muscle
- b. Megakaryocytes
- c. Splenic sinusoids filled with red blood cells
- d. Aggregations of lymphocytes within the red pulp
- e. Reticuloendothelial cells of the red pulp

FIG. 4. Red pulp of the spleen. (H&E, × 870)
- a. Splenic sinusoid
- b. Endothelial cell lining the sinusoid
- c. Mitotic figure
- d. Reticuloendothelial cells

Plate 20
Integumentary System

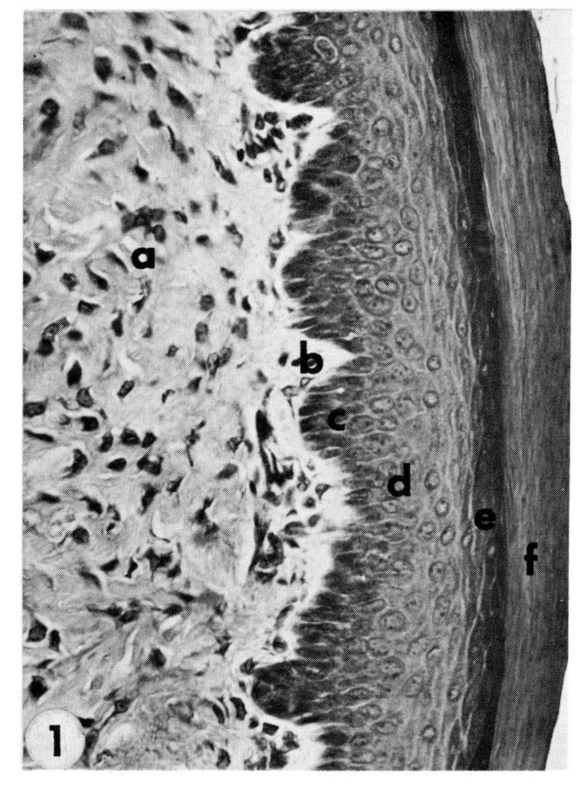

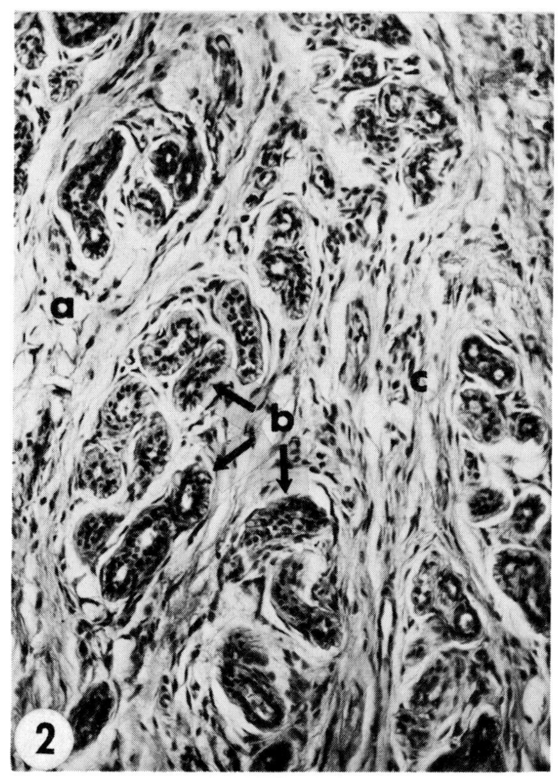

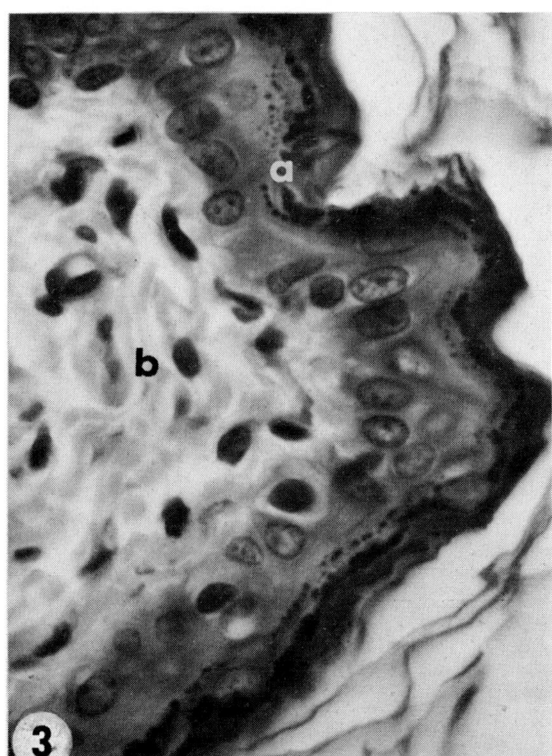

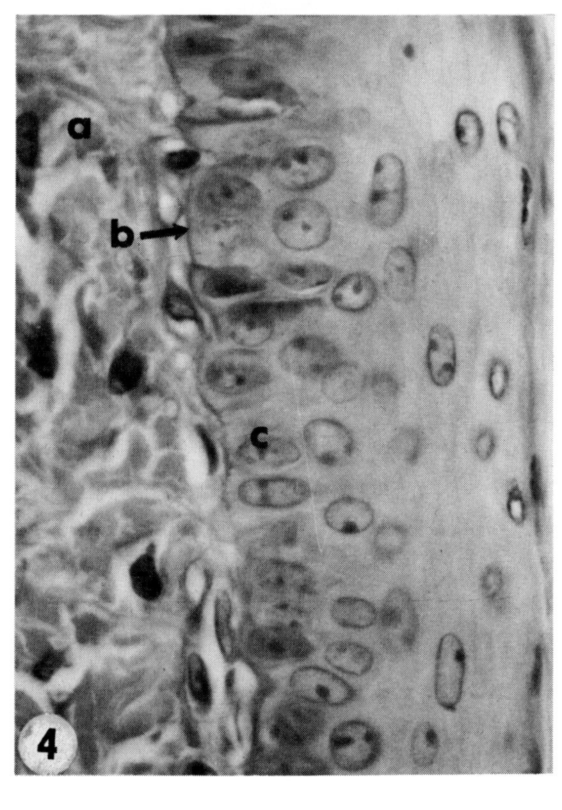

PLATE 21
Integumentary System

FIG. 1. Metacarpal pad. Cross section. Level 37. (H&E, ×395)
Dermis
a. Reticular layer
b. Papillary layer
Epidermis
c. Stratum basale
d. Stratum spinosum
e. Stratum granulosum
f. Stratum corneum

FIG. 2. Sweat glands in the metacarpal pad. Cross section. Level 40. (H&E, × 210)
a. Adipose tissue
b. Coiled tubular sweat gland
c. Loose connective tissue

FIG. 3. Stratum granulosum in the ventral tail root. Cross section. Level 20. (H&E, × 825)
a. Stratum granulosum with keratohyaline granules
b. Dermis

FIG. 4. Stratified squamous epithelium of the tail. Cross section. Level 36. (PAS, × 890)
a. Dermis
b. Basement membrane
c. Stratum basale

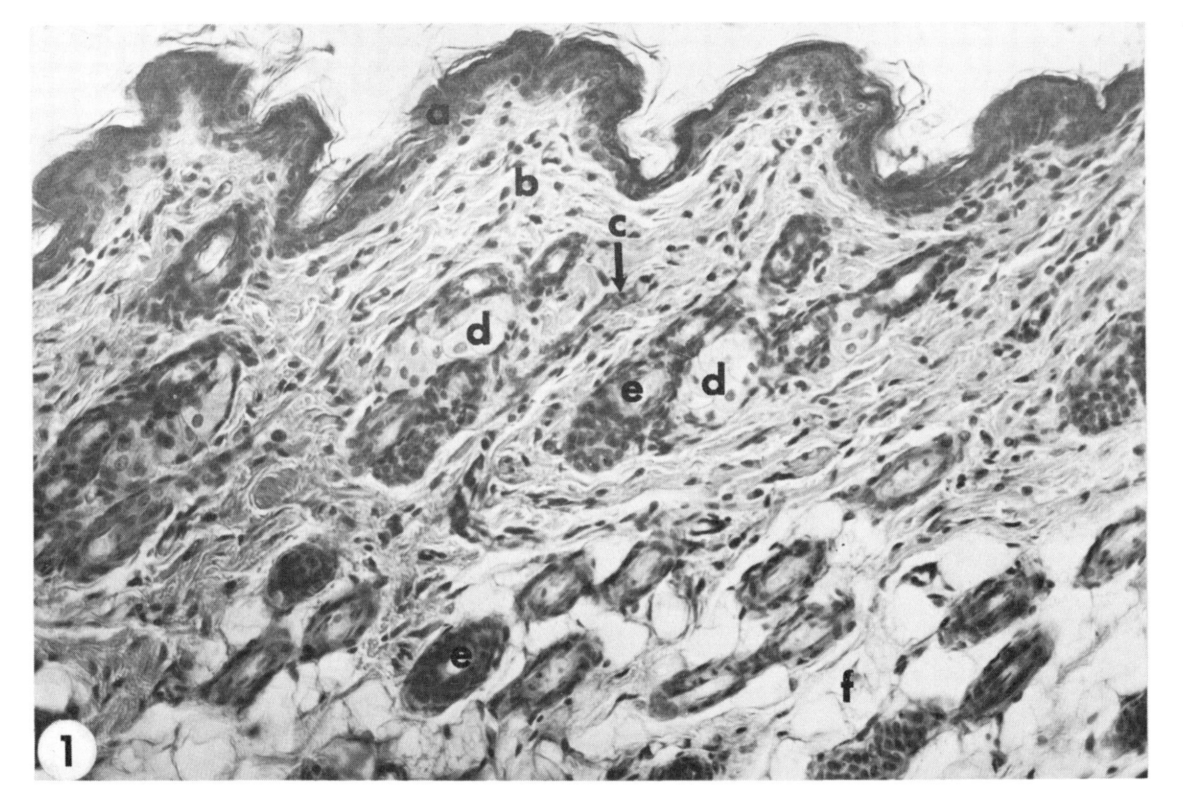

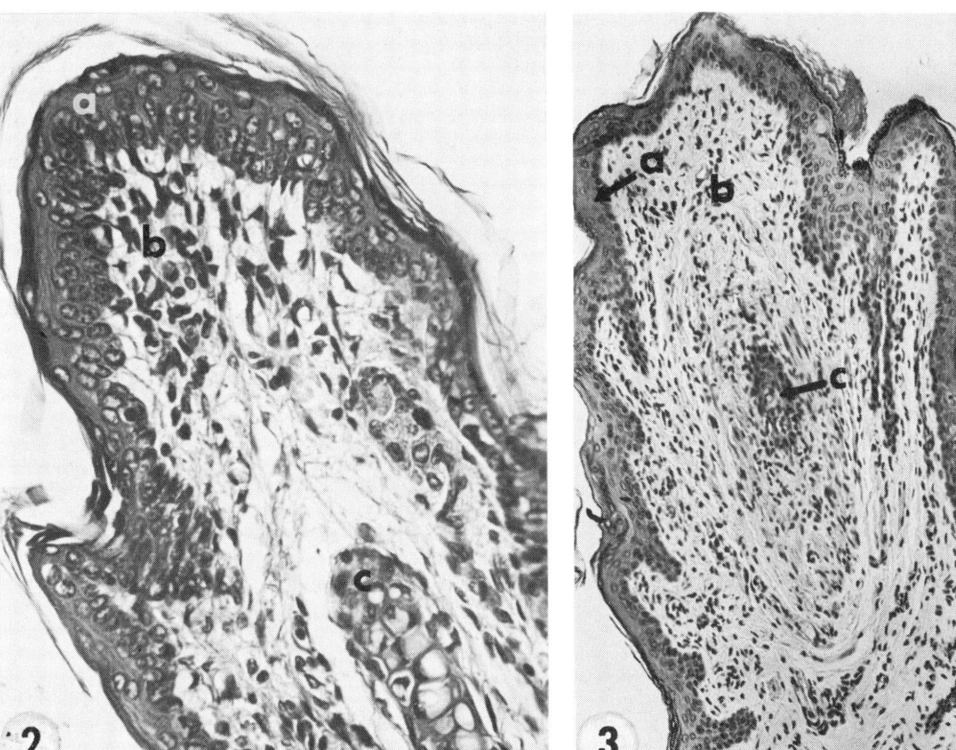

PLATE 22
Integumentary System

FIG. 1. Ventral abdominal wall. Level 28. (H&E, × 280)
- a. Epidermis
- b. Dermis
- c. Arrector pili muscle
- d. Sebaceous glands
- e. Hair follicles
- f. Panniculus adiposus

FIG. 2. Tip of the pinna. Longitudinal section. Level 1. (H&E, × 230)
- a. Epidermis
- b. Dermis
- c. Elastic cartilage

FIG. 3. Teat. Cross section. Level 30. (H&E, × 235)
- a. Epidermis
- b. Dermis
- c. Teat canal

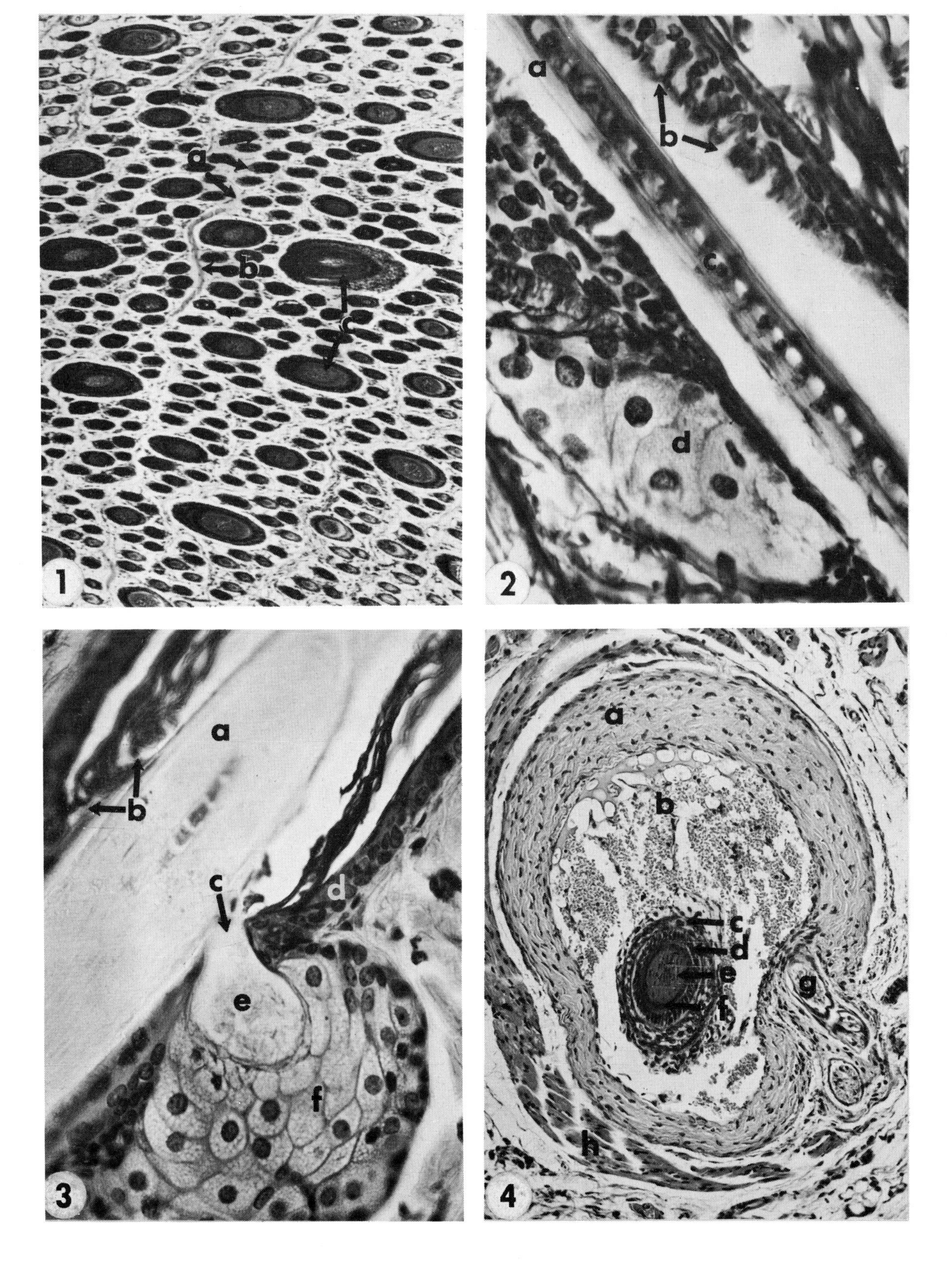

PLATE 23
Integumentary System

FIG. 1. Hair follicles in the shoulder skin. Frontal section. Level 13. (H&E, × 170)
- a. Secondary hair follicles
- b. Arrector pili muscle
- c. Central hair follicles

FIG. 2. Follicular folds in a hair follicle. Vertical section. Level 18. (H&E, × 375)
- a. Cuticle of hair shaft
- b. Follicular folds in the epithelial sheath
- c. Hair shaft
- d. Sebaceous gland

FIG. 3. Hair follicle and the associated sebaceous gland. Level 16. (H&E, × 360)
- a. Hair shaft
- b. Follicular folds
- c. Opening of the sebaceous gland into the hair follicle
- d. Epithelial sheath of the hair follicle
- e. Sebum
- f. Sebaceous gland

FIG. 4. Tactile hair in the nasal area. Cross section. Level 6. (H&E, × 135)
- a. Dermal sheath
- b. Blood sinus
- c. Outer root sheath
- d. Inner root sheath
- e. Cortex of hair
- f. Cuticle of hair
- g. Nerve bundles
- h. Skeletal muscle

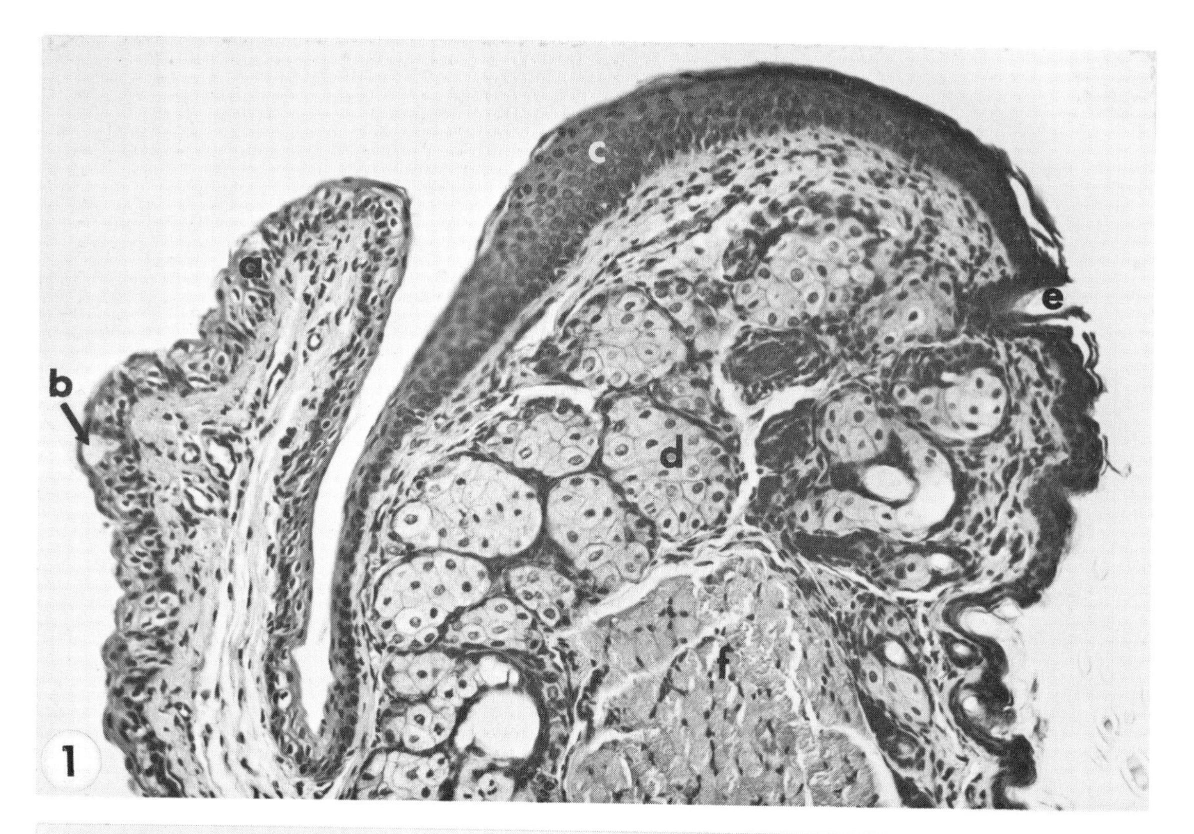

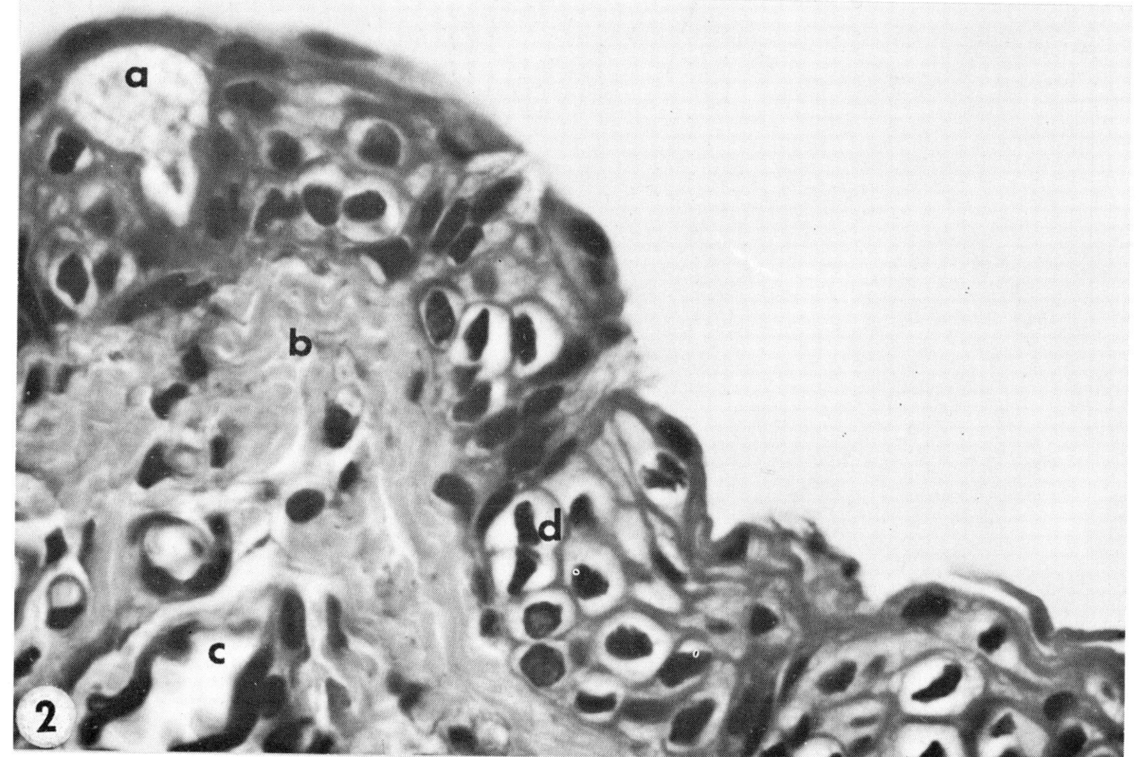

PLATE 24
Integumentary System

FIG. 1. Lower eyelid and the palpebral conjunctiva. Longitudinal section, Level 3. (H&E, × 170)
- a. Epithelium of the palpebral conjunctiva
- b. Goblet cell
- c. Stratified squamous epithelium of the lower eyelid
- d. Tarsal gland (Meibomian gland)
- e. Hair follicle opening
- f. Orbicularis oculi muscle

FIG. 2. Palpebral conjunctiva. Level 3. (H&E, × 1150)
- a. Goblet cell in epithelium
- b. White fibrous connective tissue
- c. Blood vessel
- d. Clear cells

PLATE 25
Oral Cavity

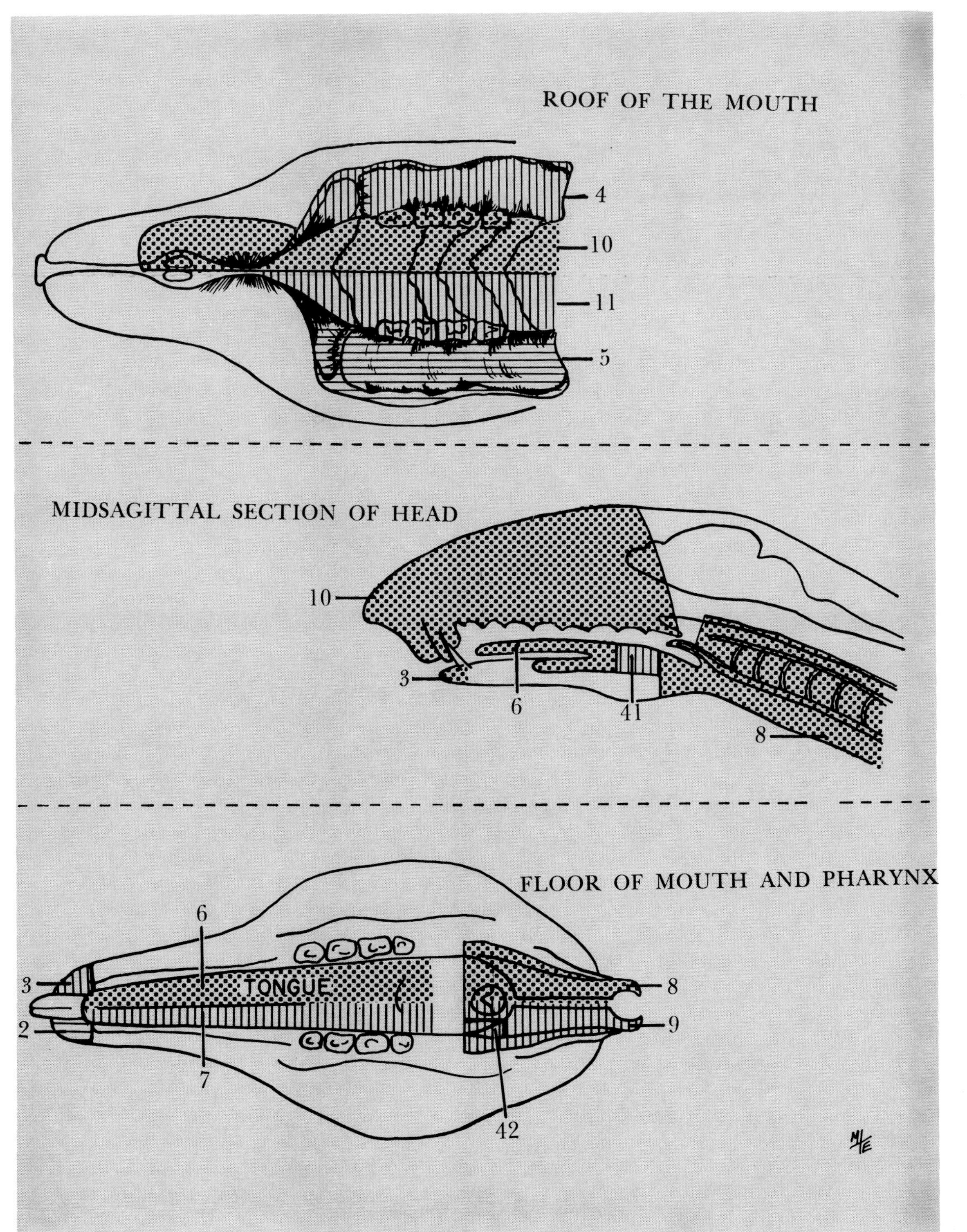

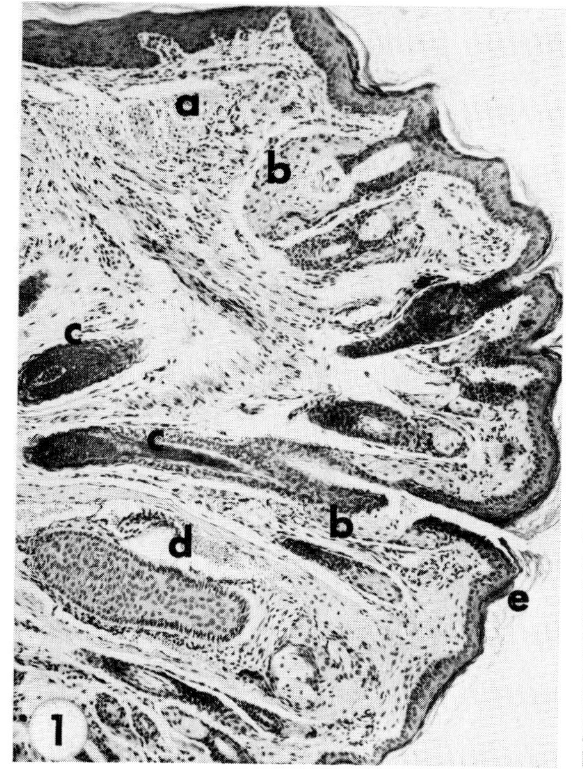

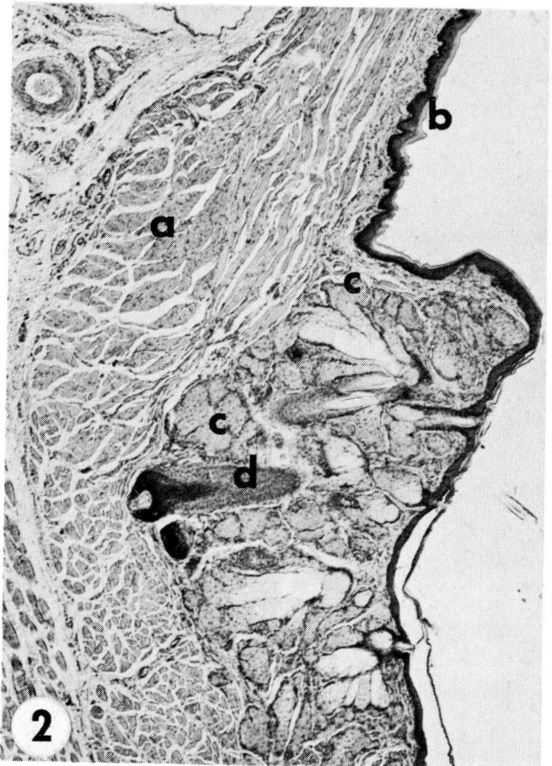

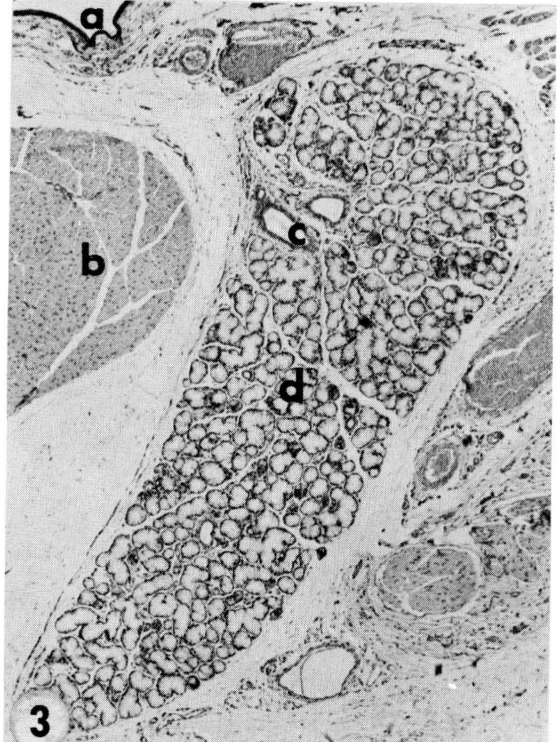

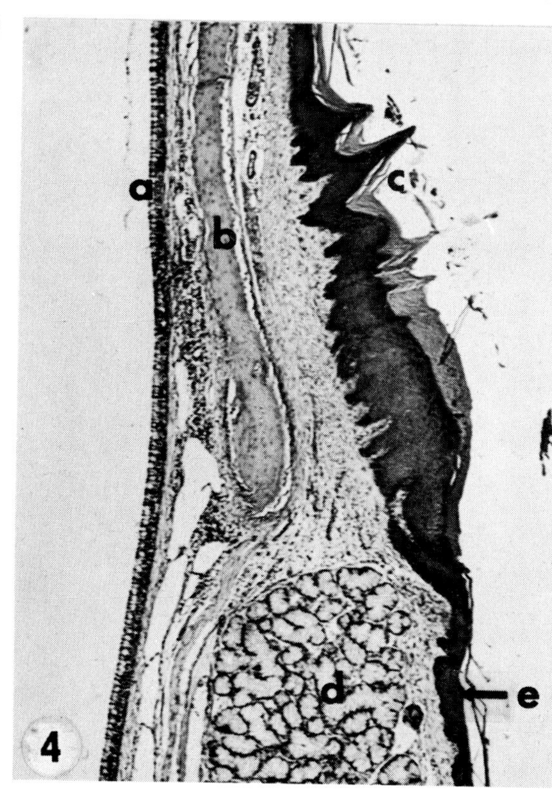

PLATE 26
Digestive System

FIG. 1. Lower lip. Sagittal section. Level 3. (H&E, × 90)

a. Skeletal muscle (orbicularis oris muscle)
b. Sebaceous glands
c. Hair follicles
d. Blood sinus of a tactile hair follicle
e. Cutaneous area with cornified stratified squamous epithelium

FIG. 2. Hairy patch of the buccal mucosa. Longitudinal section. Level 5. (H&E, × 40)

a. Skeletal muscle
b. Cornified stratified squamous epithelium of the mucosa
c. Sebaceous glands of the hairy patch
d. Hair follicle

FIG. 3. Glands of the buccal mucosa. Longitudinal section. Level 5. (H&E, × 40)

a. Oral cavity
b. Skeletal muscle
c. Duct of a gland
d. Mucous gland parenchyma

FIG. 4. Junction of the hard and soft palate. Midsagittal section. Level 10. (H&E, × 50)

a. Pseudostratified ciliated columnar epithelium of the nasal mucosa
b. Palatine bone
c. Hard palate covered with cornified stratified squamous epithelium
d. Mucous glands of the soft palate
e. Soft palate covered with stratified squamous epithelium

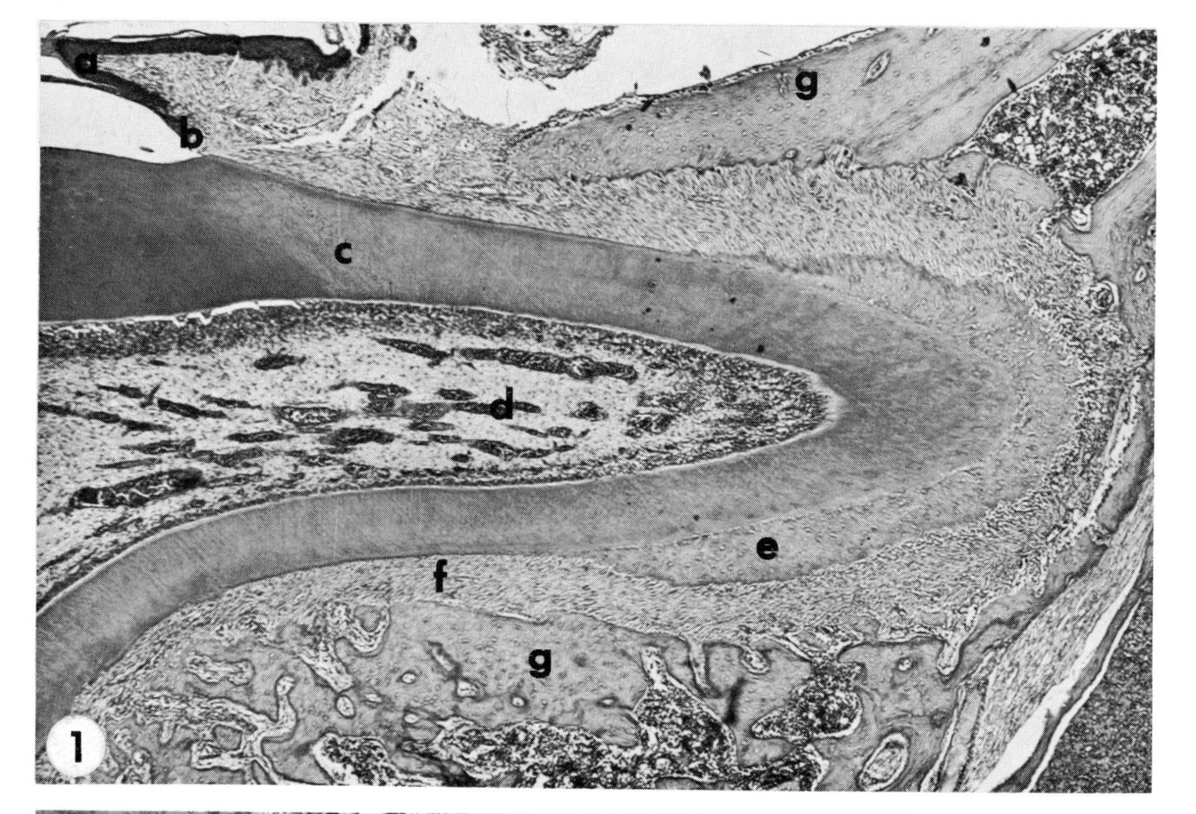

PLATE 27
Digestive System

FIG. 1. Root of a molar tooth. Sagittal section. Level 10. (H&E, × 60)

a. Gingiva
b. Area of attachment of the gingival epithelium to the tooth
c. Dentin
d. Dental pulp
e. Cementum with cementocytes in the lacunae
f. Periodontal membrane
g. Alveolar bone

FIG. 2. Tooth wall. Sagittal section. Level 10. (H&E, × 240)

a. Alveolar bone
b. Periodontal membrane with blood vessels
c. Ameloblasts
d. Enamel (note enamel prisms)
e. Dentino-enamel junction
f. Dentin (note dentinal tubules)
g. Predentin
h. Odontoblasts
i. Dental pulp

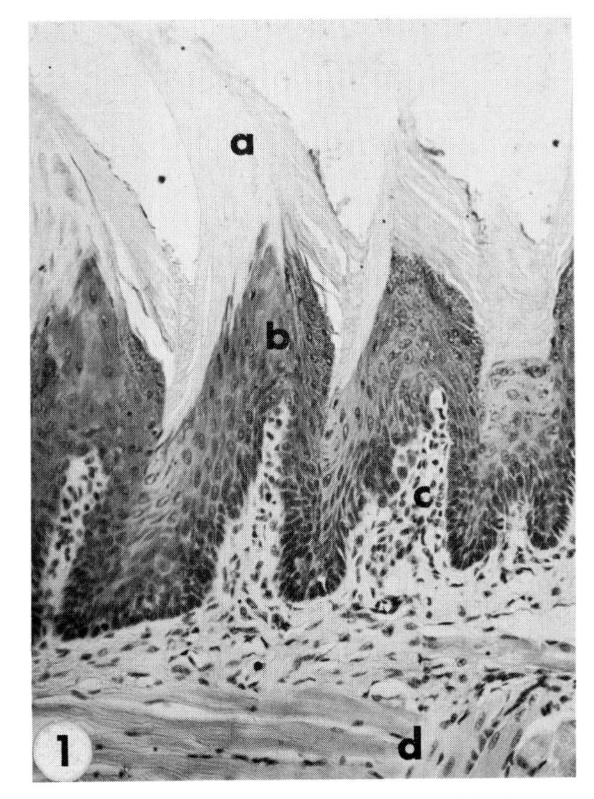

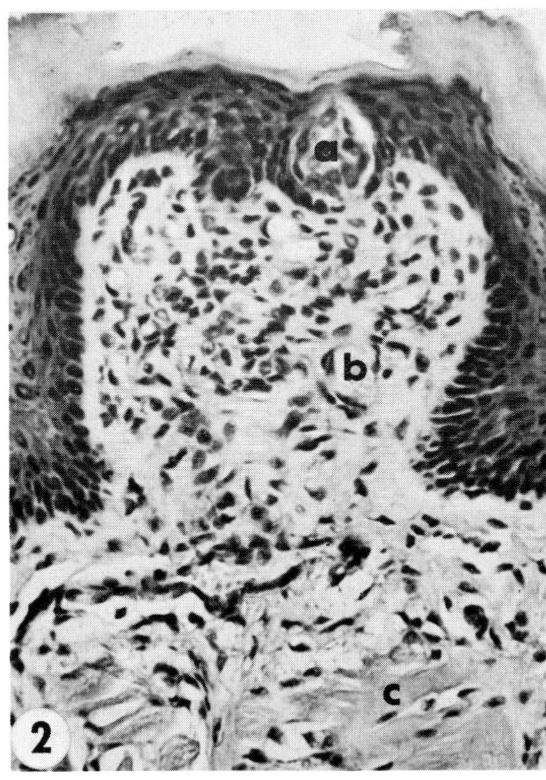

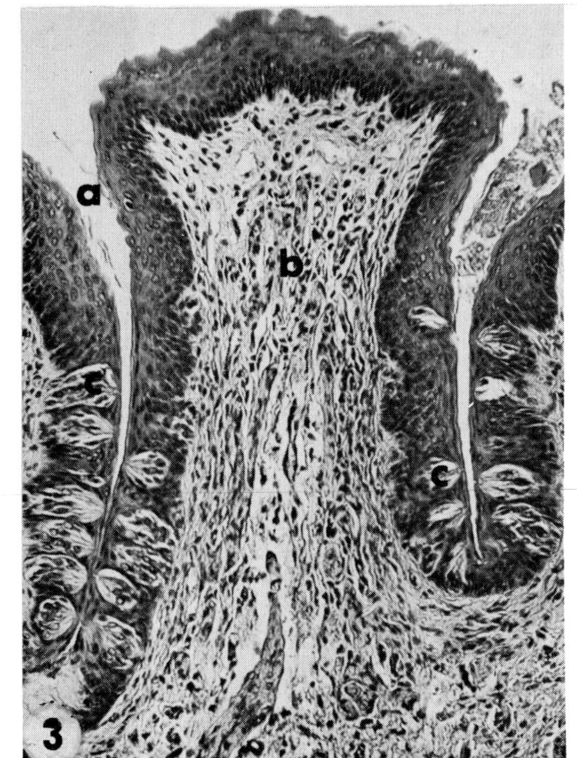

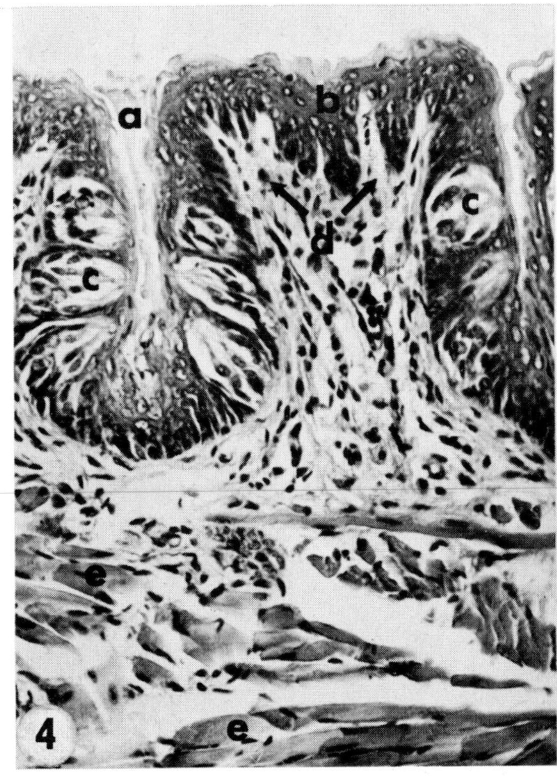

PLATE 28

Digestive System

FIG. 1. Filiform papillae of the tongue. Sagittal section. Level 6. (H&E, × 150)
- a. Cornified layer of stratified squamous epithelium
- b. Noncornified layer of stratified squamous epithelium
- c. Lamina propria
- d. Skeletal muscle

FIG. 2. Fungiform papilla with a taste bud. Sagittal section. Level 6. (H&E, × 540)
- a. Taste bud
- b. Blood vessel in the lamina propria
- c. Skeletal muscle

FIG. 3. Circumvallate papilla with taste buds. Cross section. Level 41. (H&E, × 195)
- a. Encircling gustatory furrow
- b. Lamina propria
- c. Taste buds

FIG. 4. Foliate papilla. Cross section. Level 42. (H&E, × 270)
- a. Gustatory furrow
- b. Stratified squamous epithelium
- c. Taste buds
- d. Lamina propria of a secondary papillae (arrow)
- e. Skeletal muscle

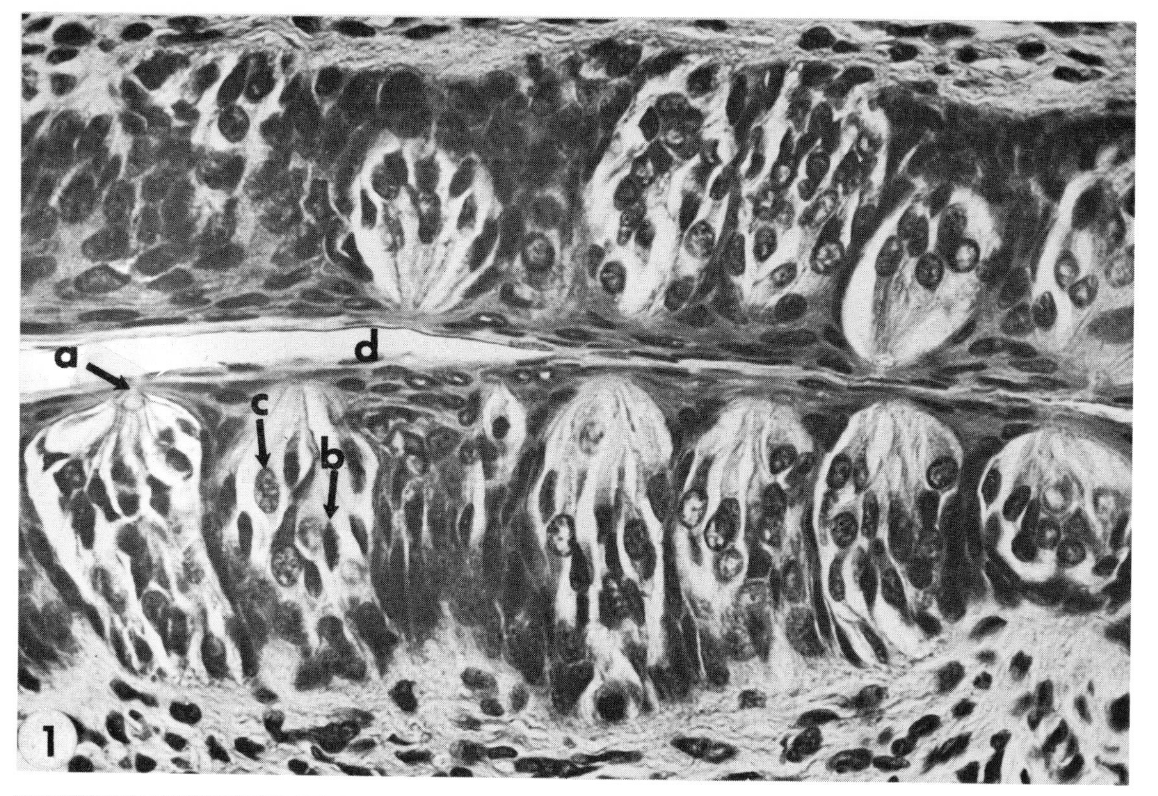

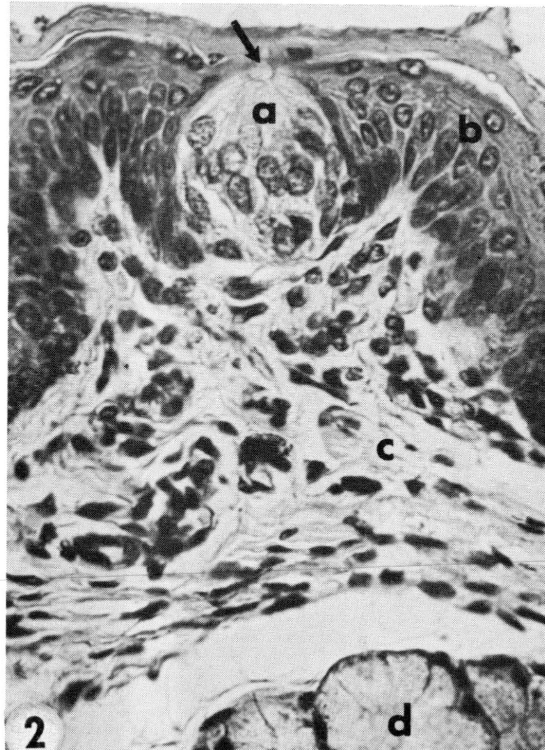

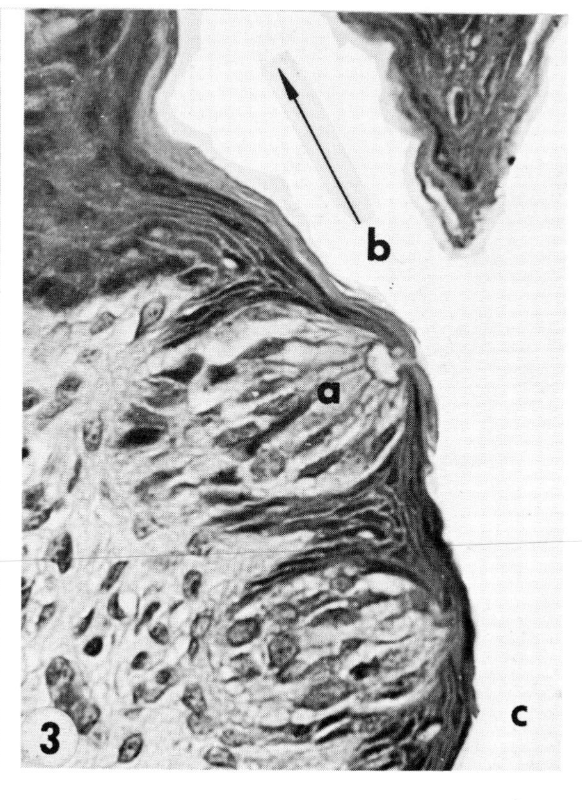

PLATE 29
Digestive System

FIG. 1. Taste buds in a circumvallate papilla. Cross section. Level 41. (H&E, × 715)
- a. Taste pore
- b. Neuroepithelial cell
- c. Sustentacular cell
- d. Circular gustatory furrow

FIG. 2. Taste bud in the soft palate. Sagittal section. Level 8. (H&E, × 320)
- a. Taste bud with a pore (arrow)
- b. Cornified stratified squamous epithelium
- c. Lamina propria
- d. Mucous glands

FIG. 3. Taste buds in the oral-nasal region. Cross section. Level 7. (H&E, × 660)
- a. Taste bud with a pore
- b. Vestibular region of the nasal cavity
- c. Oral cavity

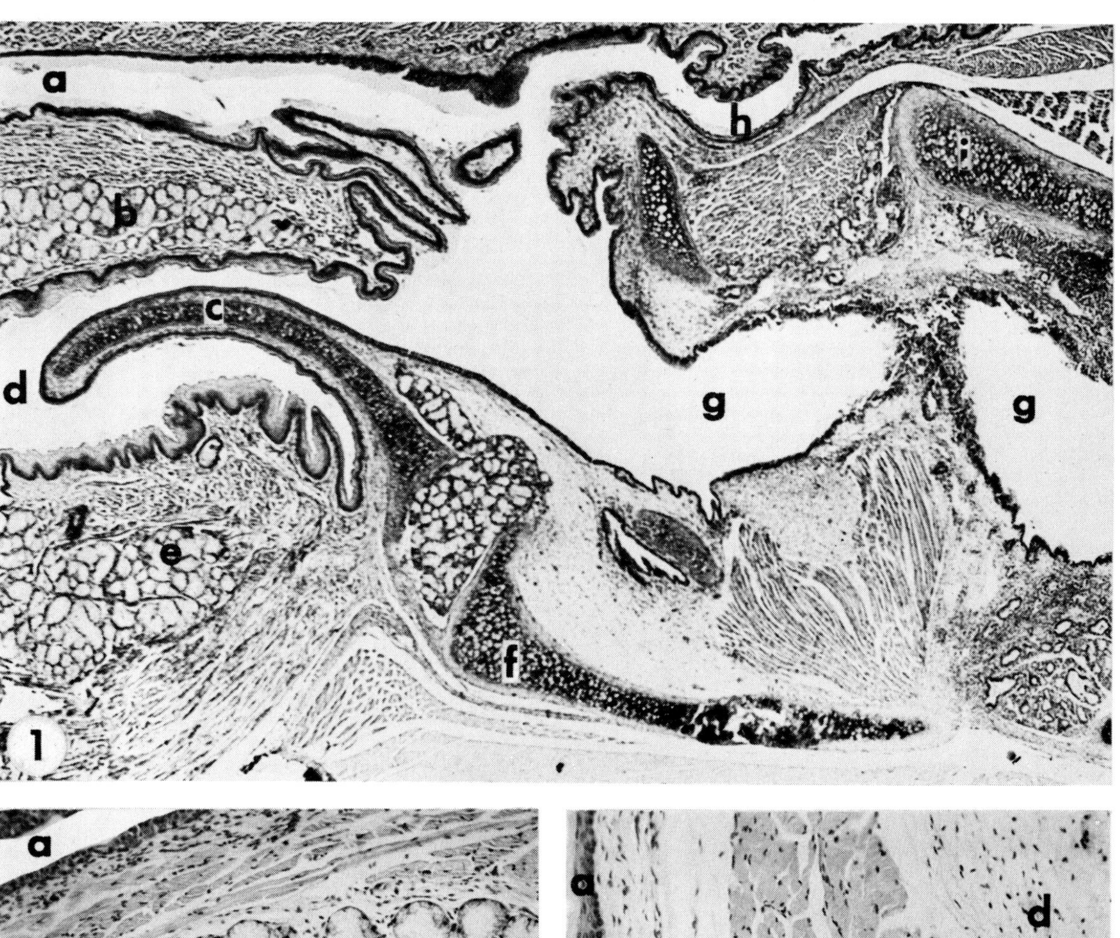

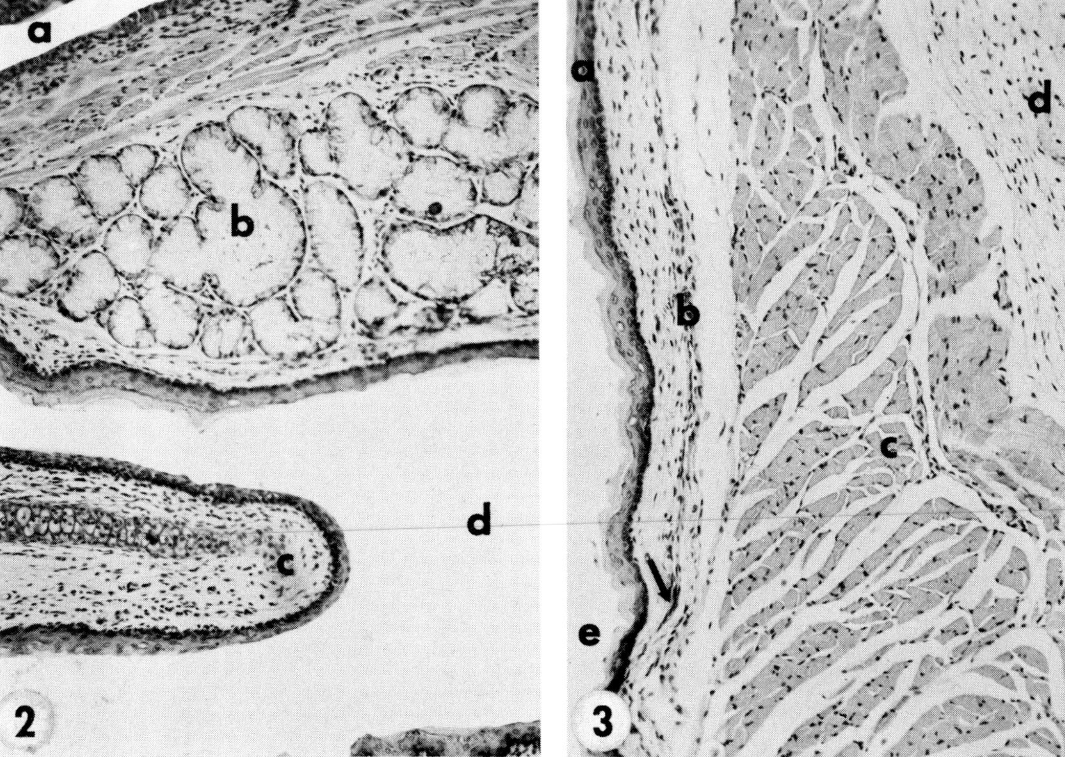

Plate 30
Digestive System

Fig. 1. Relationship of the esophagus and larynx to the nasal and oral cavities. Sagittal section. Level 8. (H&E, × 24)

a. Nasal cavity
b. Soft palate
c. Epiglottis
d. Cavity of the oropharynx
e. Mucous glands of the oropharynx
f. Thyroid cartilage of the larynx
g. Laryngeal cavity
h. Esophagus
i. Cricoid cartilage of the larynx

Fig. 2. Pharynx. Sagittal section. Level 8. (H&E, × 110)

a. Nasal cavity
b. Mucous glands in the soft palate
c. Epiglottis with elastic cartilage
d. Cavity of the oropharynx

Fig. 3. Pharyngo-esophageal junction. Sagittal section. Level 8. (H&E, × 125)

a. Stratified squamous epithelium of the esophagus
b. Muscularis mucosa (note beginning of mucularis mucosa at arrow)
c. Muscularis externa composed of inner circular and outer longitudinal skeletal muscle
d. Tunica adventitia
e. Pharyngeal cavity

PLATE 31
Digestive System

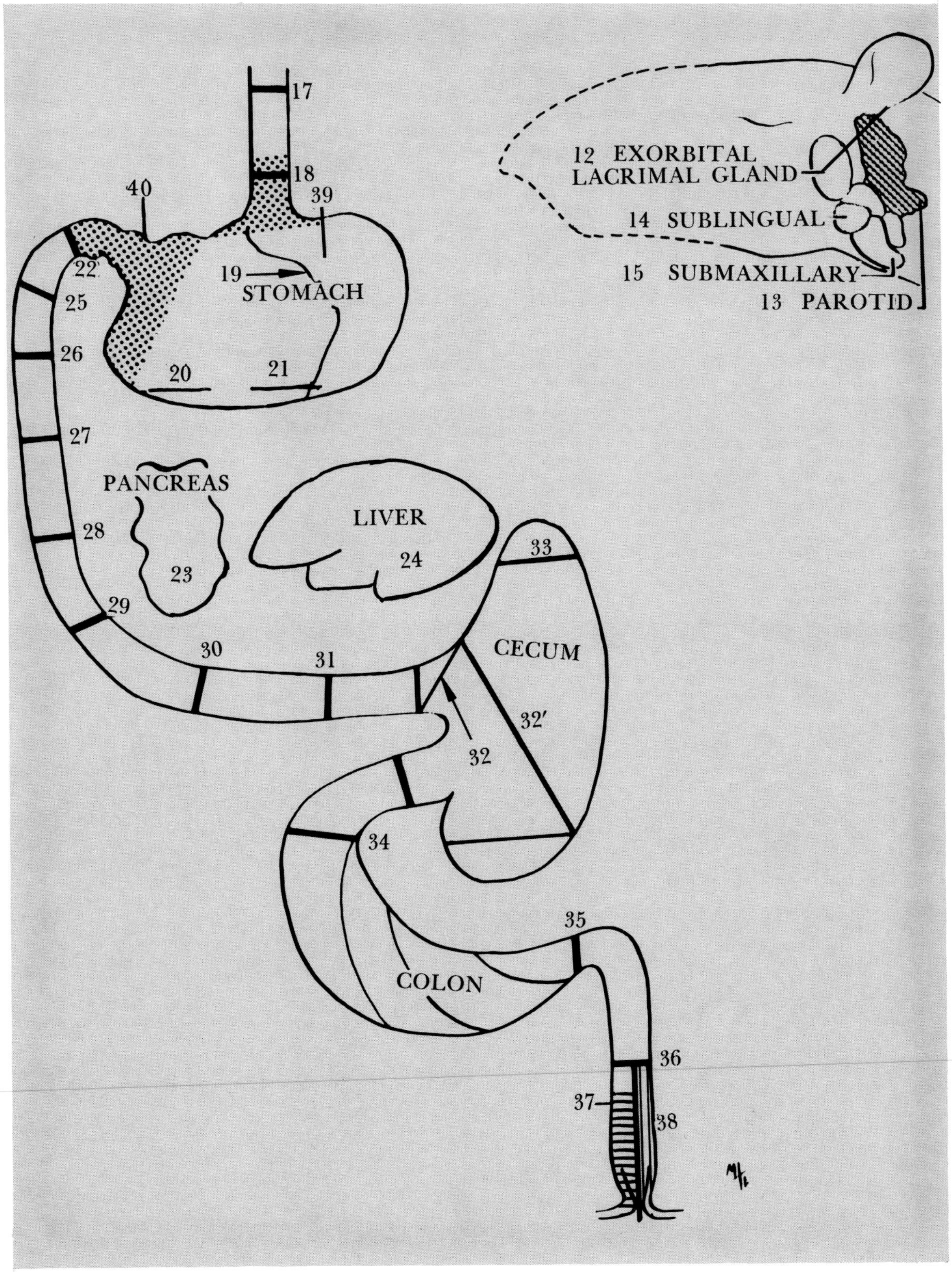

12 EXORBITAL LACRIMAL GLAND
14 SUBLINGUAL
15 SUBMAXILLARY
13 PAROTID
17
18
40
39
19
STOMACH
22
25
26
20
21
27
PANCREAS
23
LIVER
24
28
29
30
31
33
CECUM
32′
32
34
35
COLON
36
37
38

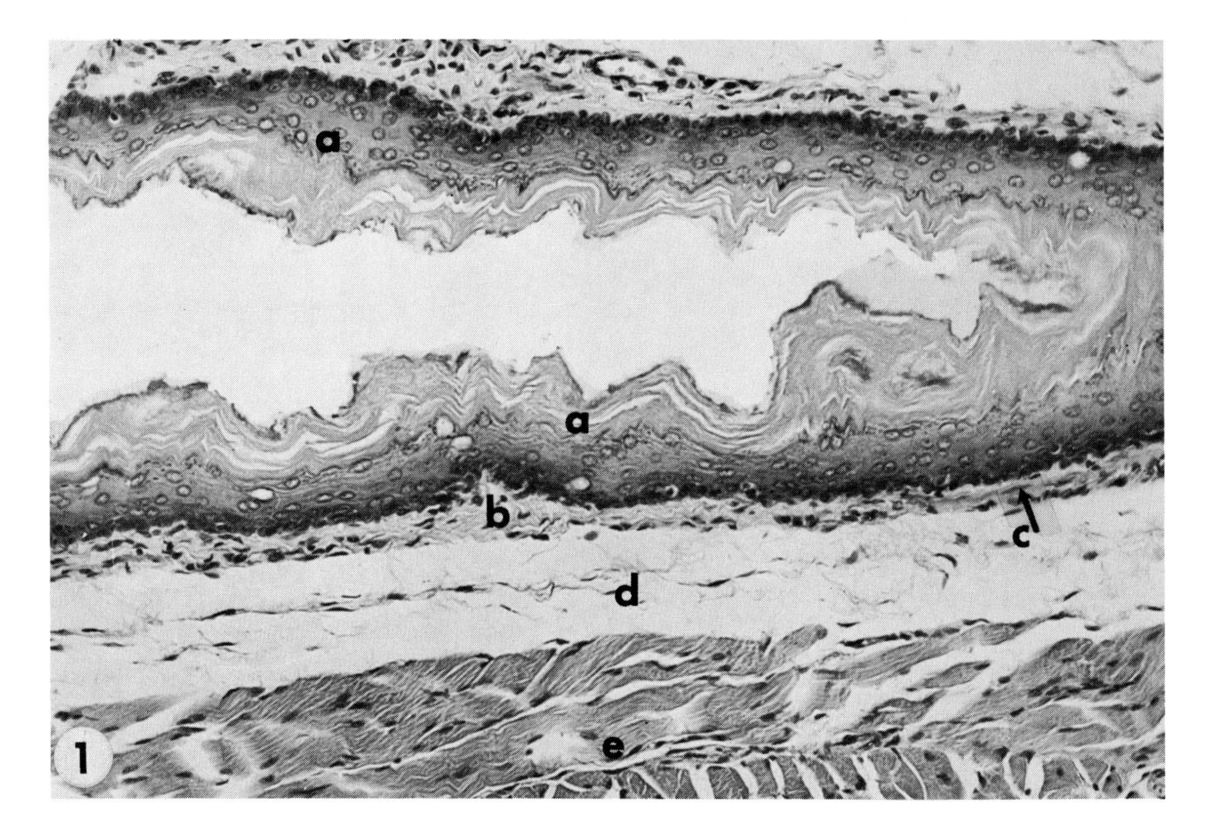

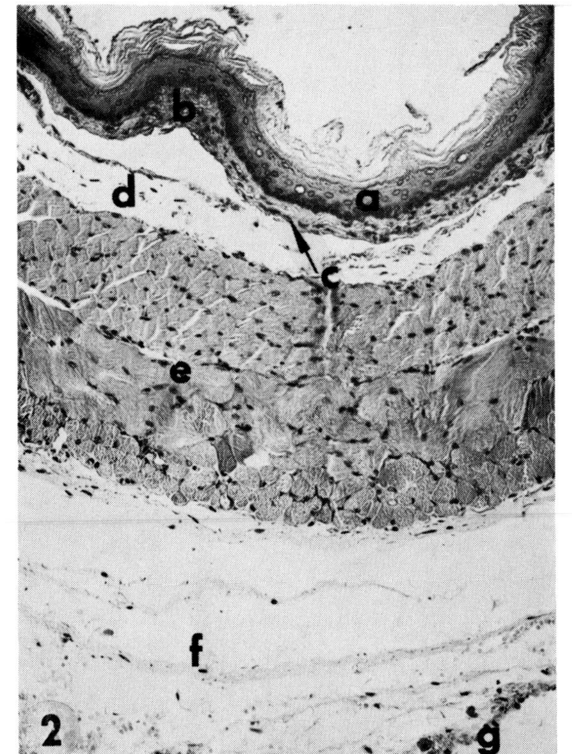

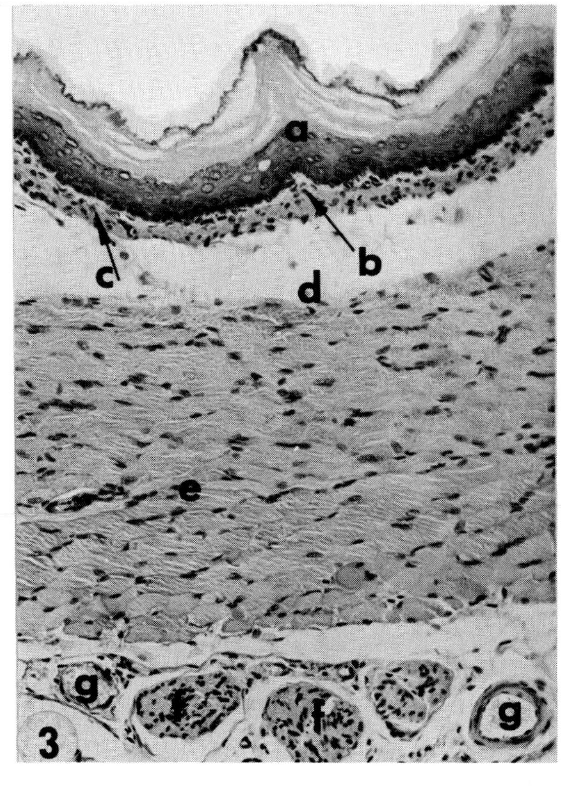

Plate 32
Digestive System

Fig. 1. Esophagus near the pharynx. Longitudinal section. Level 8. (H&E, × 250)
- a. Cornified stratified squamous epithelium
- b. Lamina propria
- c. Beginning of the muscularis mucosa
- d. Submucosa
- e. Skeletal muscle of the tunica muscularis

Fig. 2. Esophagus. Cross section. Level 17. (H&E, × 200)
- a. Cornified stratified squamous epithelium
- b. Lamina propria
- c. Muscularis mucosa (arrow)
- d. Submucosa
- e. Skeletal muscle of the tunica muscularis
- f. Tunica adventitia
- g. Mediastinum

Fig. 3. Esophagus. Cross section. Level 18. (H&E, × 250)
- a. Cornified stratified squamous epithelium
- b. Lamina propria
- c. Muscularis mucosa
- d. Submucosa
- e. Skeletal muscle of the tunica muscularis
- f. Nerve bundles
- g. Blood vessels

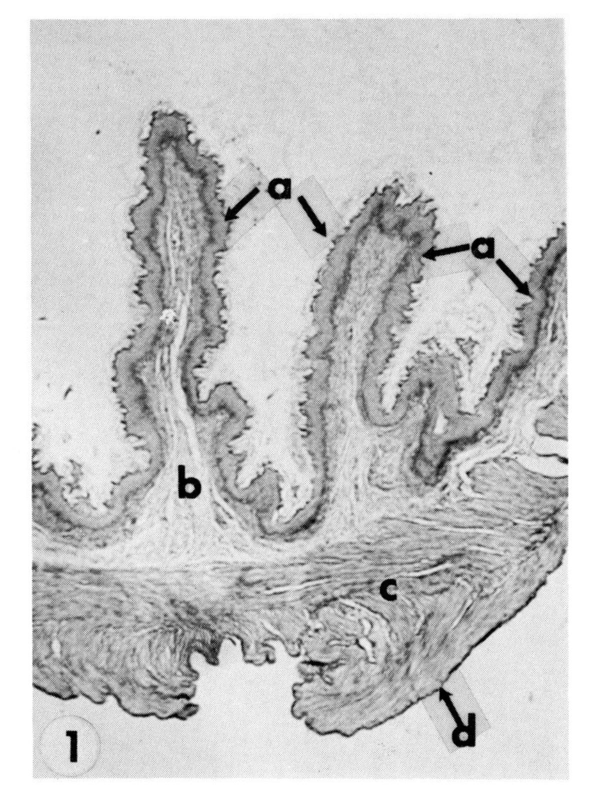

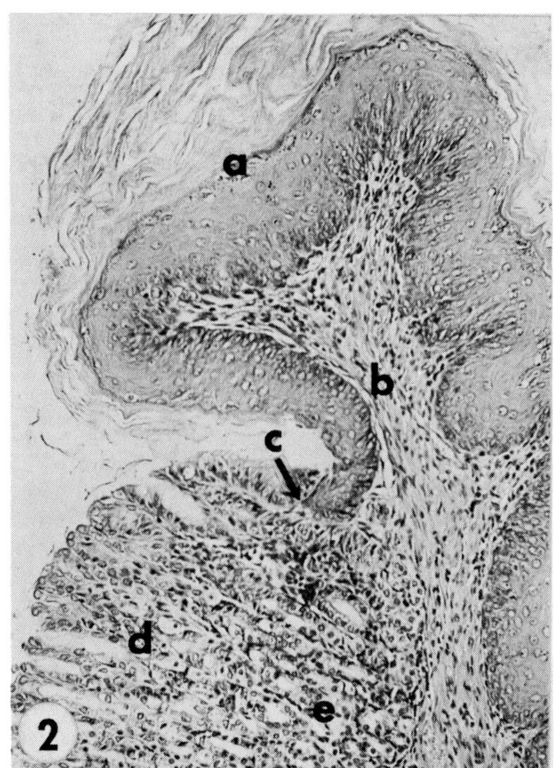

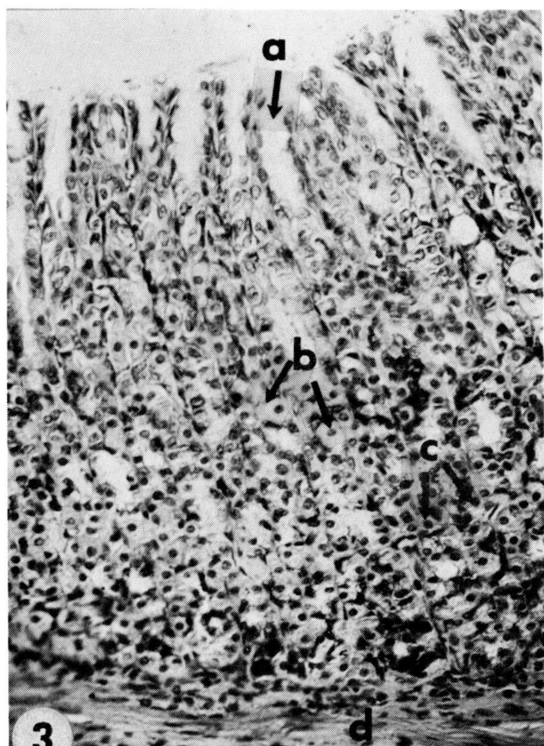

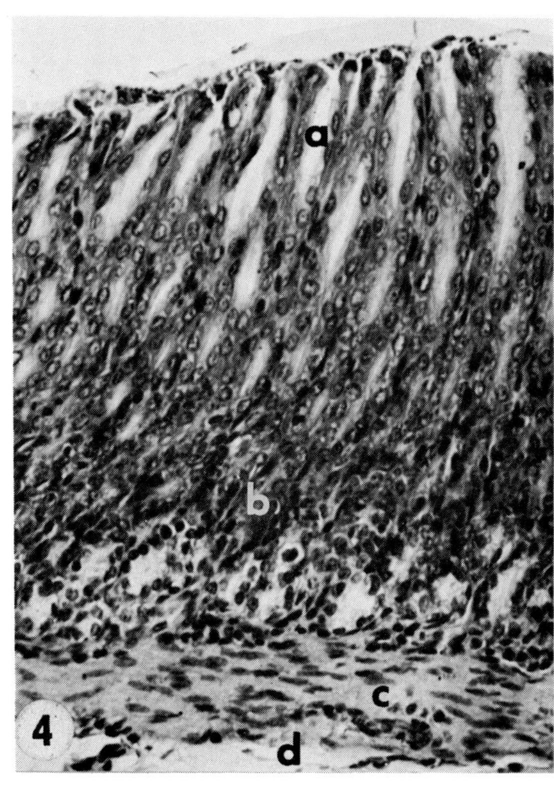

Plate 33
Digestive System

Fig. 1. Forestomach (nonglandular portion). Longitudinal section. Level 39. (H&E, $\times$ 26)

a. Rumen-like mucosal folds covered with stratified squamous epithelium
b. Lamina propria
c. Smooth muscle of the tunica muscularis
d. Serosa

Fig. 2. Junction of the forestomach and fundic stomach. Midsagittal section. Level 19. (H&E, $\times$ 136)

a. Forestomach (nonglandular) lined by cornified stratified squamous epithelium
b. Muscularis mucosa
c. Glandular and nonglandular junction
d. Columnar epithelium of the fundic stomach
e. Gastric glands

Fig. 3. Mucosa of the fundic stomach. Cross section. Level 20. (H&E, $\times$ 266)

a. Gastric pit lined with simple columnar epithelium
b. Parietal cells in the gastric glands
c. Chief cells in the gastric glands
d. Muscularis mucosa

Fig. 4. Mucosa of the pyloric stomach. Cross section. Level 40. (H&E, $\times$ 265)

a. Gastric pits
b. Pyloric glands
c. Muscularis mucosa
d. Submucosa

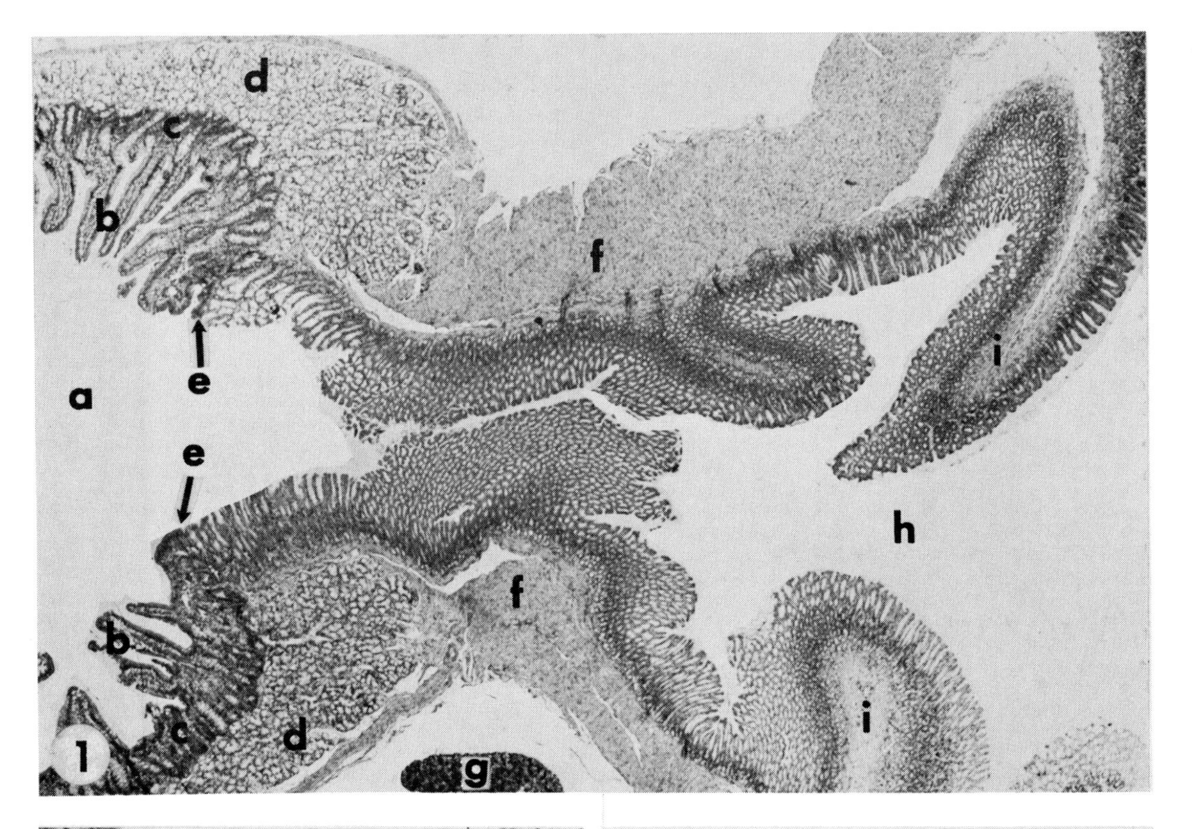

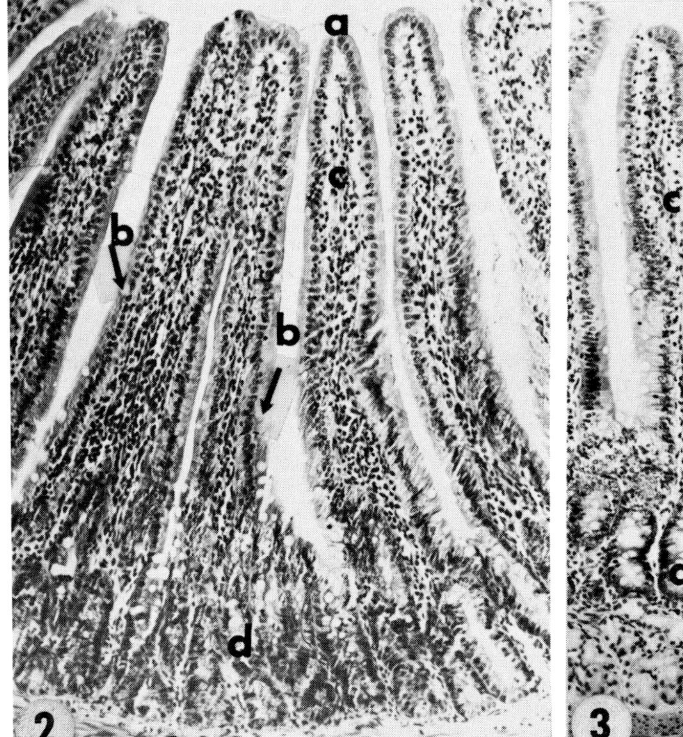

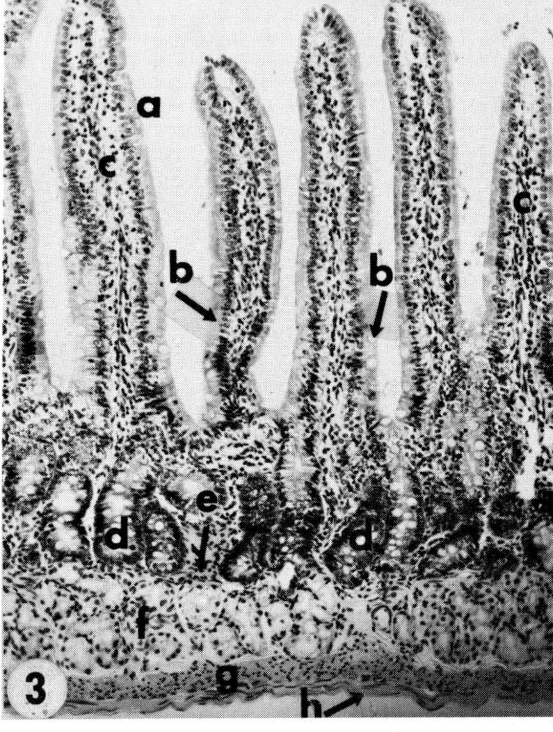

PLATE 34
Digestive System

FIG. 1. Junction of the pyloric stomach and duodenum. Midsagittal section. Level 40. (H&E, × 31)

a. Lumen of the duodenum
b. Duodenal villi
c. Intestinal glands
d. Submucosal glands (Brunner's glands)
e. Junction of the gastric and intestinal mucosa
f. Pyloric sphincter (smooth muscle)
g. Pancreas
h. Lumen of the pyloric stomach
i. Rugae of the stomach

FIG. 2. Duodenum in the area without submucosal glands. Cross section. Level 22. (H&E, × 120)

a. Simple columnar epithelium
b. Goblet cells
c. Lamina propria
d. Intestinal glands
e. Muscularis mucosa

FIG. 3. Duodenum with submucosal glands and Paneth cells. Cross section. Level 40. (H&E, × 120)

a. Simple columnar epithelium
b. Goblet cells
c. Lamina propria
d. Intestinal glands with Paneth cells
e. Muscularis mucosa
f. Submucosal glands (Brunner's glands)
g. Smooth muscle of the tunica muscularis
h. Serosa

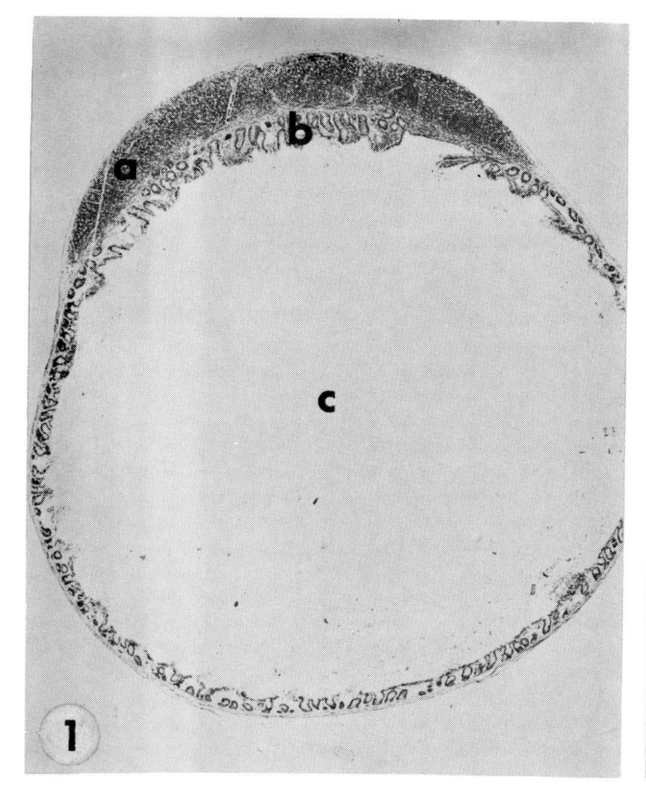

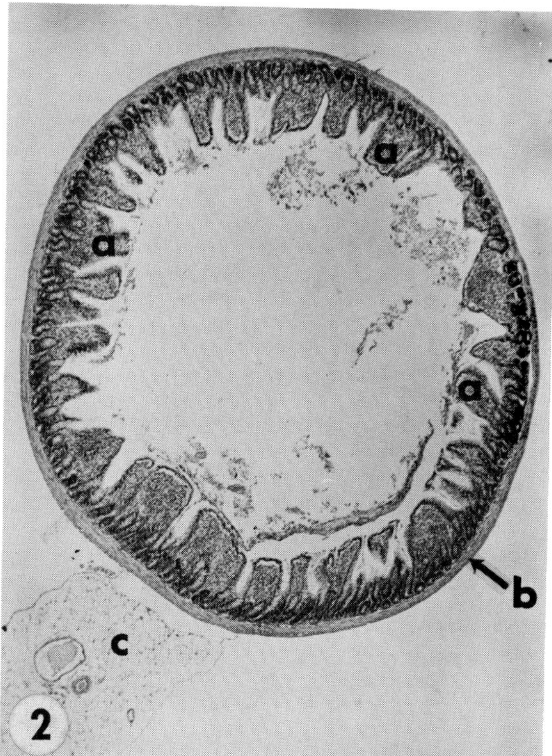

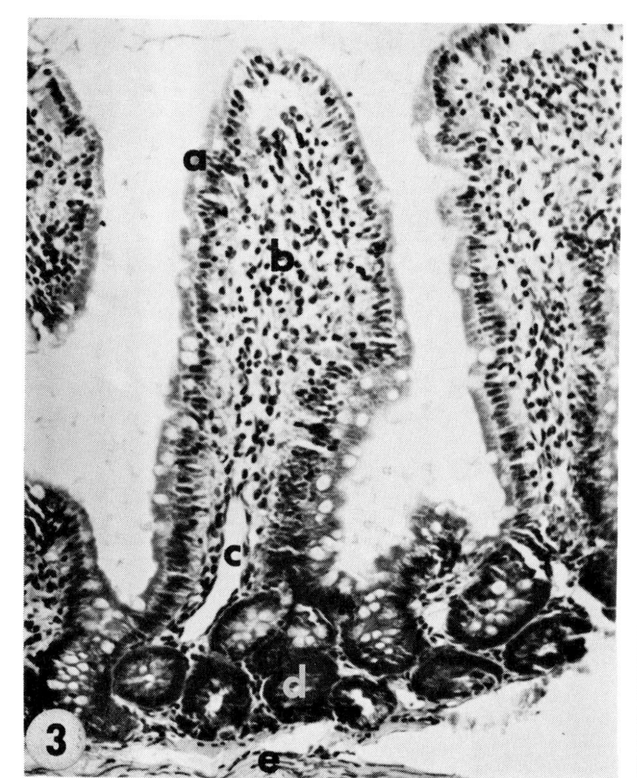

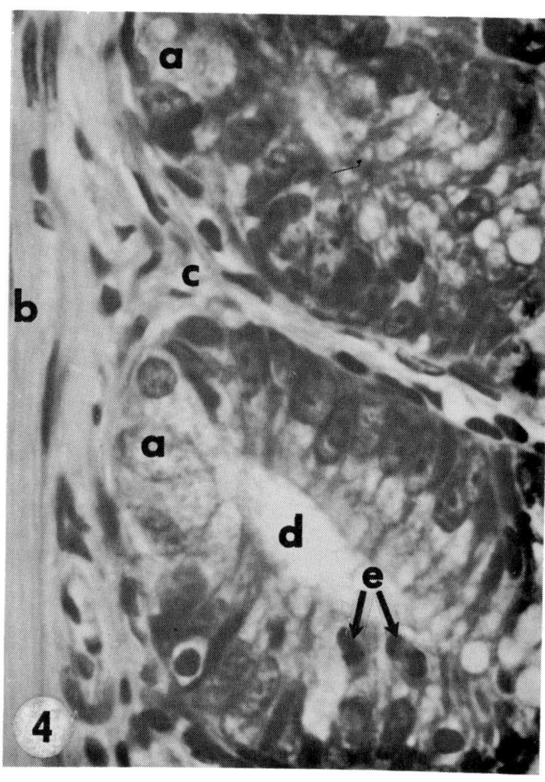

PLATE 35

Digestive System

FIG. 1. Distended ileum. Cross section. Level 30. (H&E, × 15)
- a. Aggregation of lymphoid nodules (Peyer's patch)
- b. Intestinal mucosa
- c. Lumen of the ileum

FIG. 2. Ileum. Cross section. Level 31. (H&E, × 19)
- a. Various shaped villi
- b. Tunica muscularis
- c. Mesentery

FIG. 3. Villus. Level 28. (H&E, × 195)
- a. Simple columnar epithelium with goblet cells
- b. Lamina propria
- c. Lacteal
- d. Intestinal glands
- e. Muscularis mucosa

FIG. 4. Base of the intestinal glands in the ileum. Cross section. Level 31. (H&E, × 1020)
- a. Paneth cells with cytoplasmic granules
- b. Muscularis mucosa
- c. Lamina propria
- d. Lumen of the intestinal gland (Crypt of Lieberkühn)
- e. Cells of the intestinal glands in mitosis

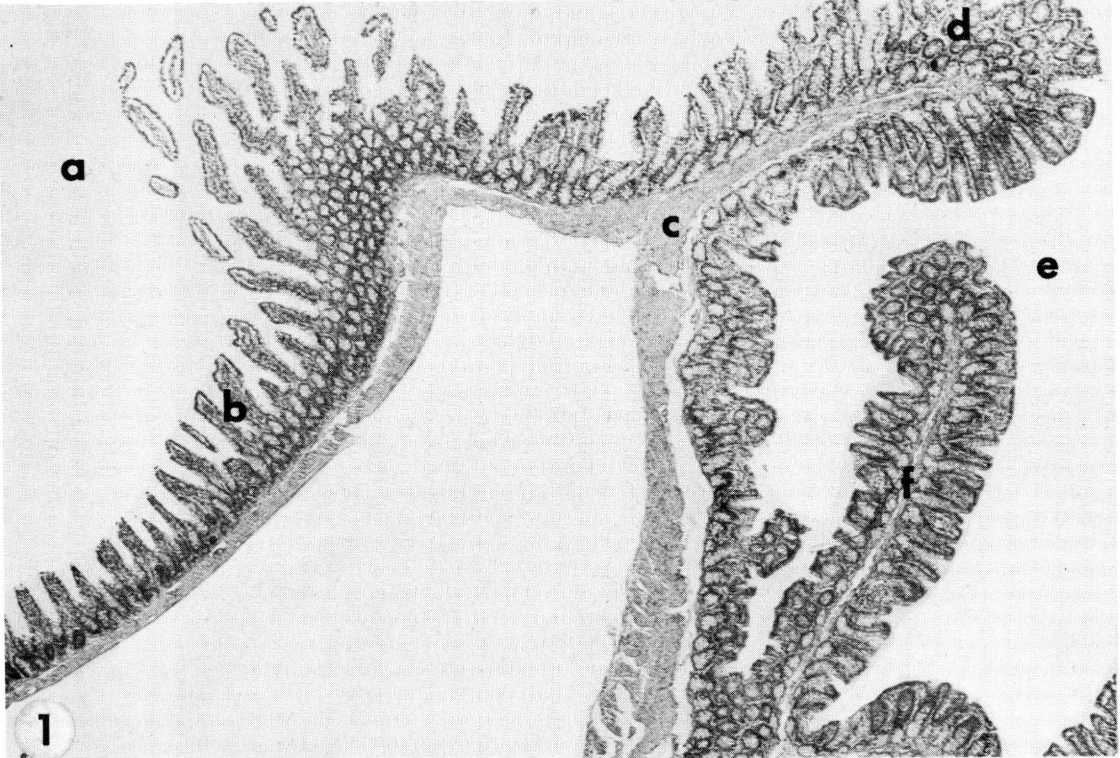

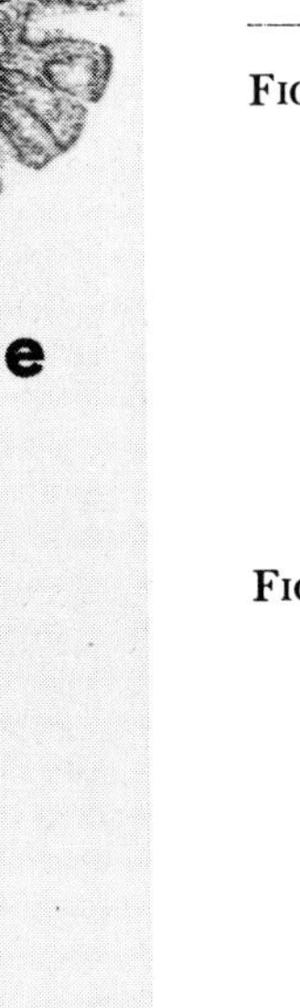

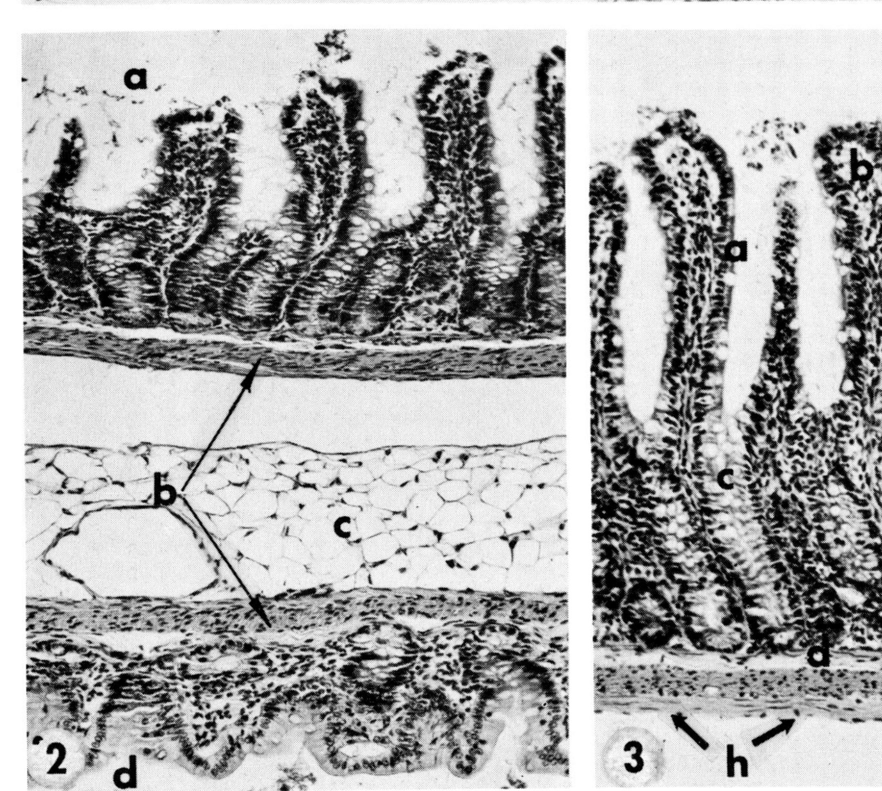

Plate 36

Digestive System

Fig. 1. Ileocecal junction. Longitudinal section. Level 32. (H&E, × 29)

a. Lumen of the ileum
b. Villi of the ileum
c. Tunica muscularis
d. Ileocecal mucosal junction
e. Lumen of the cecum
f. Fold of the cecal mucosa

Fig. 2. Ileum and cecum near the ileocecal junction. Longitudinal section. Level 32. (H&E, × 160)

a. Lumen of the ileum
b. Tunica muscularis of the ileum (above) and cecum (below)
c. Serosa of the cecum containing abundant adipose tissue
d. Lumen of the cecum

Fig. 3. Ileum. Longitudinal section. Level 32. (H&E, × 155)

a. Simple columnar epithelium with goblet cells
b. Tunica propria of the villi (note lacteals at arrows)
c. Intestinal glands (Crypts of Lieberkühn)
d. Muscularis mucosa
e. Submucosa
f. Inner circular smooth muscle layer of the tunica muscularis
g. Outer longitudinal smooth muscle layer of the tunica muscularis
h. Serosa

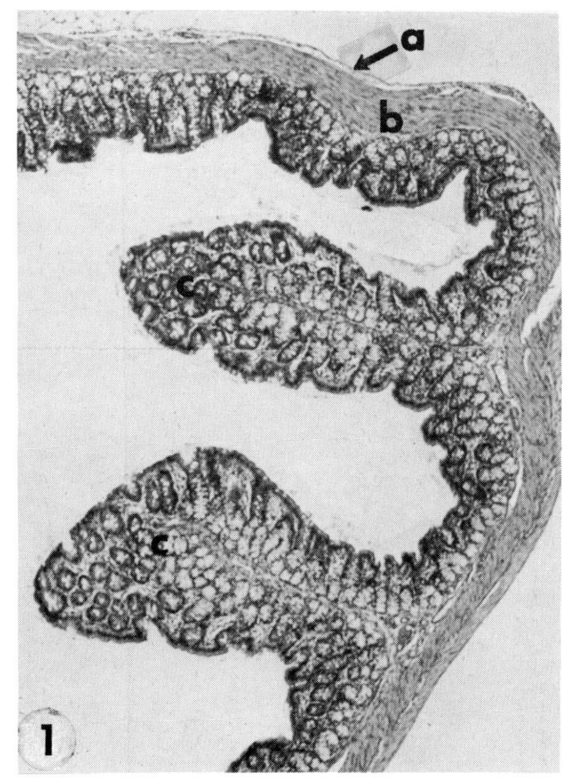

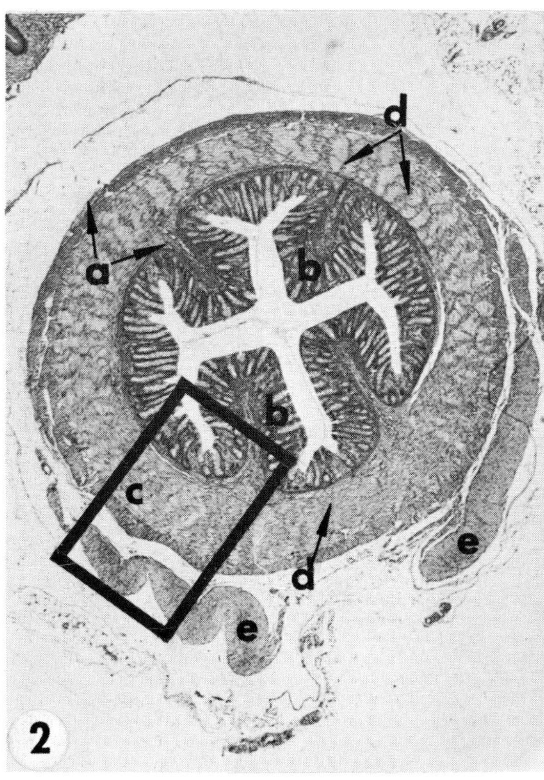

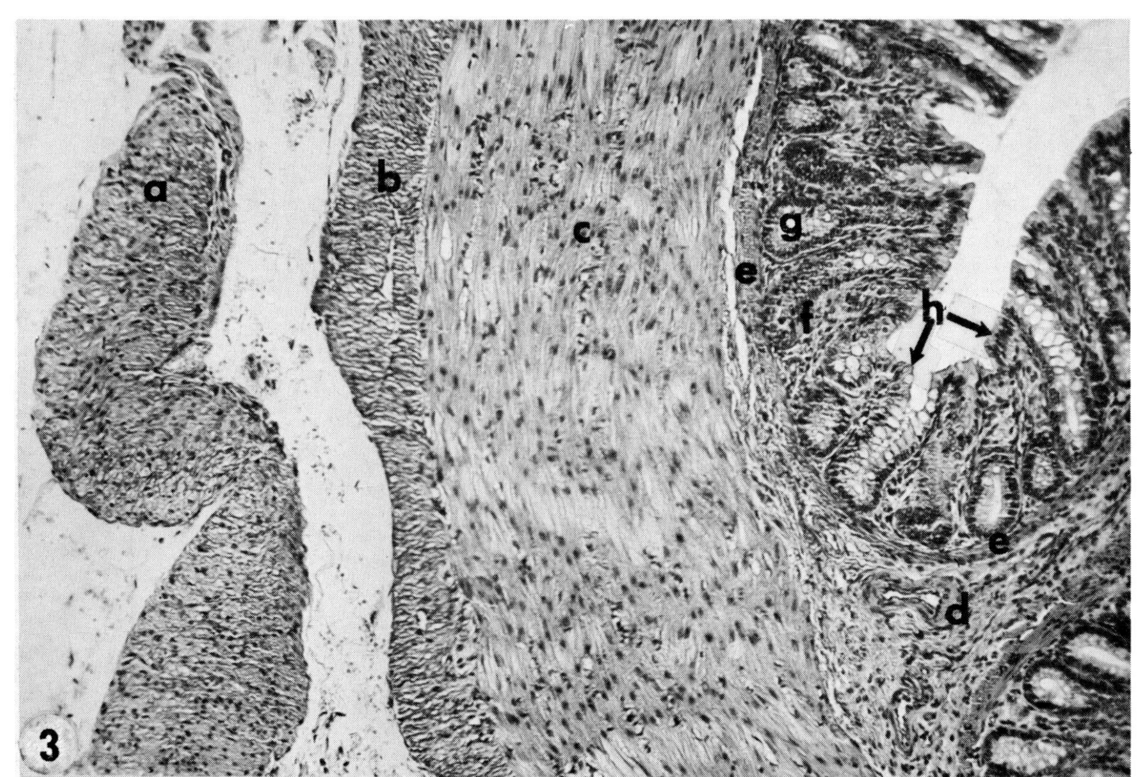

PLATE 37
Digestive System

FIG. 1. Cecum. Oblique section. Level 32. (H&E, × 135)

- a. Serosa
- b. Tunica muscularis (note spiraling of muscle layers)
- c. Longitudinal mucosal folds

FIG. 2. Colon. Cross section. Level 37. (H&E, × 24)

- a. Tunica muscularis
- b. Mucosa
- c. Area of enlargement for Fig. 3
- d. Contraction bands in the circular muscle layer
- e. Taenia coli (bands of outermost fibers in the outer longitudinal muscle layer)

FIG. 3. Colon (high power of area marked in Fig. 2). Cross section. Level 37. (H&E, × 165)

- a. Taenia coli
- b. Remaining longitudinal muscle fibers of the outer longitudinal muscle layer
- c. Inner circular layer of the tunica muscularis with contraction bands
- d. Submucosa with blood vessels
- e. Muscularis mucosa
- f. Lamina propria
- g. Intestinal gland (Crypt of Lieberkühn)
- h. Simple columnar epithelium with goblet cells

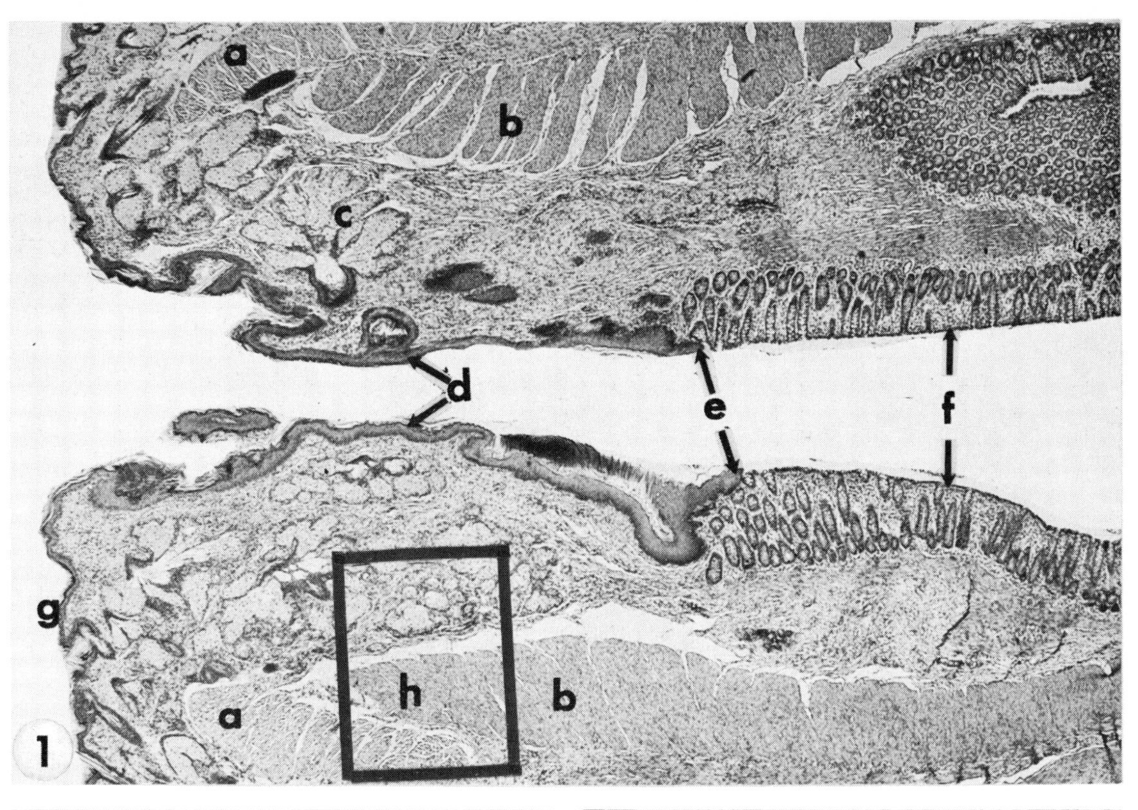

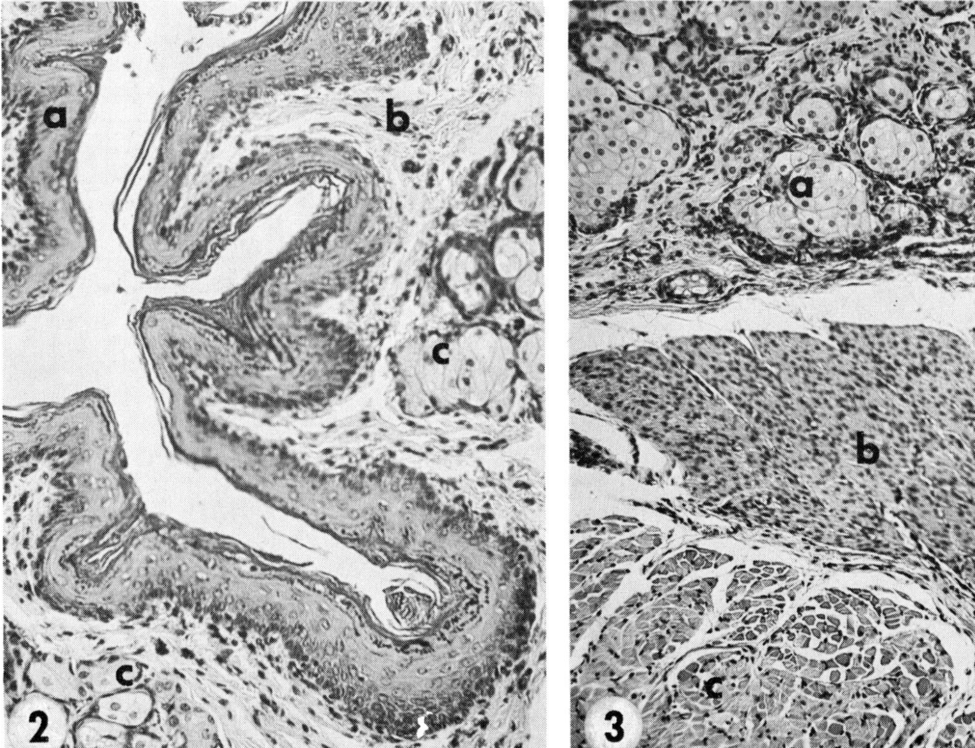

PLATE 38

Digestive System

FIG. 1. Anorectal junction. Longitudinal section. Level 38. (H&E, × 31)

a. Skeletal muscle of the external anal sphincter
b. Smooth muscle of the internal anal sphincter
c. Circumanal glands
d. Stratified squamous epithelium of the anal canal
e. Junction of the anal and rectal epithelium
f. Simple columnar epithelium of the rectal mucosa
g. Circumanal skin
h. Area of enlargement for Fig. 3

FIG. 2. Anus. Cross section. Level 37. (H&E, × 180)

a. Keratinized stratified squamous epithelium
b. Lamina propria
c. Circumanal glands (modified sebaceous type)

FIG. 3. Anorectal area (high power of area marked in Fig. 1). Longitudinal section. Level 38. (H&E, × 100)

a. Circumanal glands
b. Smooth muscle of the internal anal sphincter
c. Skeletal muscle of the external anal sphincter

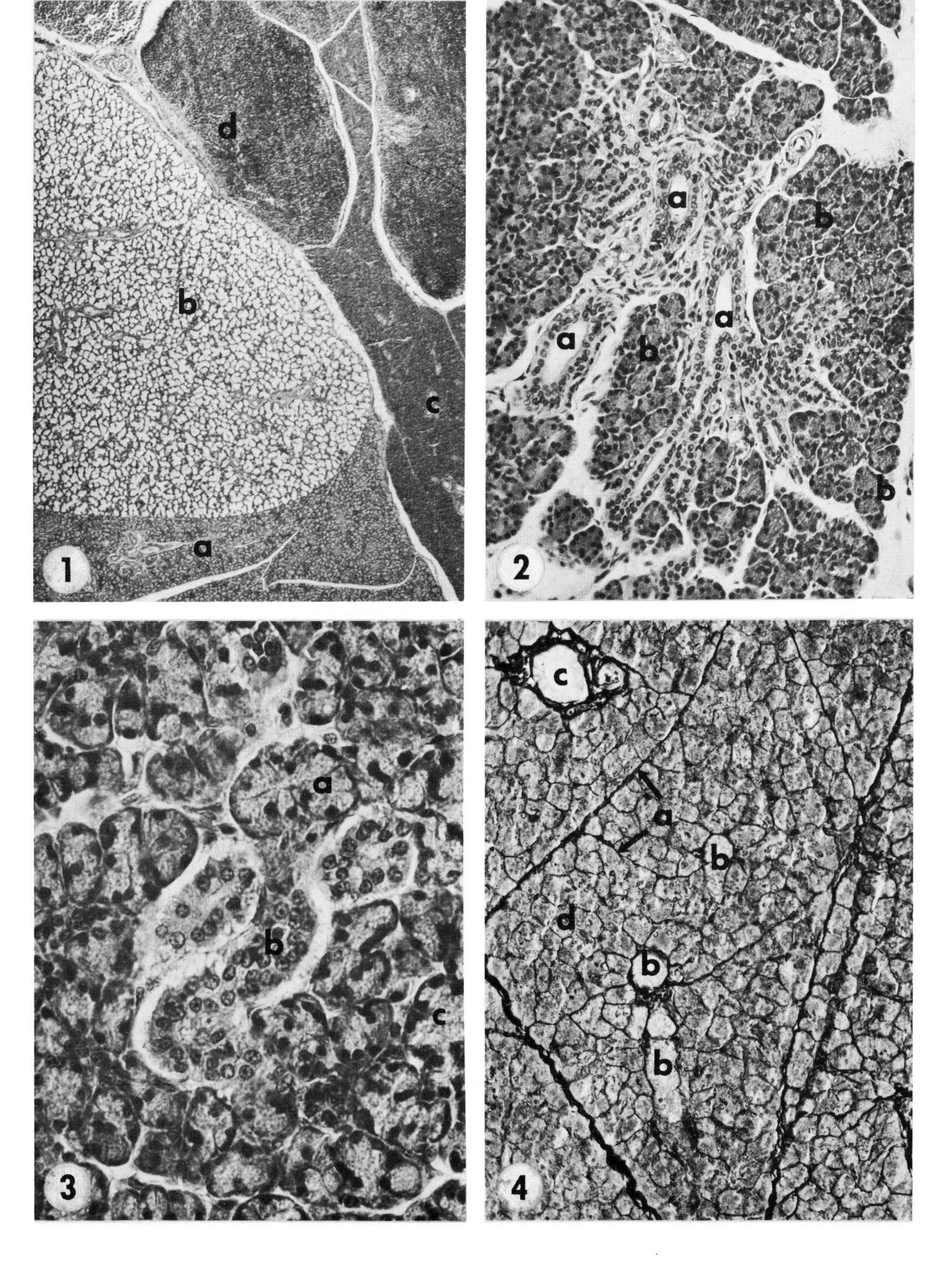

PLATE 39
Digestive System

FIG. 1. Salivary glands. Levels 13, 14 & 15. (H&E, × 23)
a. Submaxillary salivary gland
b. Sublingual salivary gland
c. Parotid salivary gland
d. Submaxillary lymph node

FIG. 2. Parotid salivary gland (serous). Level 13. (H&E, × 220)
a. Interlobular ducts
b. Alveoli of the gland parenchyma

FIG. 3. Submaxillary salivary gland (mixed). Level 15. (H&E, × 485)
a. Serous alveolus
b. Intercalated duct leaving the alveolus
c. Mucous alveolus

FIG. 4. Sublingual salivary gland (predominantly mucous). Level 14. (Reticular stain, × 150)
a. Reticular connective tissue fibers
b. Intralobular ducts
c. Interlobular duct
d. Alveoli surrounded by reticular fibers

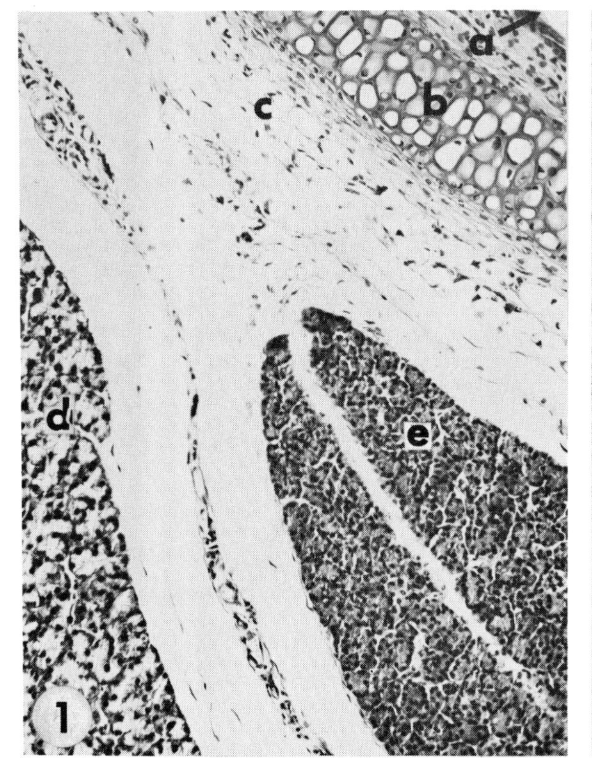

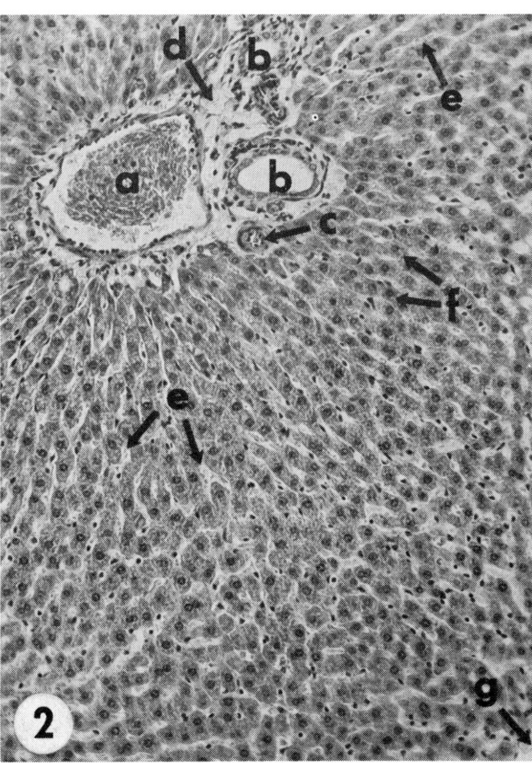

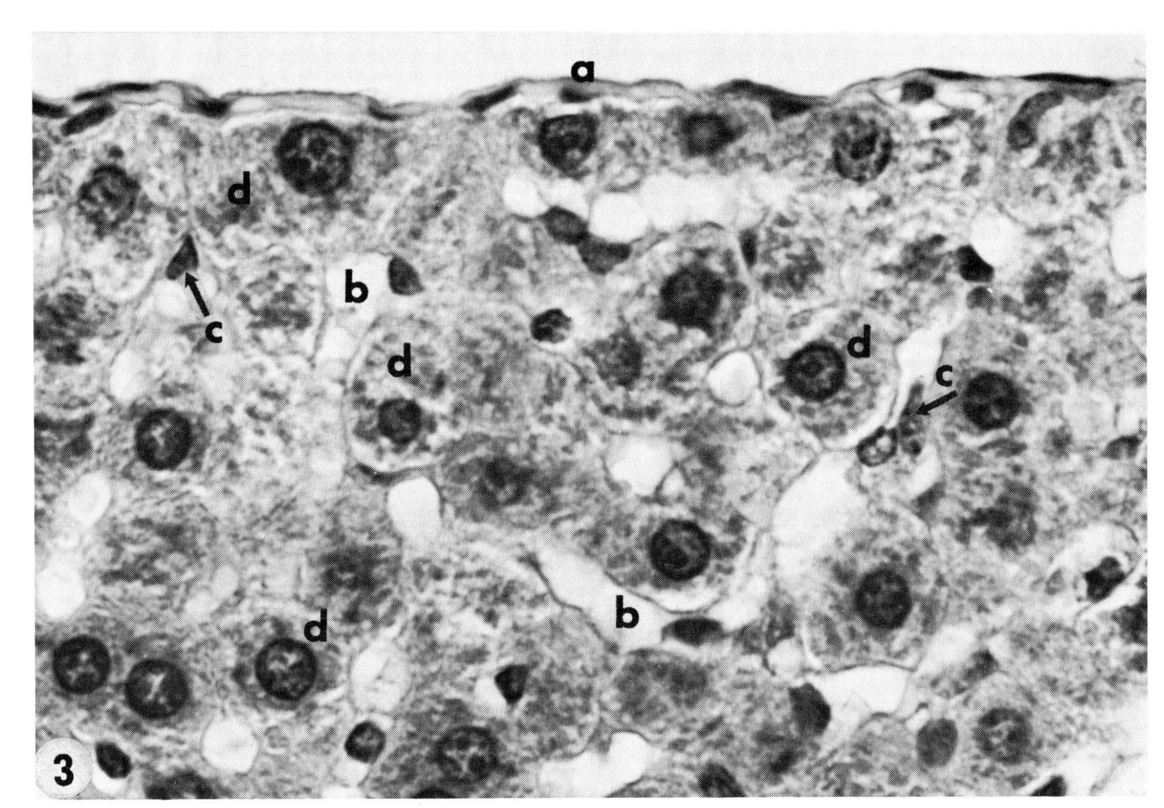

PLATE 40
Digestive System

FIG. 1. Relationship of parotid salivary gland to the exorbital lacrimal gland and the auditory canal. Longitudinal section. Level 12 to 13. (H&E, × 130)

a. Auditory canal
b. Elastic cartilage of the ear
c. Loose connective tissue
d. Exorbital lacrimal gland
e. Parotid salivary gland

FIG. 2. Portal area of the liver. Level 24. (H&E, × 155)

a. Portal vein
b. Bile ducts
c. Hepatic artery
d. Lymphatic
e. Hepatic sinusoids
f. Liver parenchyma
g. Central vein

FIG. 3. Liver. Level 24. (H&E, × 1040)

a. Connective tissue capsule with mesothelial covering
b. Sinusoids
c. Reticuloendothelial cells lining a sinusoid (Küpffer cell)
d. Hepatic cells (note prominent nucleoli)

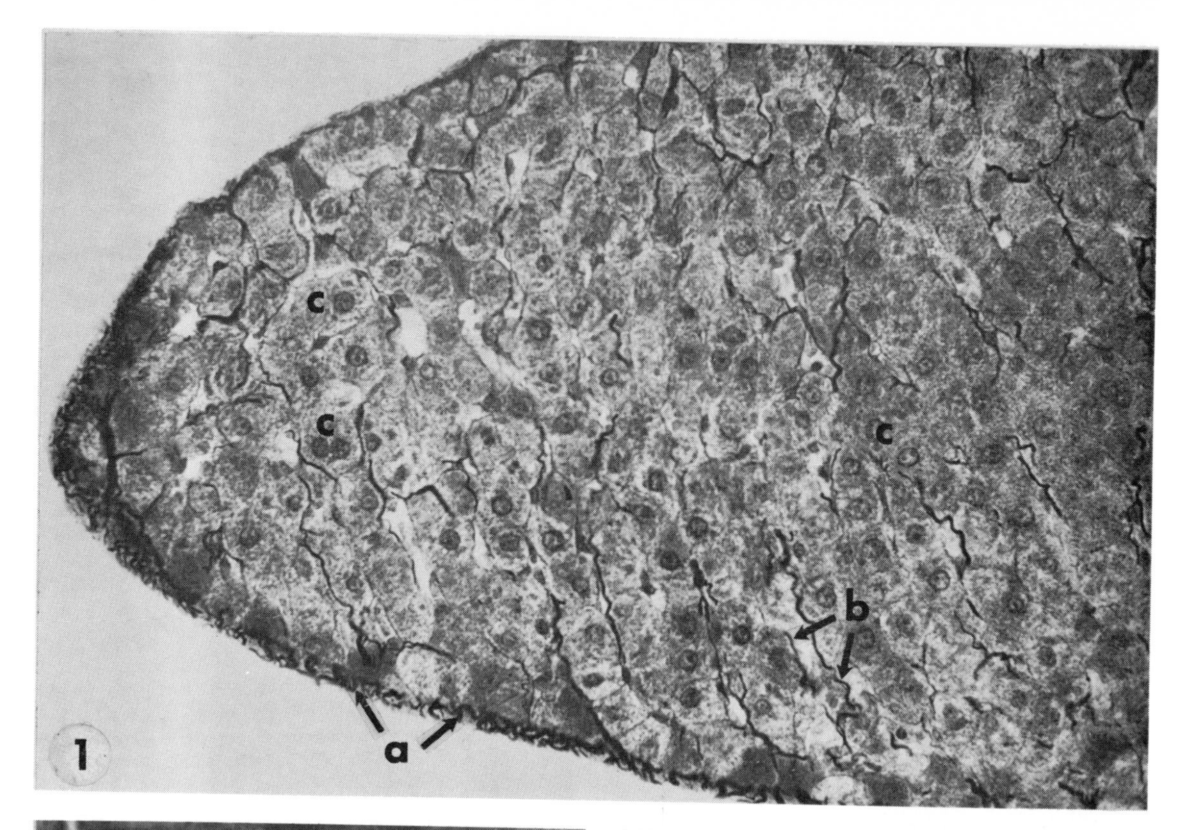

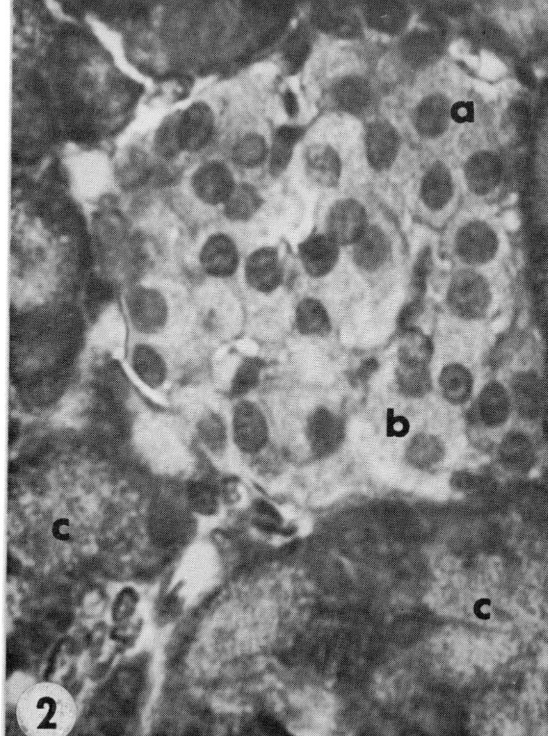

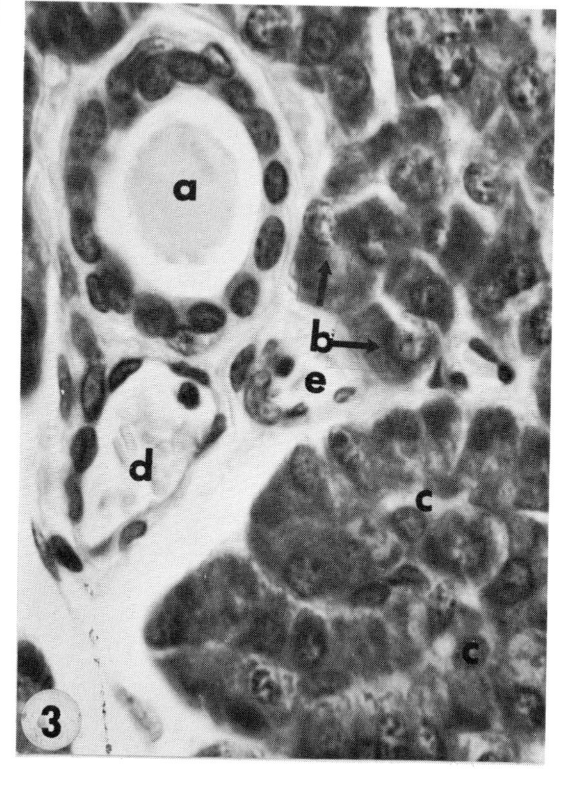

PLATE 41
Digestive System

FIG. 1. Liver. Level 24. (Reticular stain, × 415)
- a. Reticular fibers in the capsule
- b. Reticular fibers extending into the liver parenchyma
- c. Hepatic cells

FIG. 2. Pancreatic islet. Level 23. (Gomori's stain, × 1285)
- a. Alpha cells
- b. Beta cells
- c. Pancreatic acinar cells with zymogen granules

FIG. 3. Pancreas. Level 23. (H&E, × 940)
- a. Interlobular pancreatic duct
- b. Pancreatic acinar cells
- c. Centroacinar cells
- d. Vein
- e. Artery

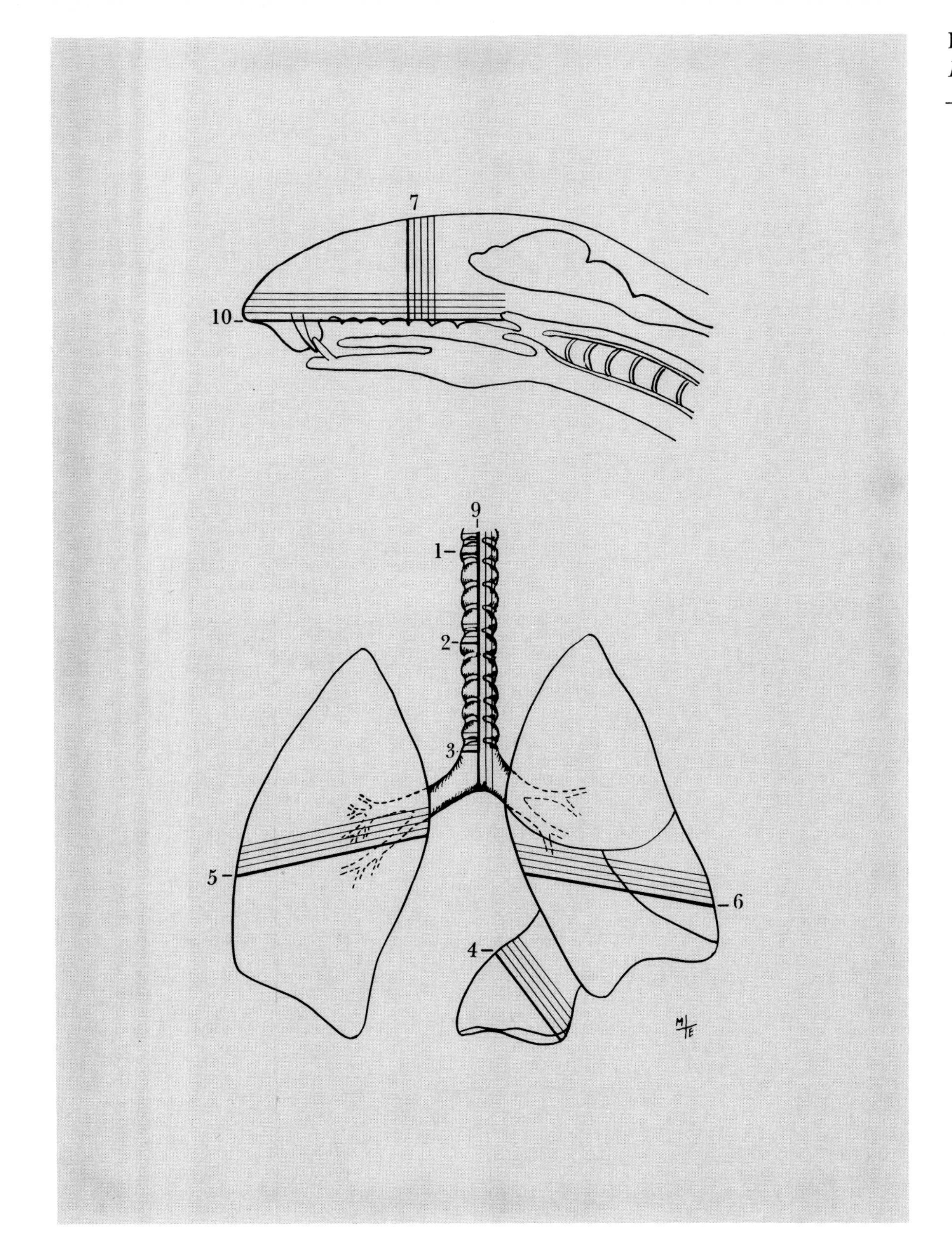

PLATE 42
Respiratory System

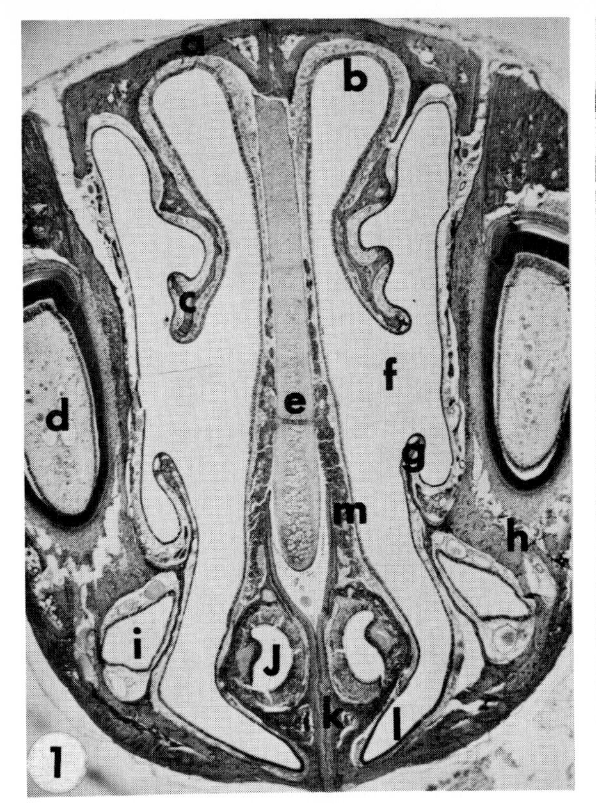

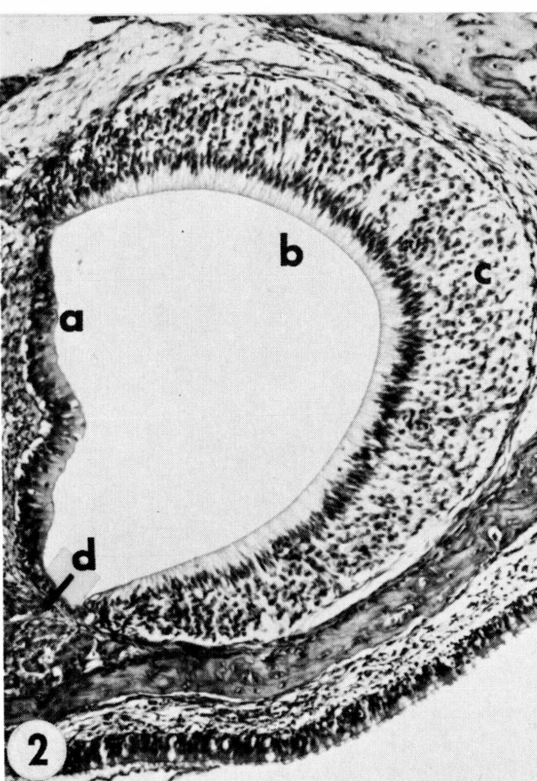

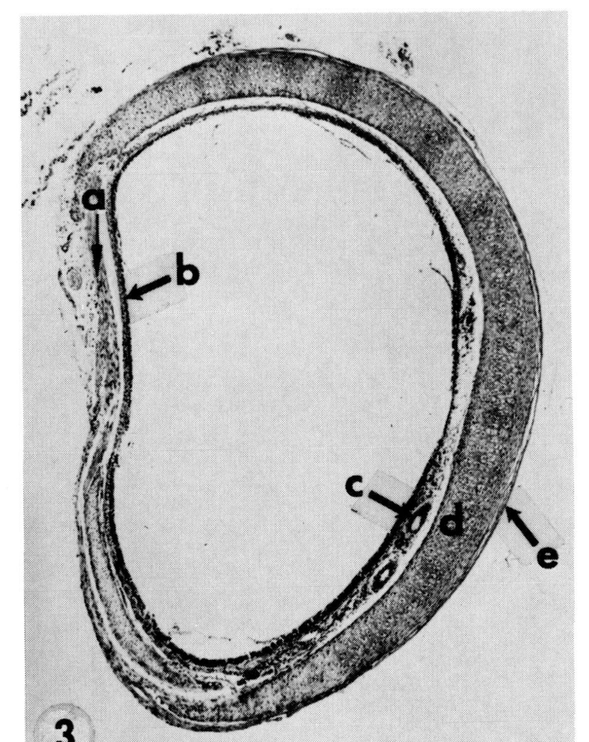

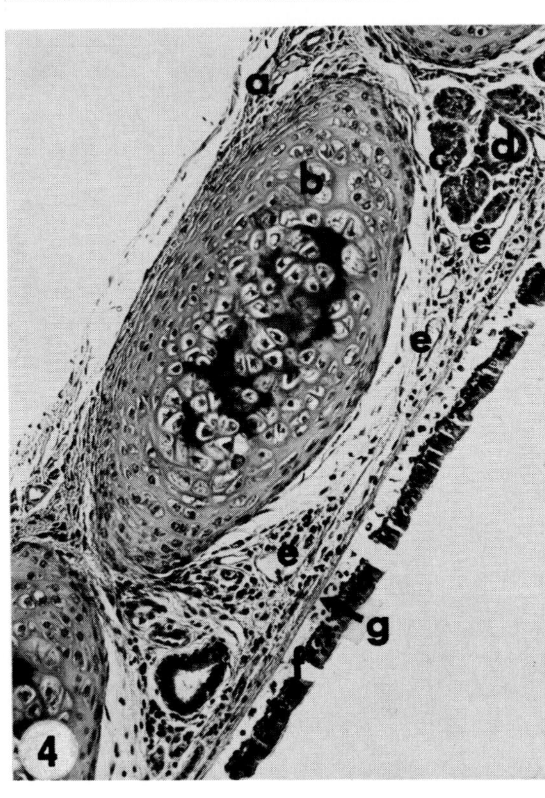

PLATE 43
Respiratory System

FIG. 1. Nasal cavity in the maxillary region. Cross section. Level 7. (H&E, × 15)

a. Frontal bone
b. Olfactory region of the nasal mucosa
c. Dorsal turbinate
d. Dental pulp of an incisor tooth
e. Hyaline cartilage of the nasal septum
f. Respiratory region of the nasal mucosa
g. Ventral turbinate
h. Maxillary bone
i. Nasolacrimal duct
j. Vomeronasal organ (Organ of Jacobson)
k. Vomer bone
l. Vestibular region of the nasal mucosa
m. Seromucous glands

FIG. 2. Vomeronasal organ. Cross section. Level 7. (H&E, × 140)

a. Respiratory epithelium on the lateral aspect of the nasal cavity
b. Olfactory epithelium on the medial aspect of the nasal cavity
c. Nonmyelinated nerve fibers
d. Serous glands

FIG. 3. Trachea. Cross section. Level 2. (H&E, × 30)

a. Trachealis muscle
b. Pseudostratified ciliated columnar epithelium
c. Ducts of the tracheal glands
d. Hyaline cartilage of the tracheal ring
e. Perichondrium

FIG. 4. Trachea. Longitudinal section. Level 9. (H&E, × 115)

a. Perichondrium
b. Hyaline cartilage of the tracheal ring (partially calcified)
c. Serous alveolus of the tracheal glands
d. Duct of the tracheal glands
e. Blood vessels
f. Pseudostratified ciliated columnar epithelium
g. Fibroelastic membrane

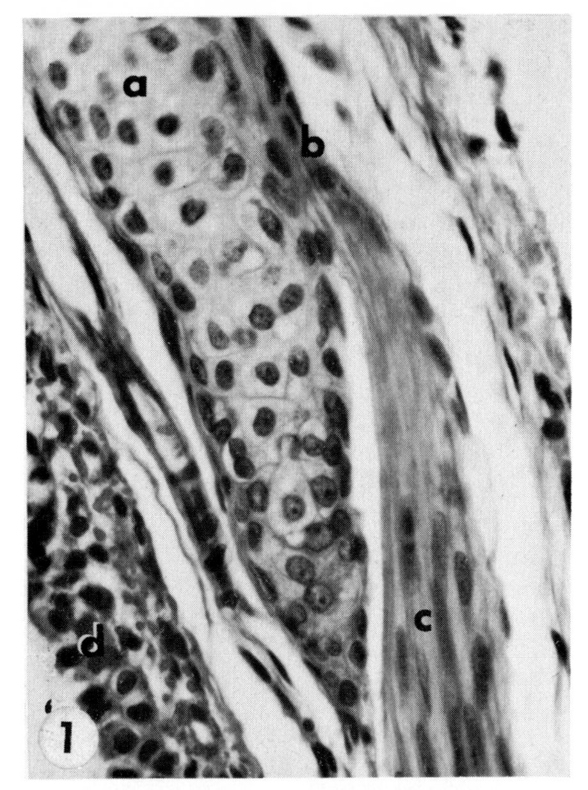

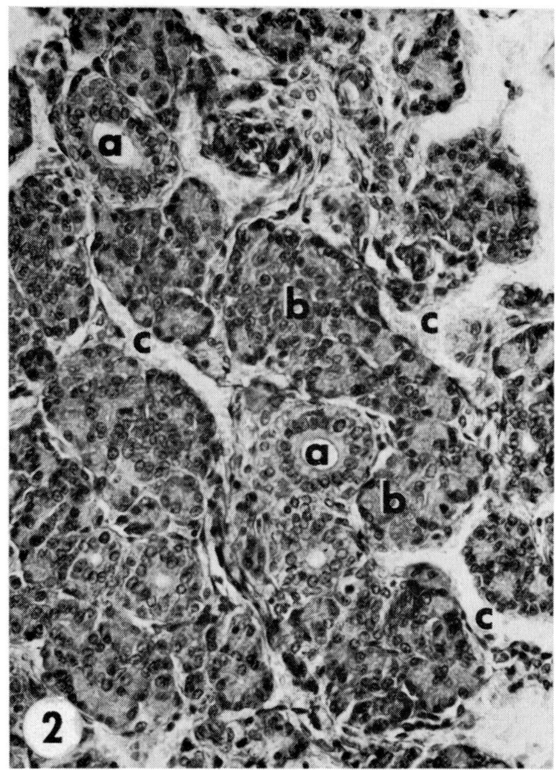

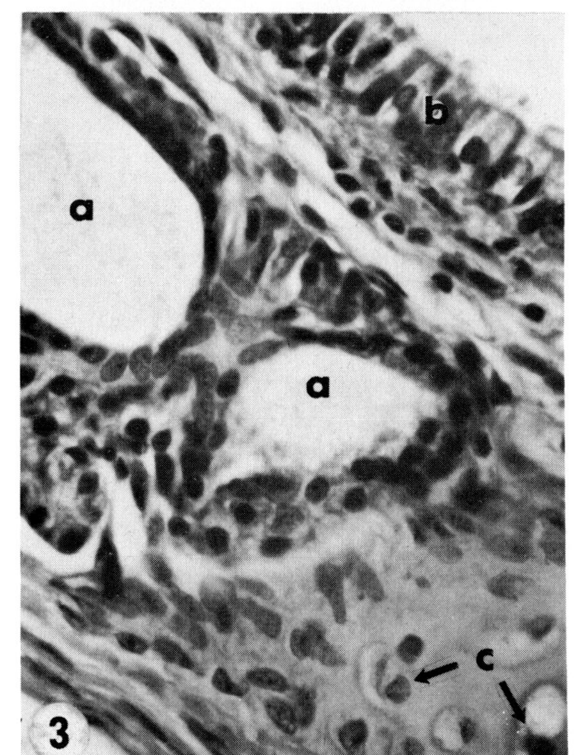

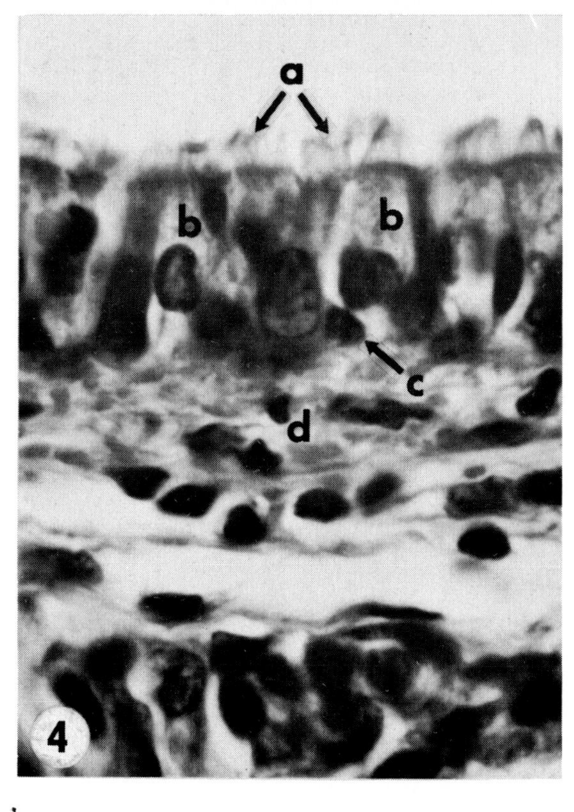

PLATE 44

Respiratory System

FIG. 1. Insertion of the trachealis muscle on the perichondrium. Cross section. Level 2. (H&E, × 630)

a. Immature hyaline cartilage of the tracheal ring
b. Area of insertion of muscle on the perichondrium
c. Smooth muscle fibers of the trachealis muscle
d. Pseudostratified ciliated columnar epithelium

FIG. 2. Tracheal glands. Cross section. Level 2. (H&E, × 345)

a. Ducts
b. Serous alveoli
c. Capillaries

FIG. 3. Trachea. Cross section. Level 2. (H&E, × 680)

a. Ducts of the tracheal glands
b. Pseudostratified ciliated columnar epithelium
c. Hyaline cartilage of a tracheal ring (note chondrocytes at arrows)

FIG. 4. Tracheal mucosa. Cross section. Level 2. (H&E, × 1390)

a. Cilia
b. Pseudostratified ciliated columnar epithelium
c. Basal cell
d. Lamina propria

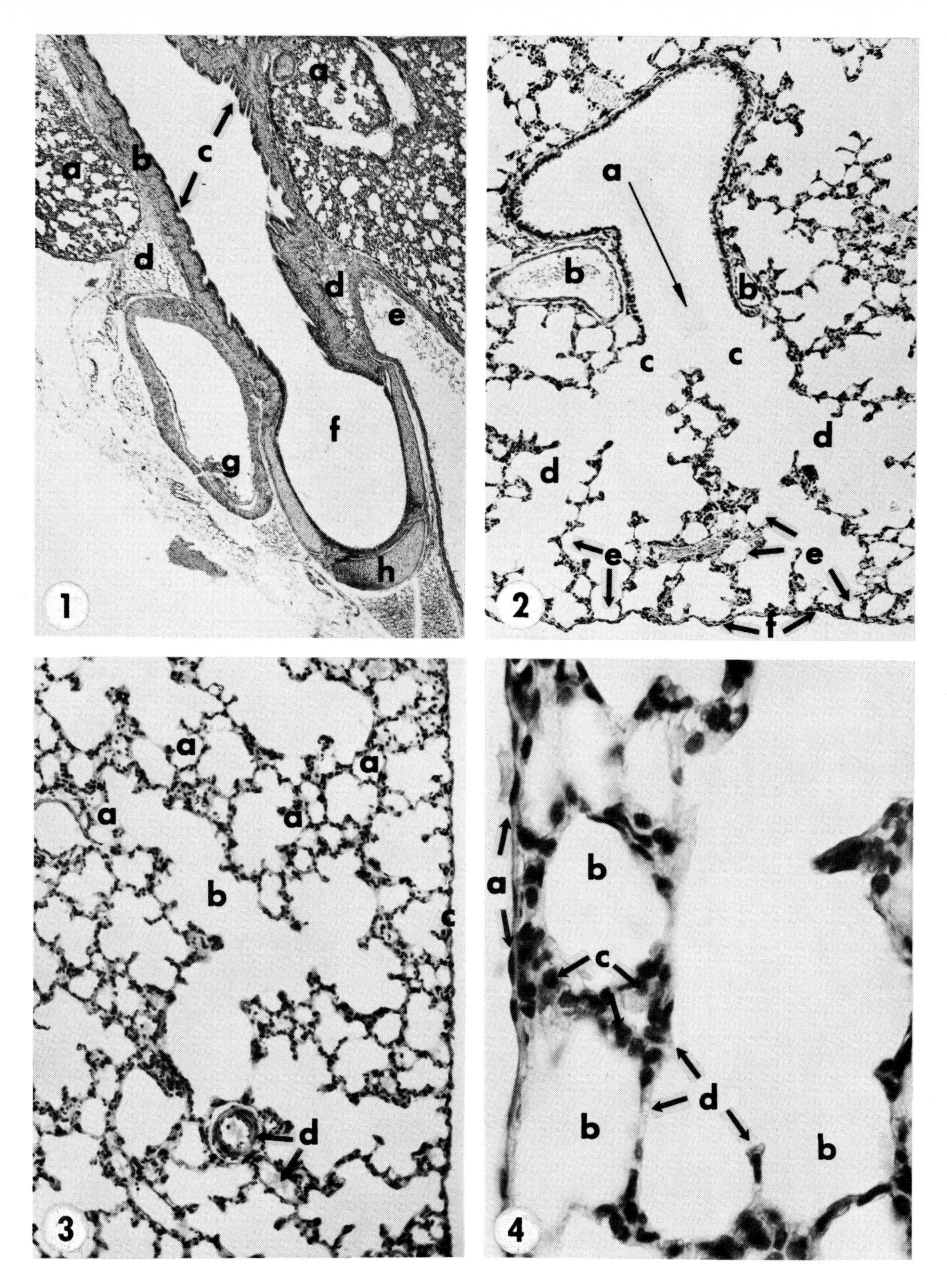

PLATE 45
Respiratory System

FIG. 1. Junction of the primary and secondary bronchi. Longitudinal section. Level 5. (H&E, × 30)

a. Pulmonary alveoli
b. Circular smooth muscle of a secondary bronchus
c. Mucosal folds
d. Adipose tissue
e. Pulmonary vein
f. Primary bronchus
g. Pulmonary artery
h. Hyaline cartilage plate of the primary bronchus

FIG. 2. Terminal bronchiole and the pulmonary alveoli. Longitudinal section. Level 6. (H&E, × 85)

a. Terminal bronchiole
b. Veins
c. Respiratory bronchiole
d. Alveolar duct
e. Alveoli
f. Visceral pleura

FIG. 3. Lung parenchyma. Level 6. (H&E, × 150)

a. Alveoli
b. Alveolar duct
c. Visceral pleura
d. Small artery and vein

FIG. 4. Lung parenchyma. Level 5. (H&E, × 740)

a. Visceral pleura
b. Alveoli
c. Septal cells
d. Alveolar wall

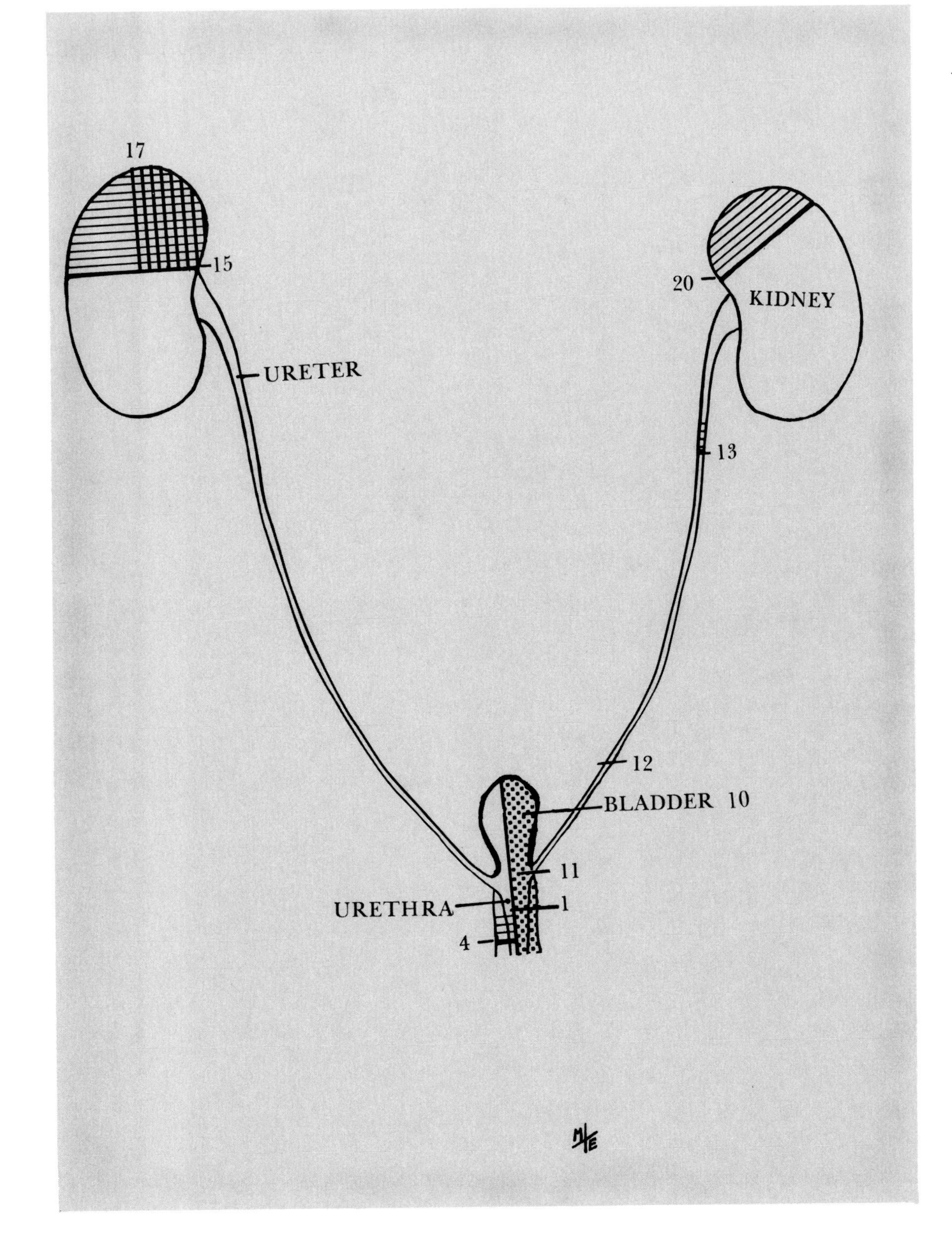

PLATE 46
Urinary System

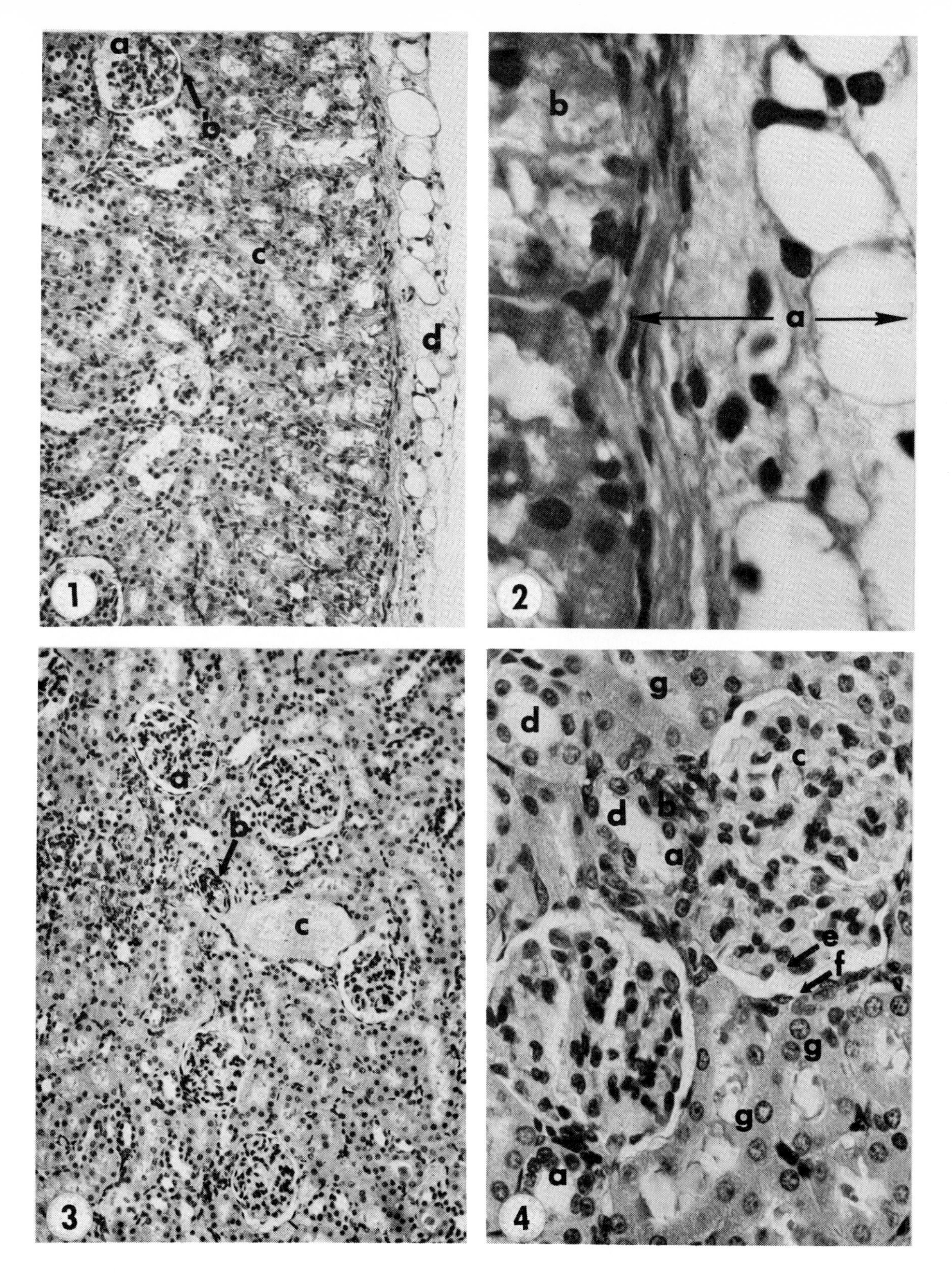

PLATE 47
Urinary System

FIG. 1. Cortex of the kidney. Level 17. (H&E, × 175)
- a. Glomerulus of the renal corpuscle
- b. Epithelial cells of the parietal layer of the glomerular (Bowman's) capsule
- c. Uriniferous tubules
- d. Kidney capsule with adipose tissue

FIG. 2. Kidney capsule. Level 17. (H&E, × 750)
- a. Capsule composed of outer adipose and inner fibrous layers
- b. Kidney parenchyma

FIG. 3. Interlobular artery and vein of the renal cortex. Level 17. (H&E, × 240)
- a. Renal corpuscle
- b. Interlobular artery
- c. Interlobular vein

FIG. 4. Renal corpuscles with an adjacent macula densa. Level 17. (H&E, × 605)
- a. Macula densa in a distal convoluted tubule
- b. Juxtaglomerular apparatus
- c. Glomerulus
- d. Distal convoluted tubule
- e. Visceral layer of the glomerular capsule
- f. Parietal layer of the glomerular capsule
- g. Proximal convoluted tubule

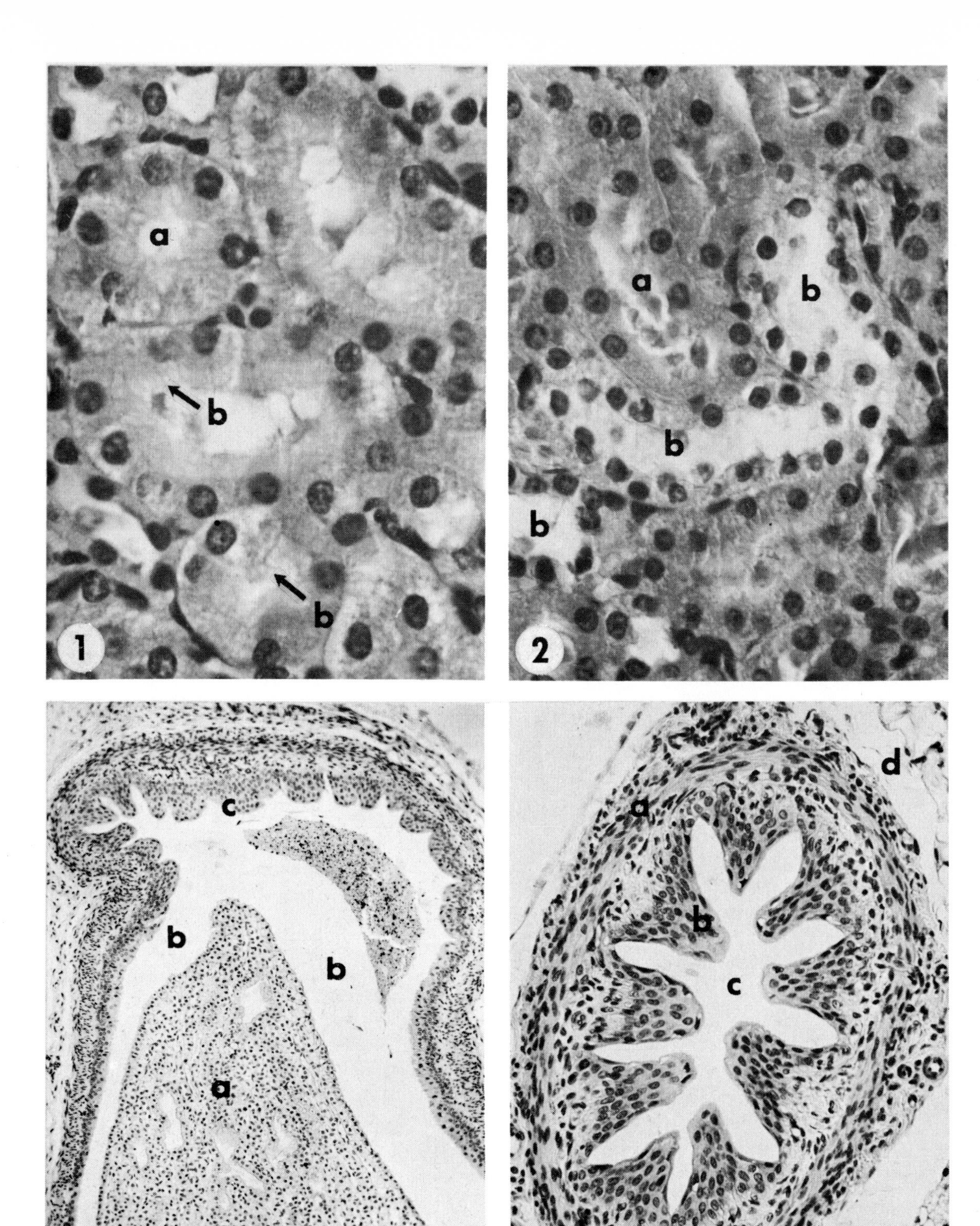

PLATE 48
Urinary System

FIG. 1. Proximal convoluted tubules of the kidney. Level 17. (H&E, × 925)
a. Lumen
b. Tubular epithelium with microvilli (brush border)

FIG. 2. Convoluted tubules of the kidney. Level 17. (H&E, × 735)
a. Proximal convoluted tubule
b. Distal convoluted tubule

FIG. 3. Junction of the kidney pelvis and the ureter. Level 15. (H&E, × 135)
a. Renal papilla
b. Renal pelvis
c. Transitional epithelium of the ureter

FIG. 4. Ureter. Cross section. Level 13. (H&E, × 255)
a. Smooth muscle fibers of the tunica muscularis
b. Transitional epithelium
c. Lumen
d. Adventitia

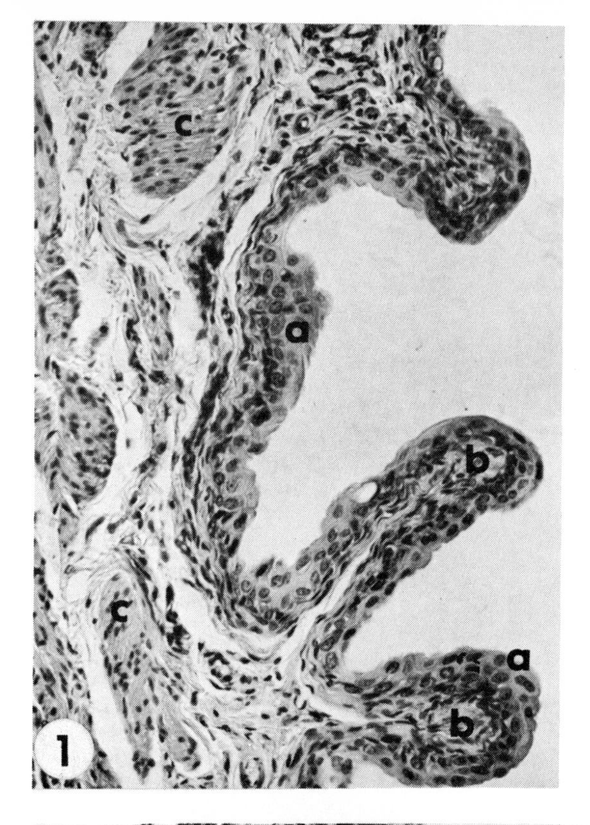

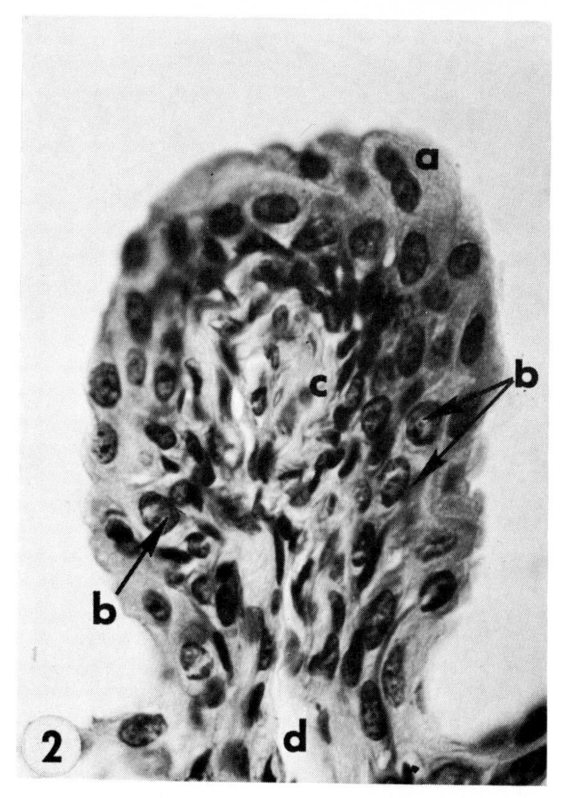

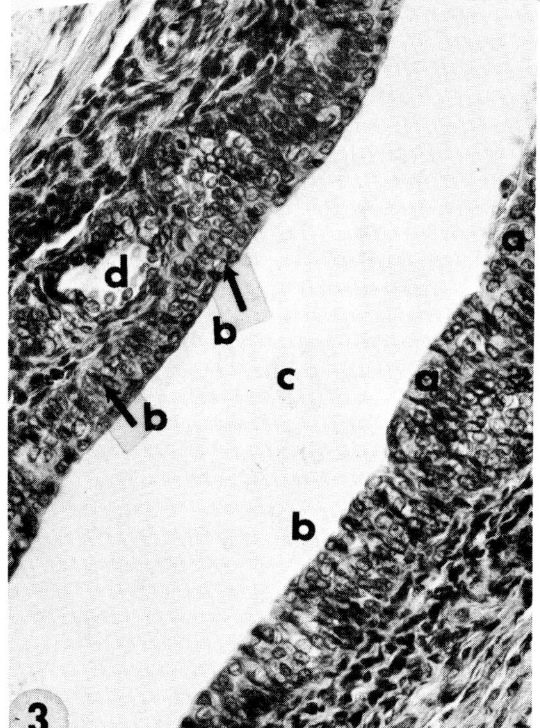

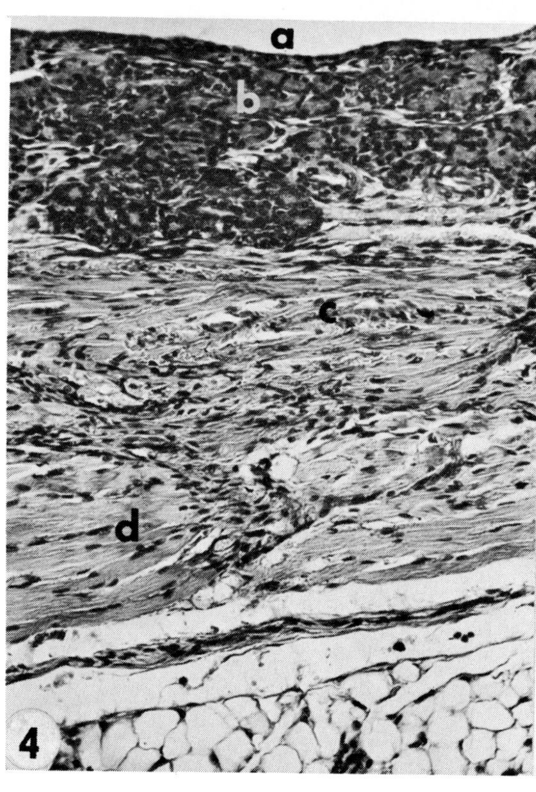

PLATE 49

Urinary System

FIG. 1. Urinary bladder. Longitudinal section. Level 10. (H&E, × 240)
- a. Transitional epithelium
- b. Lamina propria
- c. Smooth muscle of the bladder wall

FIG. 2. Urinary bladder mucosa. Level 10. (H&E, × 610)
- a. Flattened binucleated transitional epithelial cell
- b. Polygonal cells of the basal layer
- c. Lamina propria
- d. Capillary

FIG. 3. Neck of the urinary bladder. Longitudinal section. Level 11. (H&E, × 275)
- a. Patches of transitional epithelium
- b. Stratified columnar epithelium
- c. Lumen
- d. Mucosal gland

FIG. 4. Pelvic urethra (male). Longitudinal section. Level 1. (H&E, × 230)
- a. Urethral lumen
- b. Serous glands in the mucosa lined with low transitional epithelium
- c. Smooth muscle
- d. Skeletal muscle

PLATE 50
Male Urogenital System

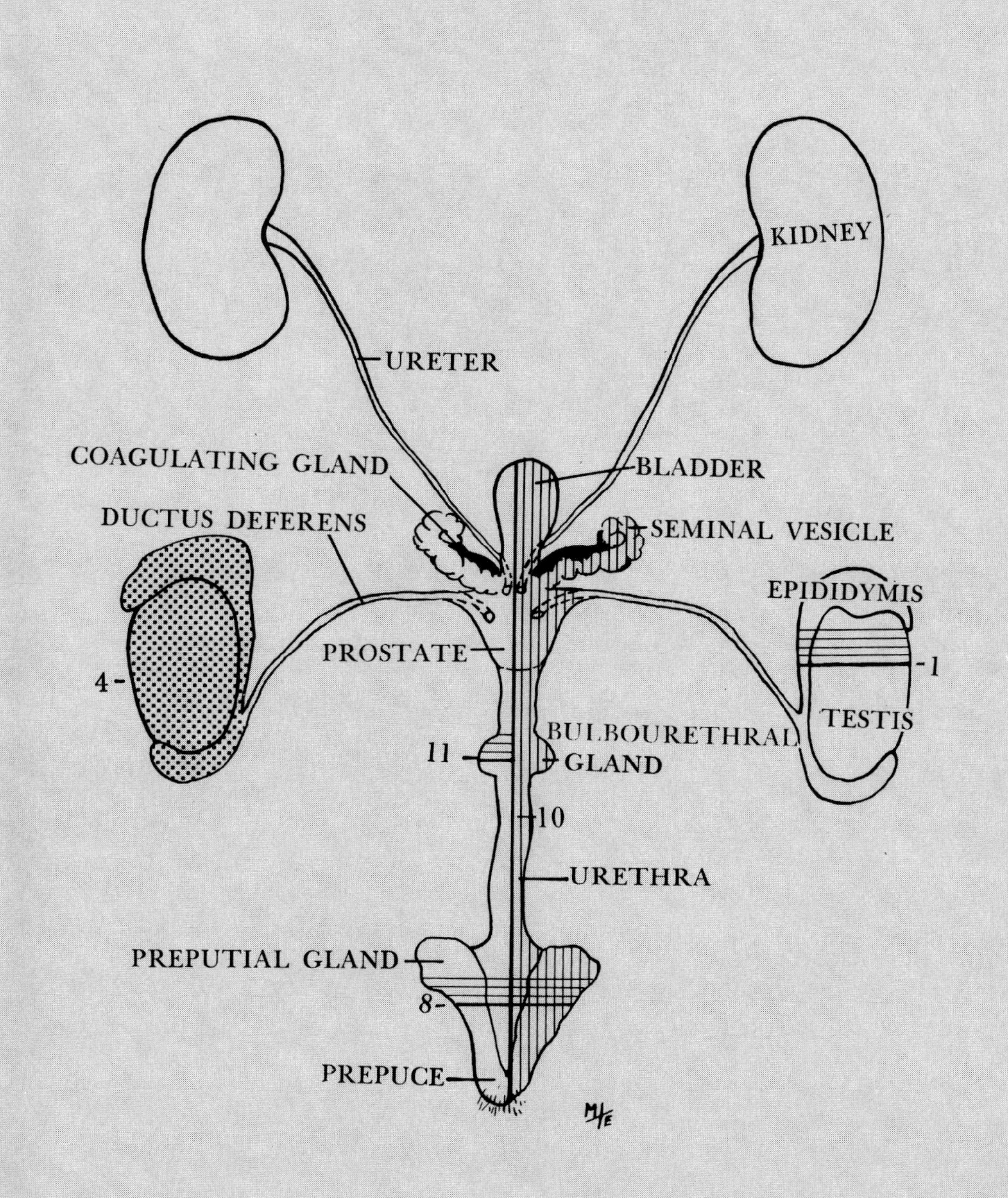

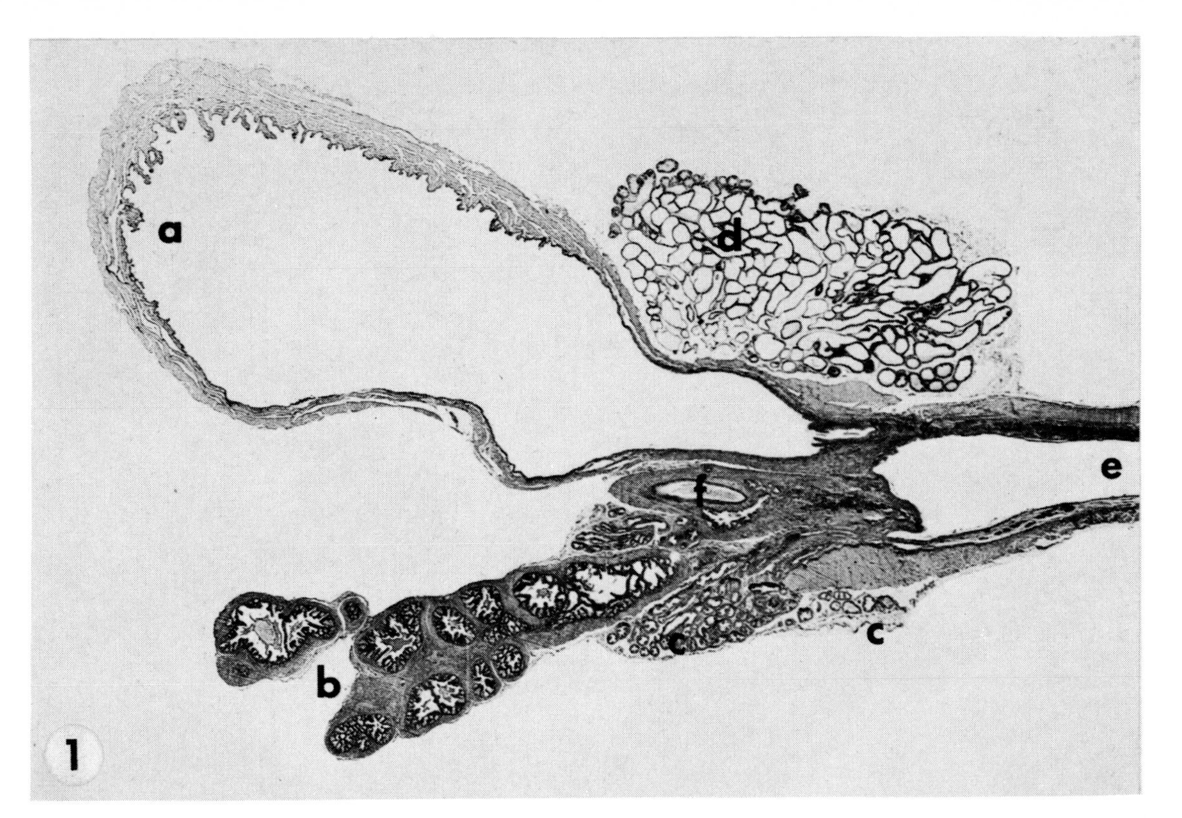

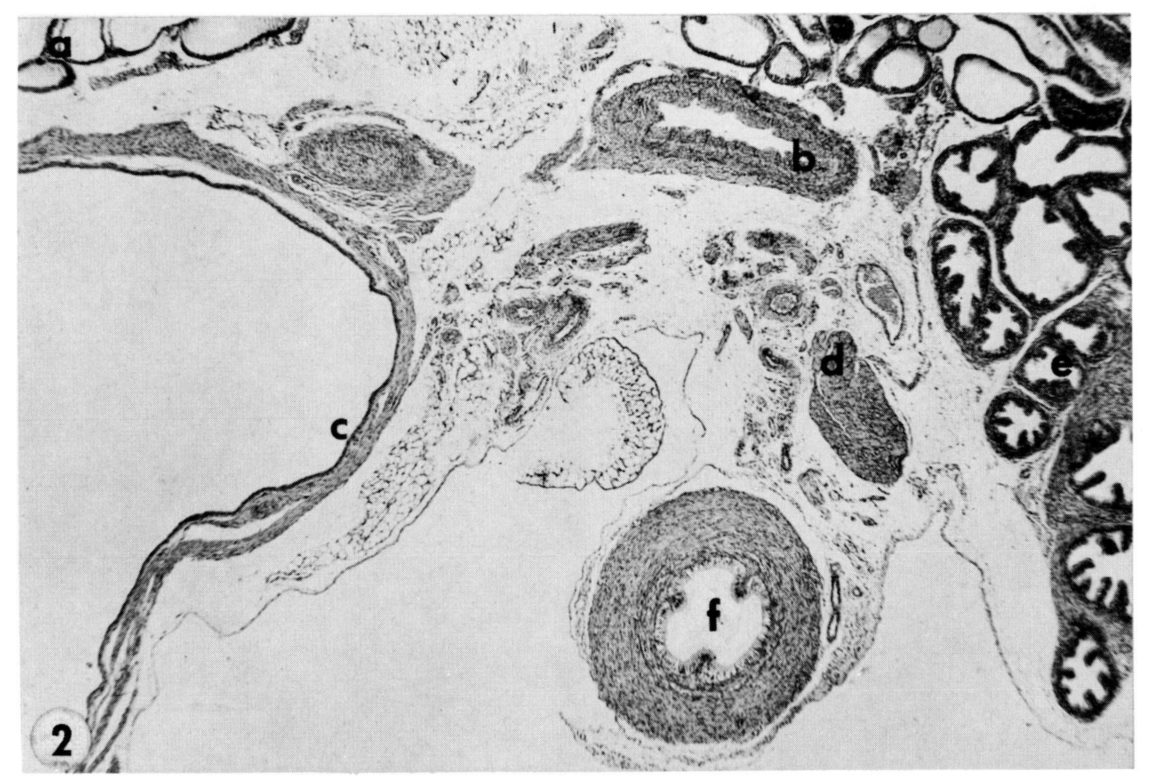

PLATE 51
Male Urogenital System

FIG. 1. Urinary bladder and accessory sex glands. Longitudinal section at midline. Level 10. (H&E, $\times$ 40)
- a. Urinary bladder
- b. Seminal vesicle
- c. Coagulating gland
- d. Prostate
- e. Urethra
- f. Ductus deferens

FIG. 2. Urinary bladder and accessory sex glands. Longitudinal section lateral to midline. Level 10. (H&E, $\times$ 50)
- a. Prostate gland
- b. Ureter
- c. Urinary bladder
- d. Ganglion
- e. Seminal vesicle
- f. Ductus deferens

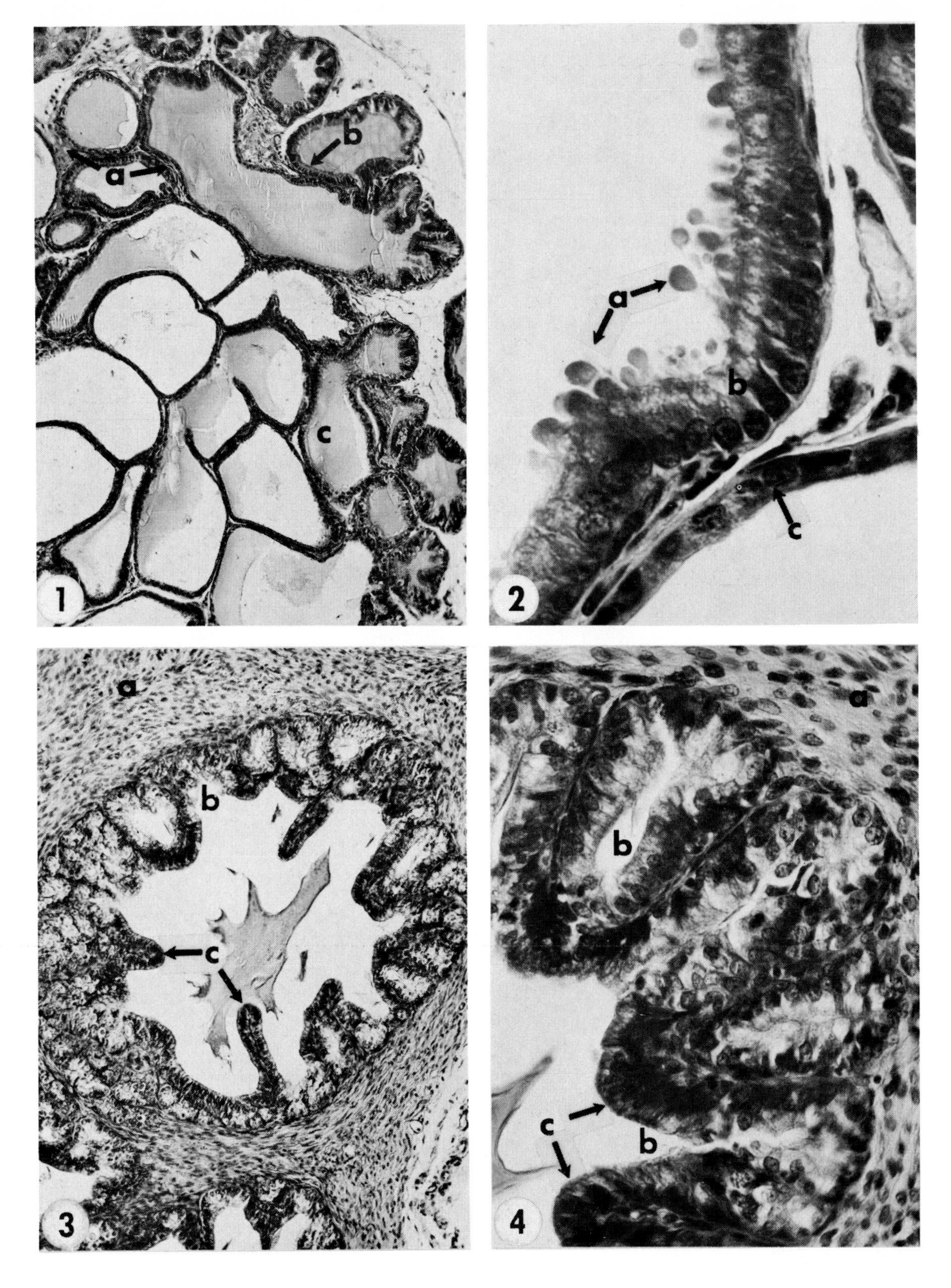

PLATE 52
Male Urogenital System

FIG. 1. Prostate gland. Level 10. (H&E, × 70)
a. Fibro-muscular septum
b. Simple columnar epithelium
c. Prostatic secretion in an alveolus

FIG. 2. Prostate gland showing alveolar epithelium in active and inactive secretory phases. Level 10. (H&E, × 1000)
a. Secretion blebs
b. Simple columnar epithelium in secretory phase
c. Simple cuboidal epithelium in nonsecretory phase

FIG. 3. Seminal vesicle tubule. Level 10. (H&E, × 130)
a. Smooth muscle septa
b. Crypt
c. Simple columnar epithelium

FIG. 4. Mucosa of the seminal vesicle tubule. Level 10. (H&E, × 360)
a. Smooth muscle
b. Crypts
c. Simple columnar epithelium

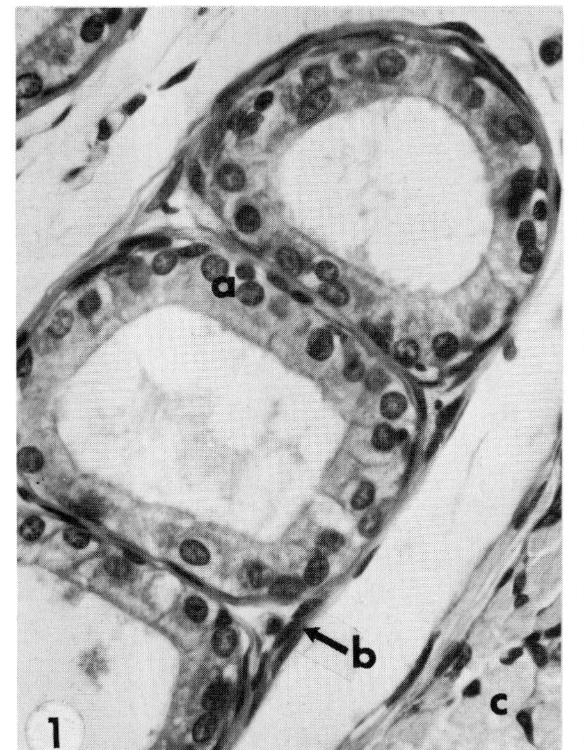

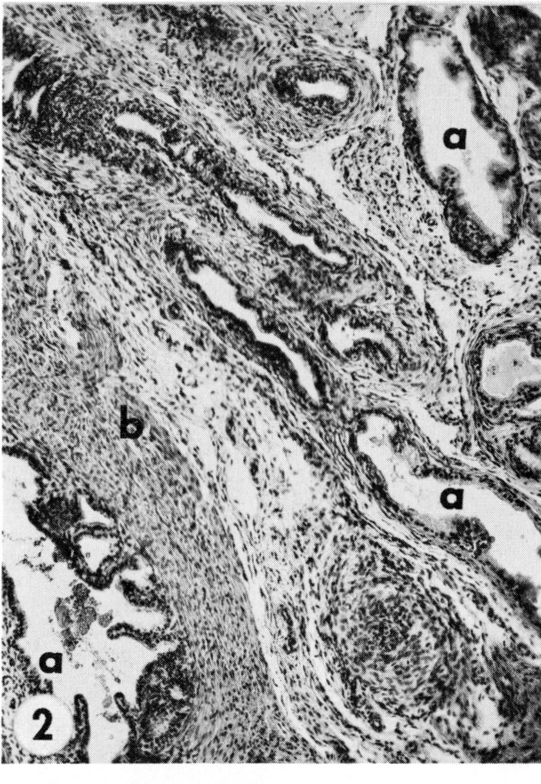

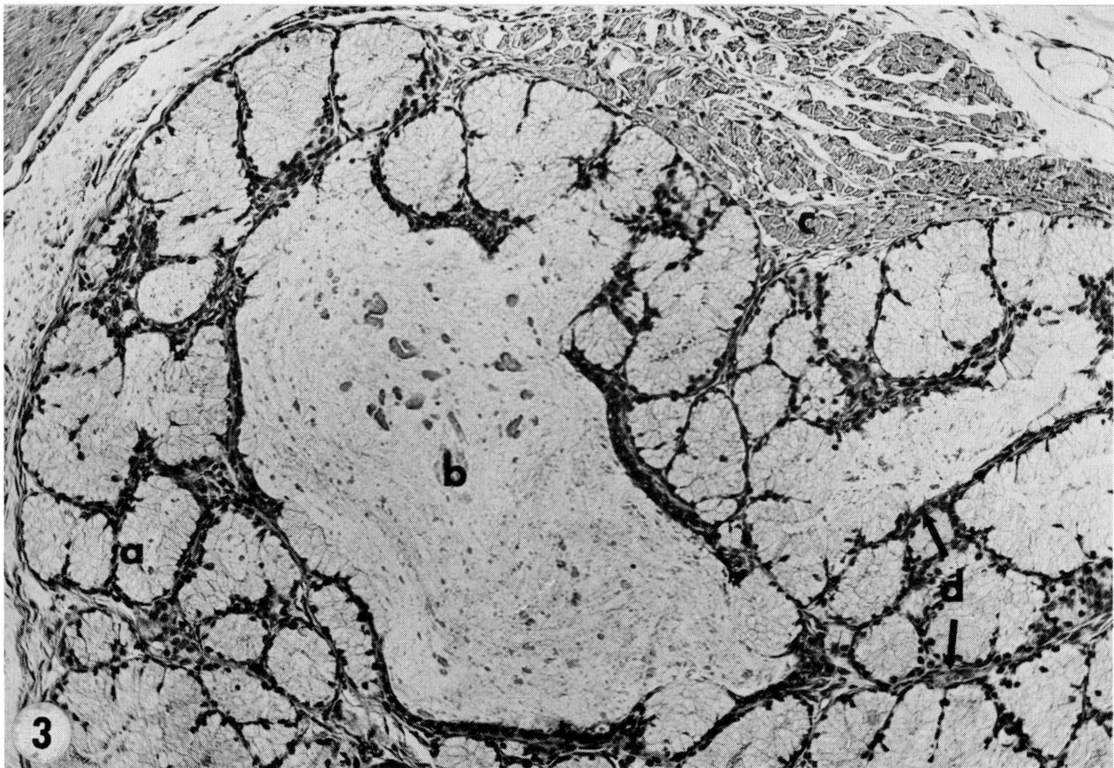

PLATE 53

Male Urogenital System

FIG. 1. Coagulating gland alveoli. Longitudinal section. Level 10. (H&E, × 680)

a. Simple columnar epithelial cells
b. Smooth muscle fibers
c. Skeletal muscle in cross section

FIG. 2. Ducts of the coagulating gland. Longitudinal section. Level 10. (H&E, × 65)

a. Lumen of the ducts
b. Connective tissue stroma

FIG. 3. Bulbourethral gland. Cross section. Level 11. (H&E, × 185)

a. Mucus-secreting columnar cells
b. Excretory duct filled with mucous secretion
c. Fibro-muscular capsule
d. Connective tissue capsule

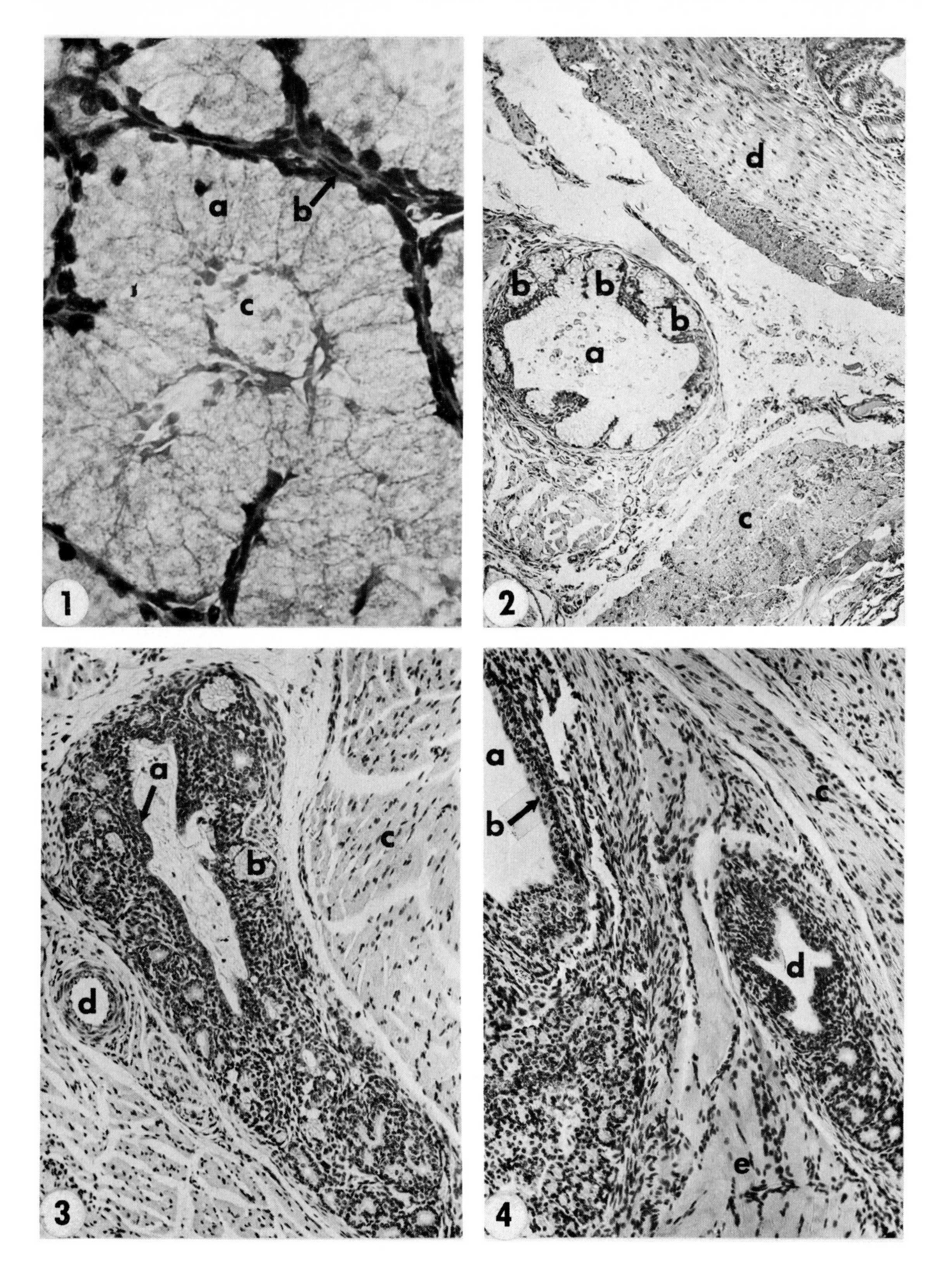

PLATE 54
Male Urogenital System

FIG. 1. Bulbourethral gland. Cross section. Level 11. (H&E, × 820)
a. Mucus-secreting columnar cells with basal nuclei
b. Connective tissue septa
c. Mucus-filled lumen of the alveolus

FIG. 2. Duct of the bulbourethral gland. Cross section. Level 11. (H&E, × 85)
a. Lumen of the duct
b. Mucus-secreting alveoli of the bulbourethral duct
c. Skeletal muscle
d. Cross section of the large intestine

FIG. 3. Bulbourethral duct—middle portion. Level 11. (H&E, × 140)
a. Stratified cuboidal epithelium
b. Mucus-secreting alveolus
c. Skeletal muscle
d. Blood vessel

FIG. 4. Bulbourethral duct—distal portion. Level 11. (H&E, × 130)
a. Urethral lumen
b. Transitional epithelium of the urethra
c. Smooth muscle
d. Lumen of the bulbourethral duct
e. Skeletal muscle

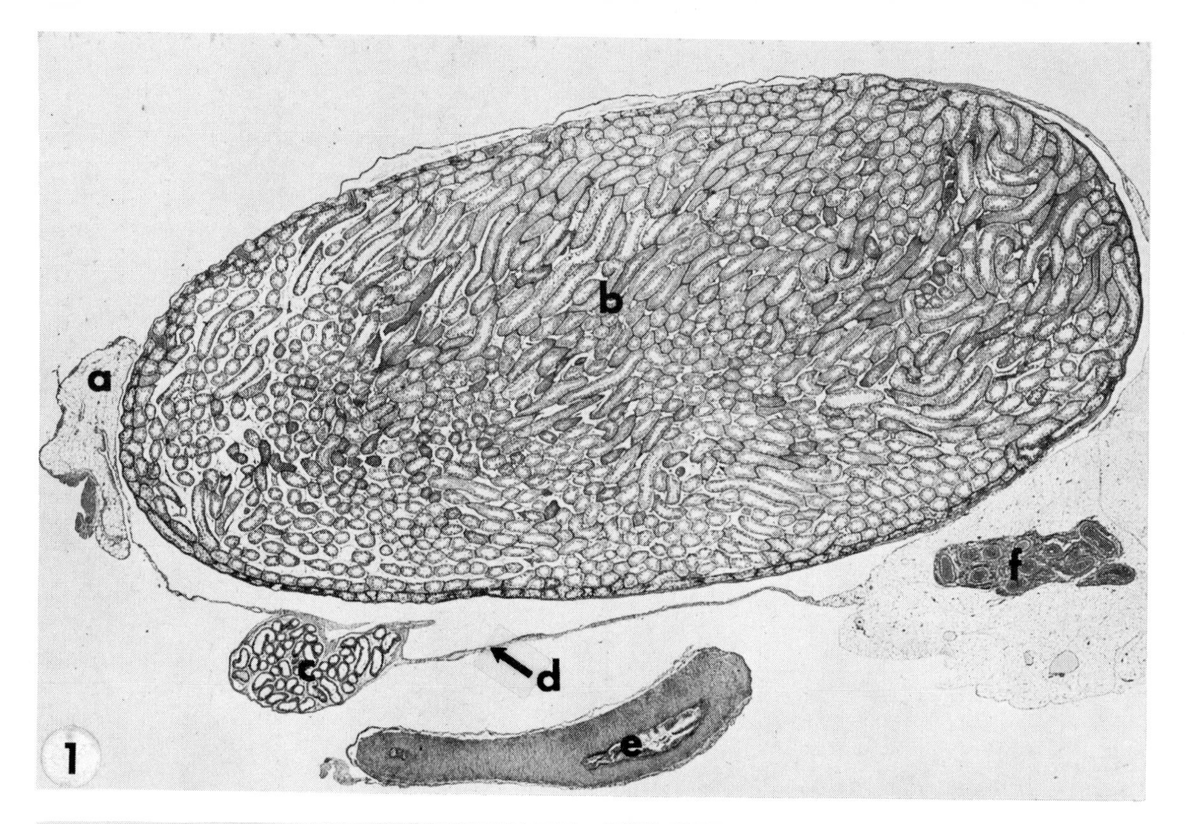

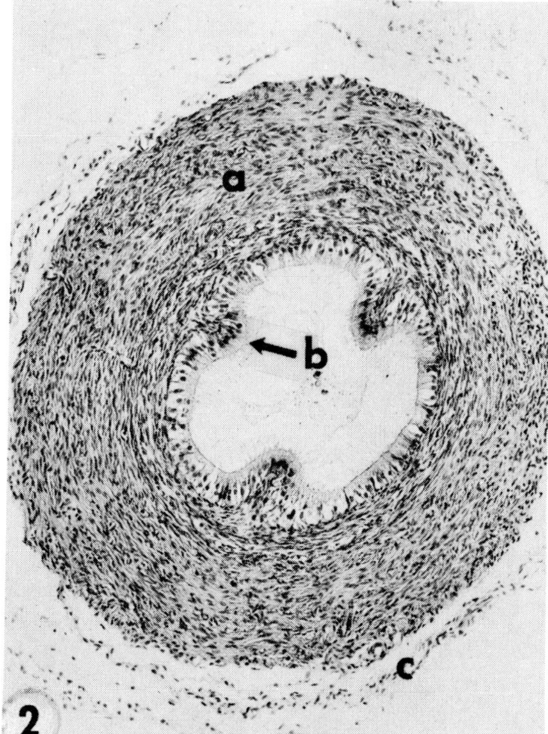

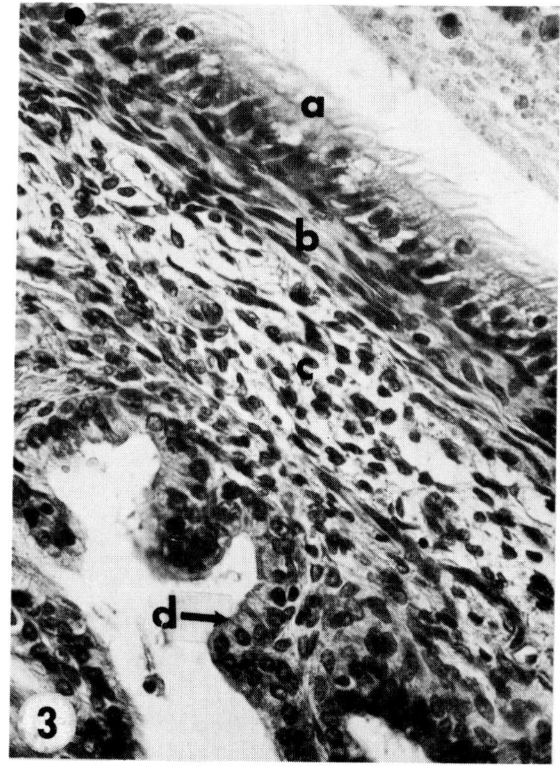

Plate 55
Male Urogenital System

Fig. 1. Testis. Longitudinal section. Level 4. (H&E, × 9)
- a. Adipose tissue
- b. Seminiferous tubules
- c. Epididymis
- d. Tunica vaginalis parietalis
- e. Ductus deferens
- f. Pampiniform plexus

Fig. 2. Ductus deferens—middle portion. Cross section. (H&E, × 115)
- a. Tunica muscularis
- b. Ciliated columnar epithelium
- c. Tunica adventitia

Fig. 3. Ductus deferens and the prostate gland. Longitudinal section. Level 10. (H&E, × 355)
- a. Ciliated columnar epithelium of the ductus deferens
- b. Smooth muscle fibers of the tunica muscularis
- c. Areolar connective tissue
- d. Nonciliated columnar epithelium of the prostate gland

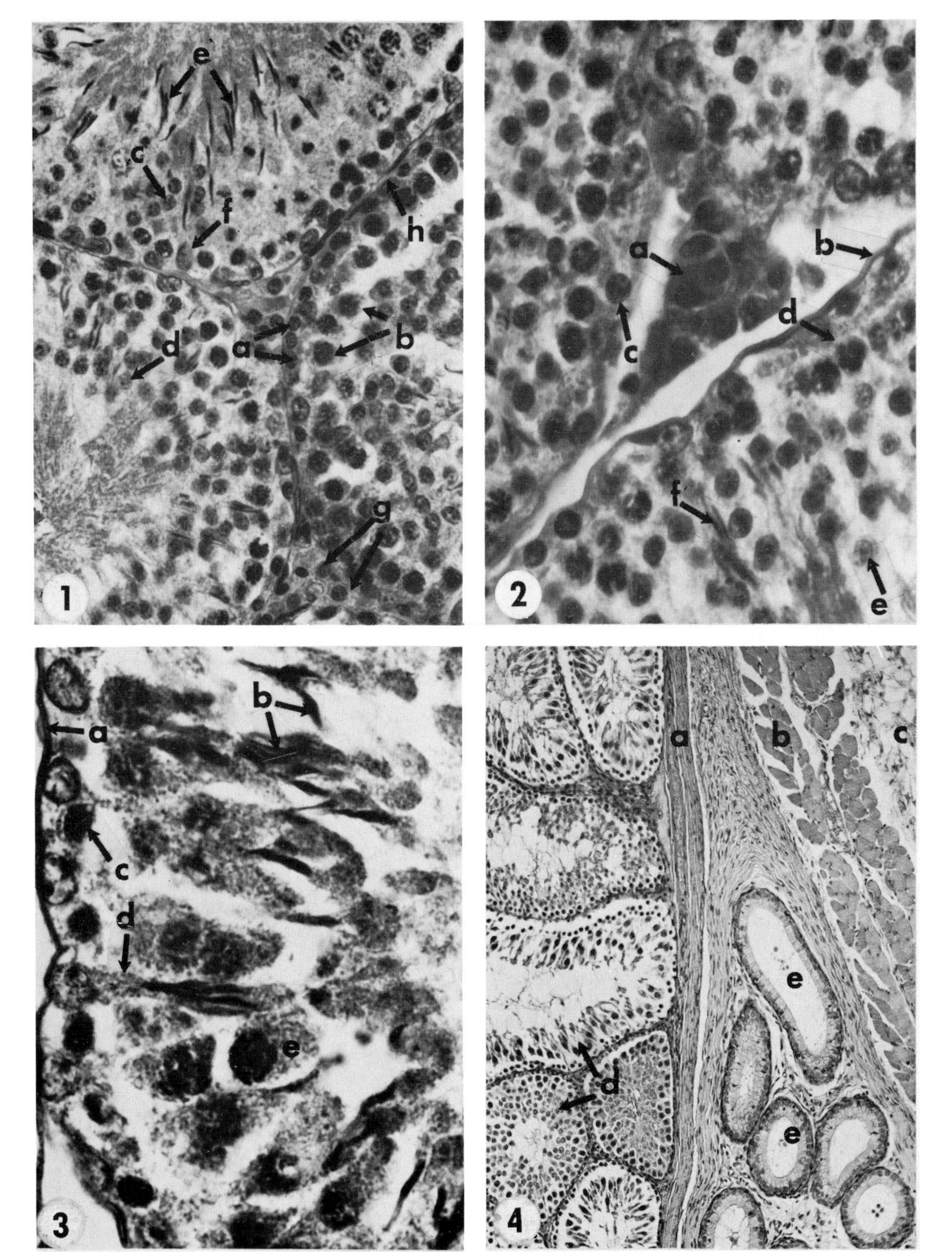

PLATE 56
Male Urogenital System

FIG. 1. Seminiferous tubules. Cross section. Level 1. (H&E, × 710)
- a. Spermatogonia
- b. Primary spermatocyte
- c. Secondary spermatocyte
- d. Young spermatids prior to transformation
- e. Maturing spermatids
- f. Sustentacular cell (Cell of Sertoli)
- g. Interstitial cells (Cells of Leydig)
- h. Basement membrane

FIG. 2. Interstitial cells of the testis. Cross section. Level 1. (H&E, × 1025)
- a. Interstitial cells (Cells of Leydig)
- b. Basement membrane
- c. Spermatogonium
- d. Primary spermatocyte
- e. Young spermatid
- f. Maturing spermatids

FIG. 3. Seminiferous tubule. Cross section. Level 1. (Trichrome, × 1410)
- a. Basement membrane
- b. Maturing spermatids
- c. Spermatogonium
- d. Sustentacular cell with an attached spermatid
- e. Primary spermatocyte

FIG. 4. Testis and the epididymis. Level 4. (H&E, × 130)
- a. Tunica albuginea
- b. Skeletal muscle fibers of the cremaster muscle
- c. Scrotal fascia
- d. Seminiferous tubules in the different stages of spermatogenesis
- e. Ductus epididymis

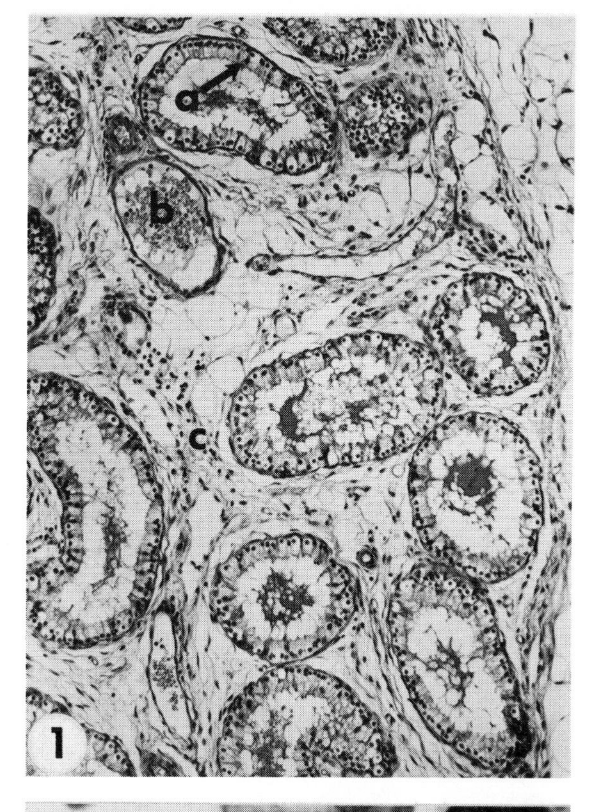

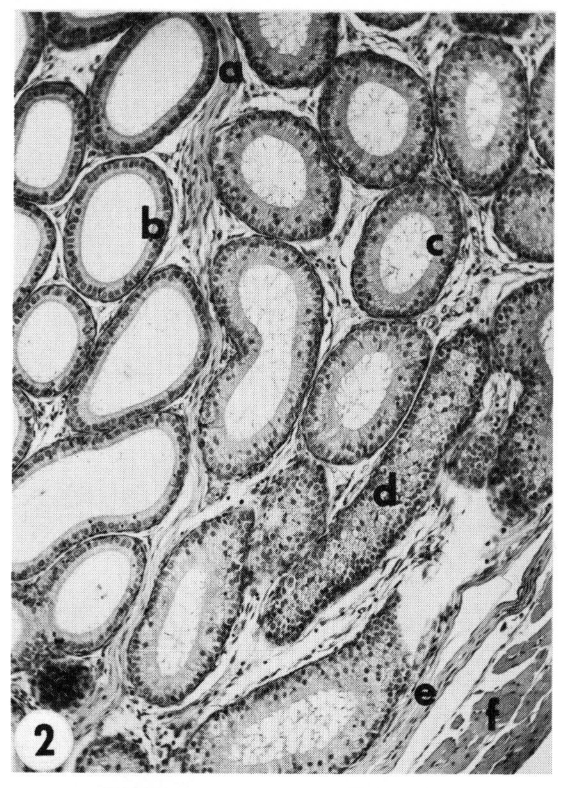

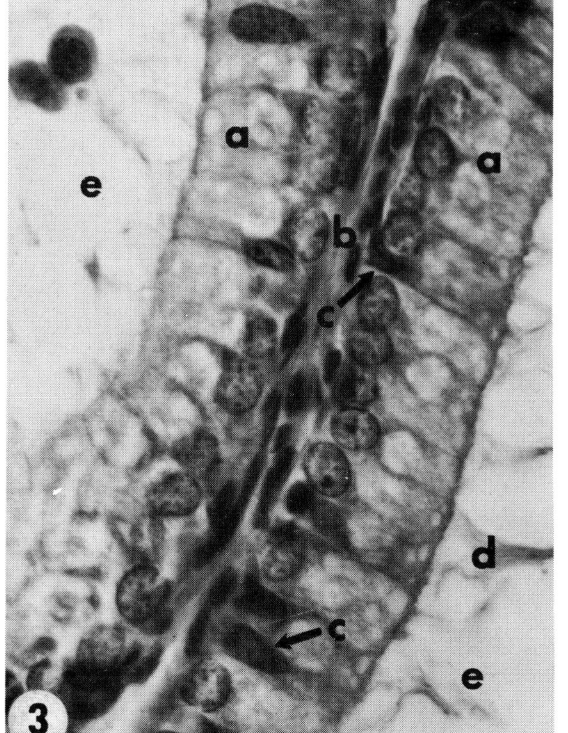

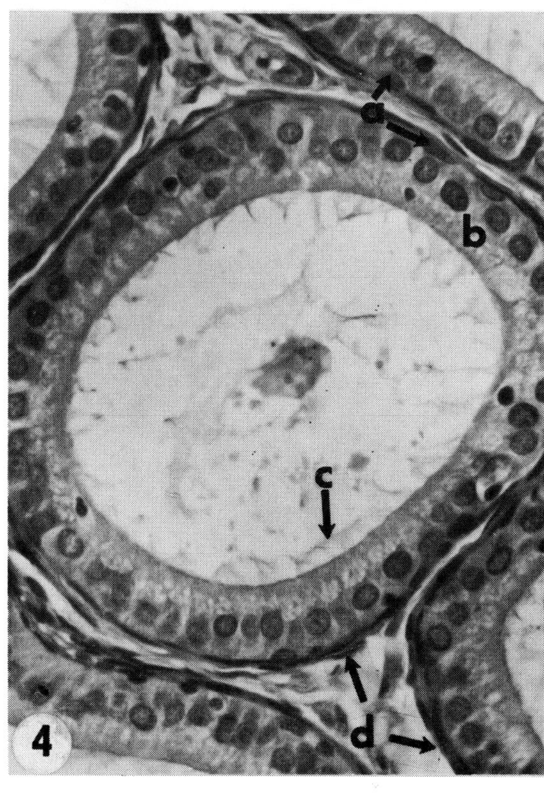

PLATE 57
Male Urogenital System

FIG. 1. Ductuli efferentes. Cross section. Level 4. (H&E, × 115)
- a. Columnar epithelium
- b. Blood vessel
- c. Loose connective tissue

FIG. 2. Epididymis. Cross section. Level 4. (H&E, × 115)
- a. Interstitial connective tissue
- b. Low pseudostratified ciliated columnar epithelium
- c. Tall pseudostratified ciliated columnar epithelium
- d. Wall of the epididymal tubule cut longitudinally
- e. Tunica albuginea
- f. Skeletal muscle fibers of the cremaster muscle

FIG. 3. Body of the epididymis. Cross section. Level 1. (H&E, × 1085)
- a. Light-staining columnar cells with vacuolated cytoplasm
- b. Connective tissue septa
- c. Dark-staining columnar cells
- d. Stereocilia
- e. Lumen

FIG. 4. Tail of the epididymis. Cross section. Level 4. (H&E, × 600)
- a. Basal epithelial cells
- b. Ciliated columnar cells with granular cytoplasm
- c. Stereocilia
- d. Smooth muscle fibers

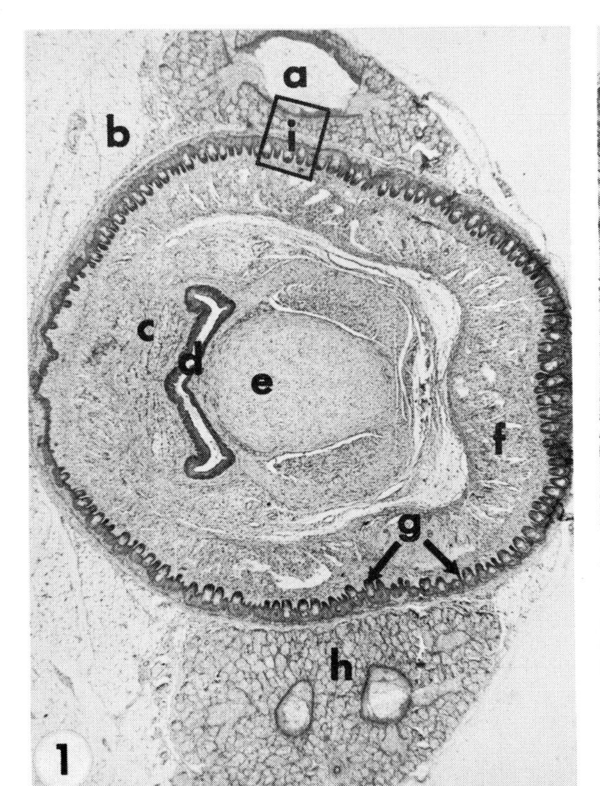

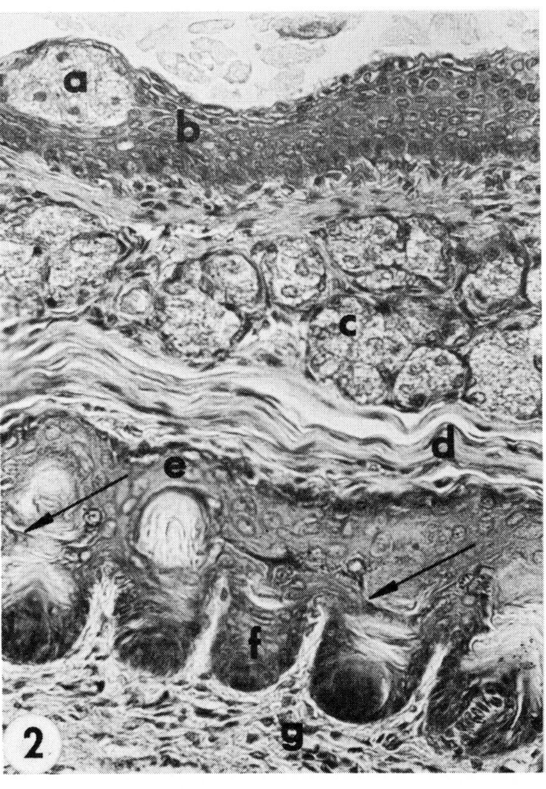

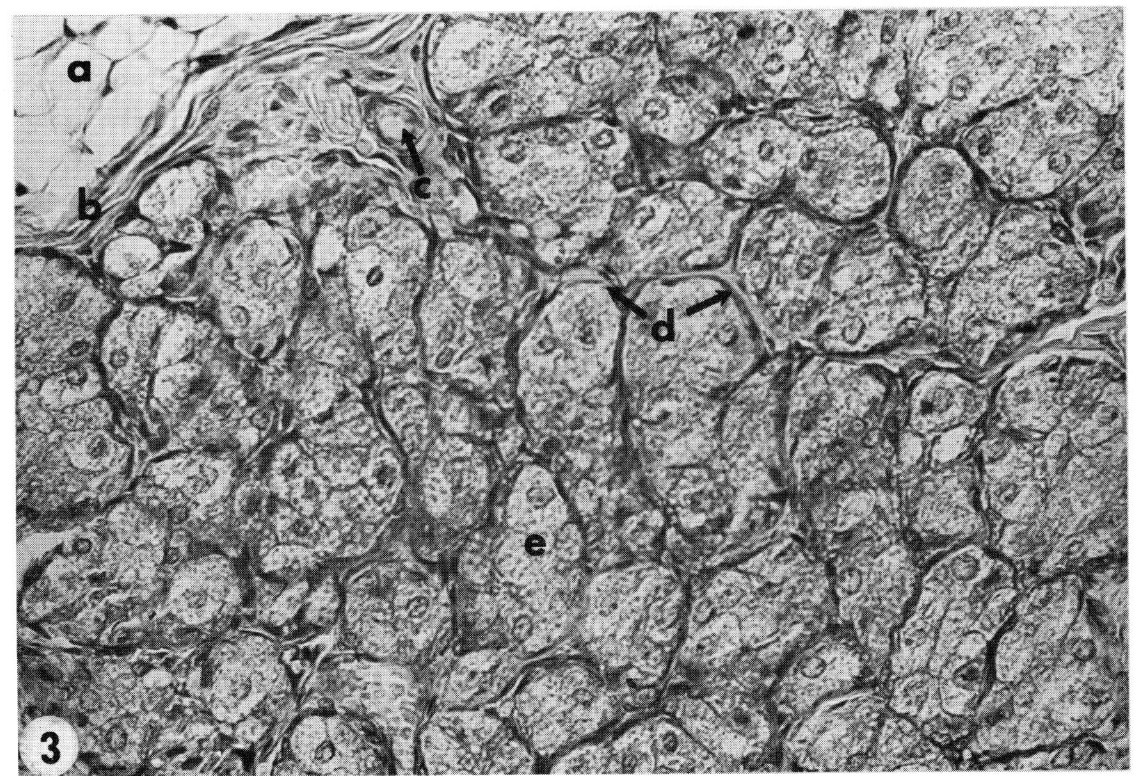

PLATE 58
Male Urogenital System

FIG. 1. Penis. Cross section. Level 8. (H&E, × 30)
- a. Excretory duct of the preputial gland
- b. Adipose connective tissue
- c. Corpus cavernosum urethra
- d. Urethra
- e. Developing os penis
- f. Corpus cavernosum penis
- g. Balano-preputial fold with developing epithelial spines
- h. Preputial gland with modified sebaceous type cells
- i. Area shown in Fig. 2

FIG. 2. Developing prepuce. Level 8. (H&E, × 305)
- a. Glandular pocket in the excretory duct of the preputial gland
- b. Stratified squamous epithelium of the excretory duct
- c. Preputial gland
- d. White fibrous connective tissue
- e. Parietal layer of the developing prepuce
- f. Visceral layer of the developing prepuce (beginning of separation at arrows)
- g. Connective tissue of the penis

FIG. 3. Preputial gland. (H&E, × 375)
- a. Adipose tissue
- b. Fibrous connective tissue capsule
- c. Blood vessel
- d. Fibrous connective tissue septa
- e. Sebaceous type acinar cells with foamy appearing cytoplasm

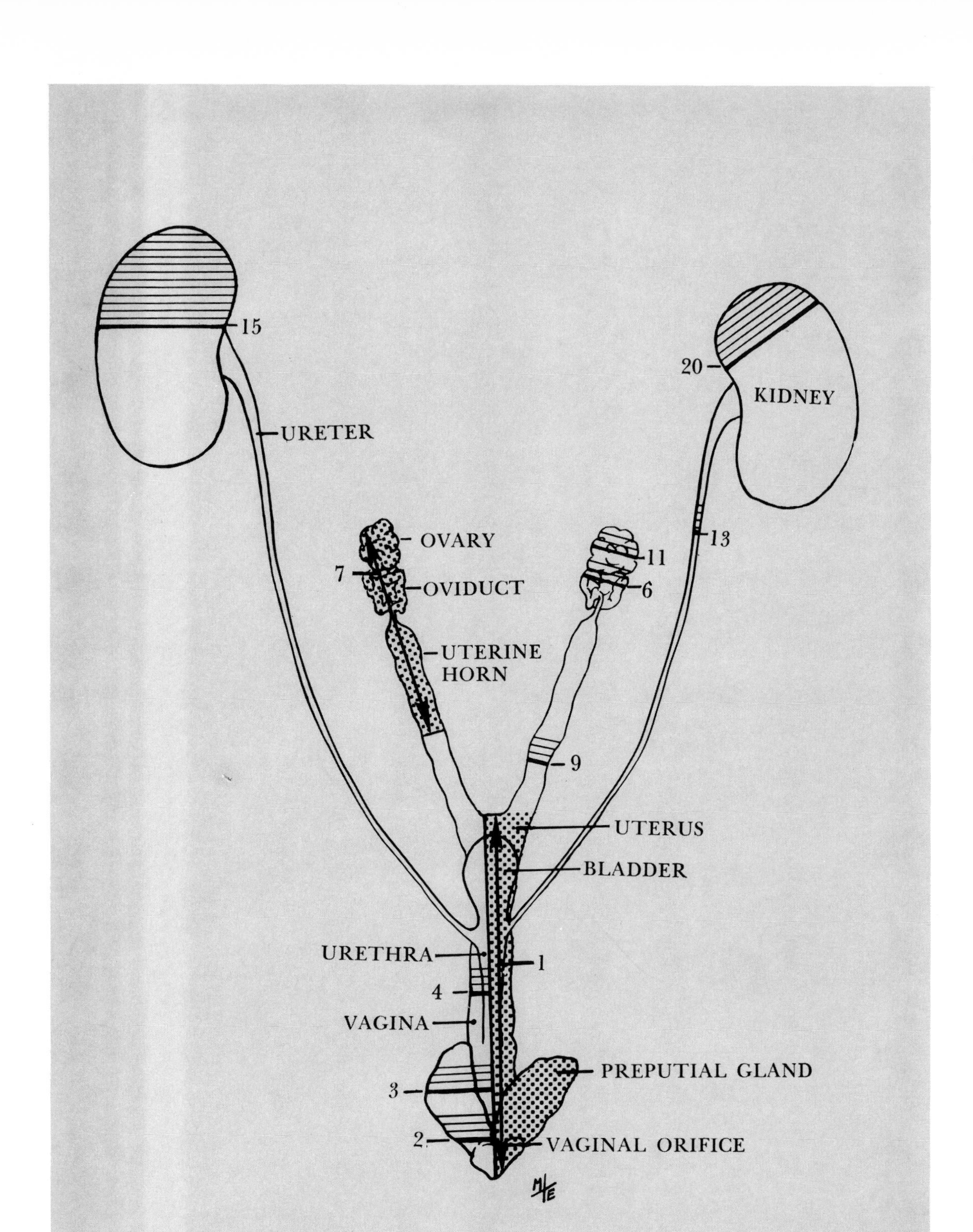

PLATE 59
Female Urogenital System

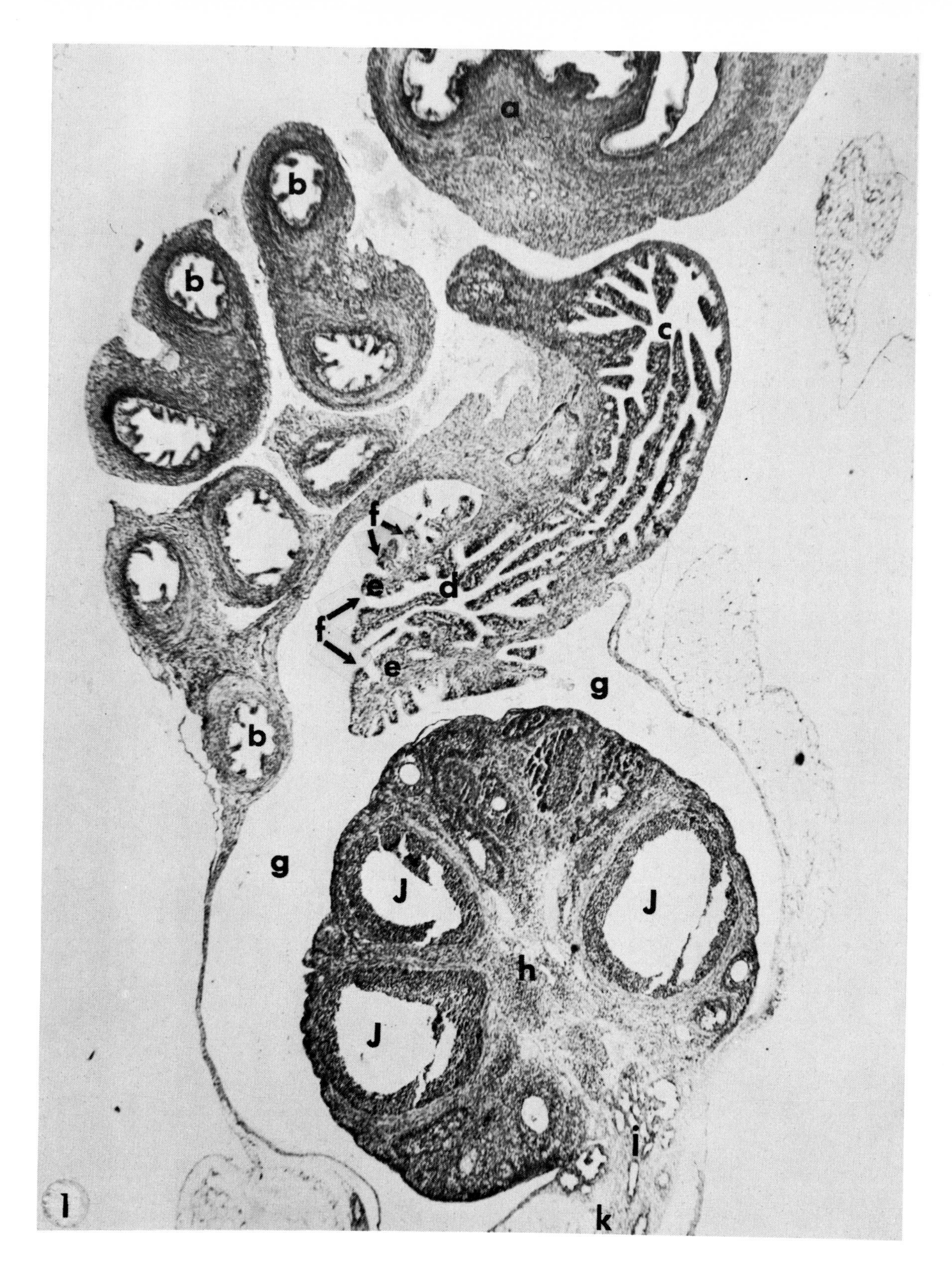

PLATE 60
Female Urogenital System

FIG. 1. Ovary, oviduct, and uterus. Transverse section. Level 7. (H&E, $\times$ 45)

- a. Uterus
- b. Isthmus of the oviduct
- c. Ampulla of the oviduct
- d. Infundibular portion of the oviduct
- e. Fimbriated end of the oviduct
- f. Ovarian bursa opening into the oviduct
- g. Ovarian bursa
- h. Ovary with maturing follicles
- i. Rete ovarii
- j. Maturing follicles
- k. Mesovarium

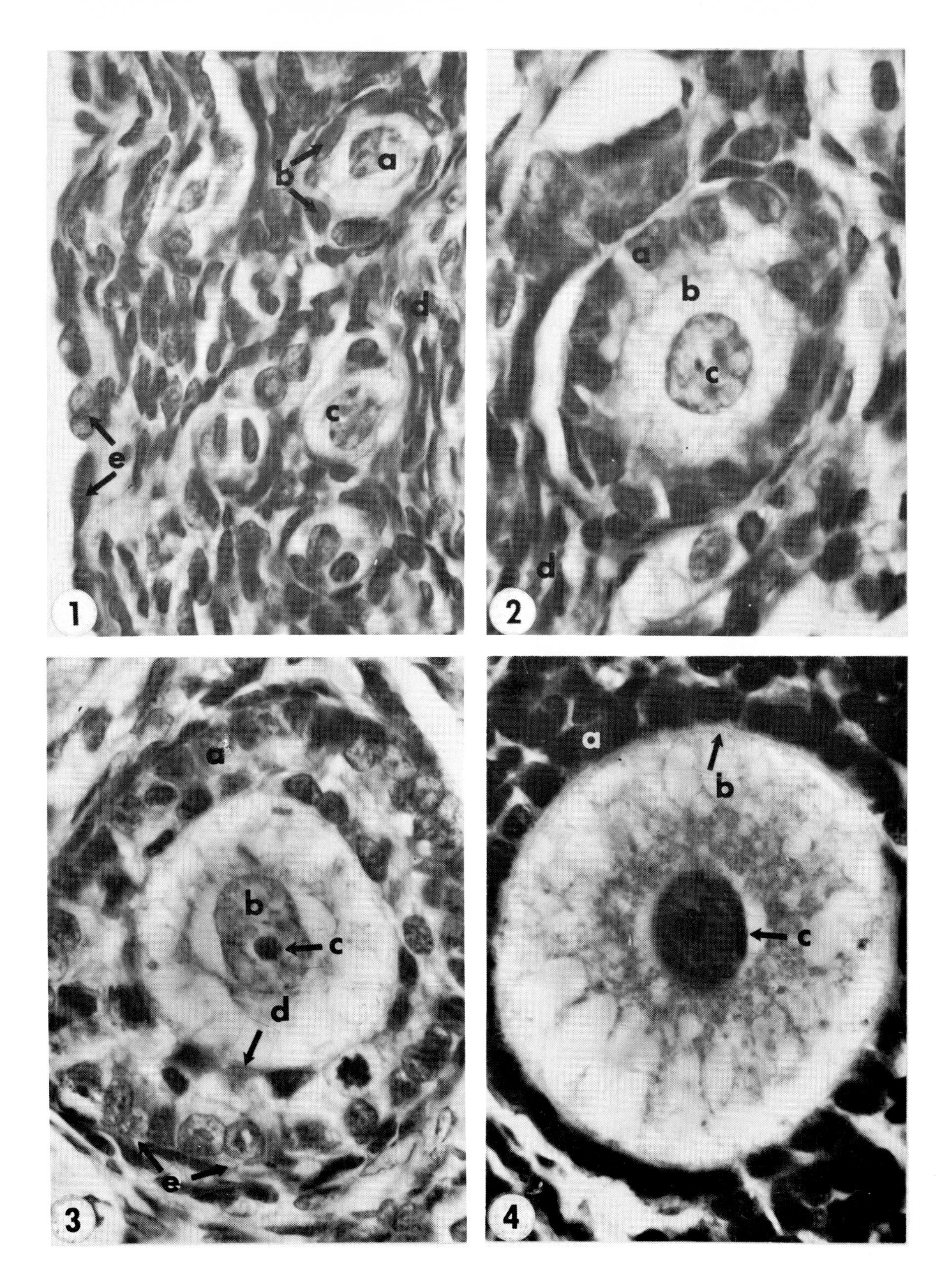

Plate 61
Female Urogenital System

Fig. 1. Primary ovarian follicles. Level 11. (H&E, × 1100)
- a. Primary oöcyte surrounded with flattened follicular cells
- b. Follicular cells
- c. Developing oöcyte
- d. Ovarian stroma
- e. Epithelial covering of the ovary

Fig. 2. Primary follicle with an oöcyte. Level 11. (H&E, × 1485)
- a. Single layer of cuboidal follicular cells
- b. Cytoplasm of the oöcyte
- c. Nucleus of the oöcyte
- d. Ovarian stroma

Fig. 3. Secondary follicle with a secondary oöcyte. Level 11. (H&E, × 1100)
- a. Stratified follicular cells
- b. Nucleus of the oöcyte
- c. Nucleolus of the oöcyte
- d. Zona pellucida
- e. Basement membrane

Fig. 4. Maturing oöcyte with a corona radiata. Level 11. (H&E, × 1190)
- a. Cells of the corona radiata
- b. Zona pellucida
- c. Nucleus of the oöcyte

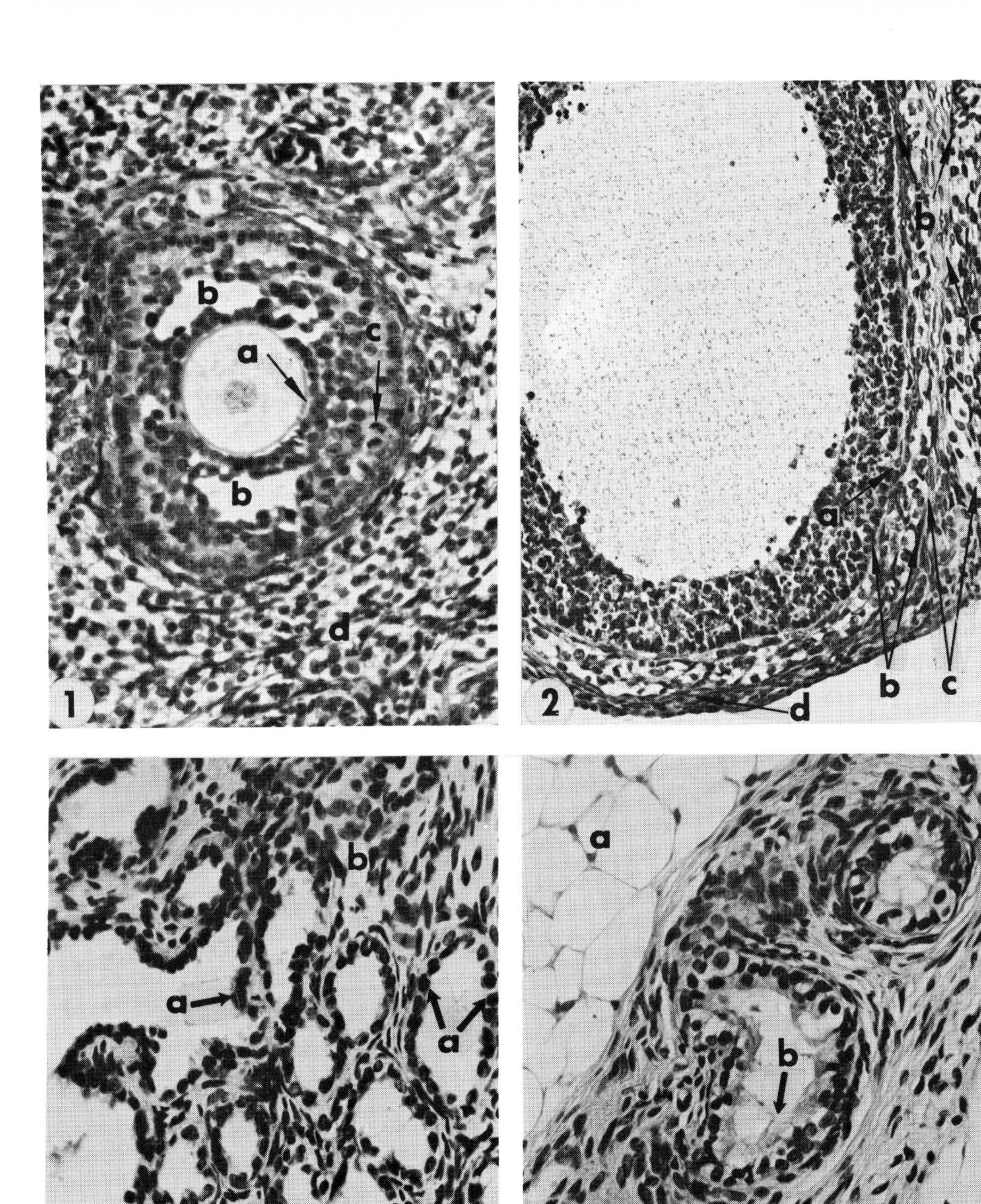

PLATE 62
Female Urogenital System

FIG. 1. Secondary follicle with a developing antrum. Level 11. (H&E, × 370)
- a. Oöcyte with nucleus and zona pellucida (arrow)
- b. Follicular antrum
- c. Membrana granulosa (mitotic figures at arrow)
- d. Ovarian stroma

FIG. 2. Mature follicle (oöcyte not seen here). Level 11. (H&E, × 270)
- a. Membrana granulosa
- b. Theca interna
- c. Theca externa
- d. Tunica albuginea

FIG. 3. Rete ovarii. Level 11. (H&E, × 370)
- a. Cuboidal epithelium
- b. Ovarian stroma

FIG. 4. Epoöphoron. Level 11. (H&E, × 365)
- a. Adipose tissue
- b. Columnar epithelium

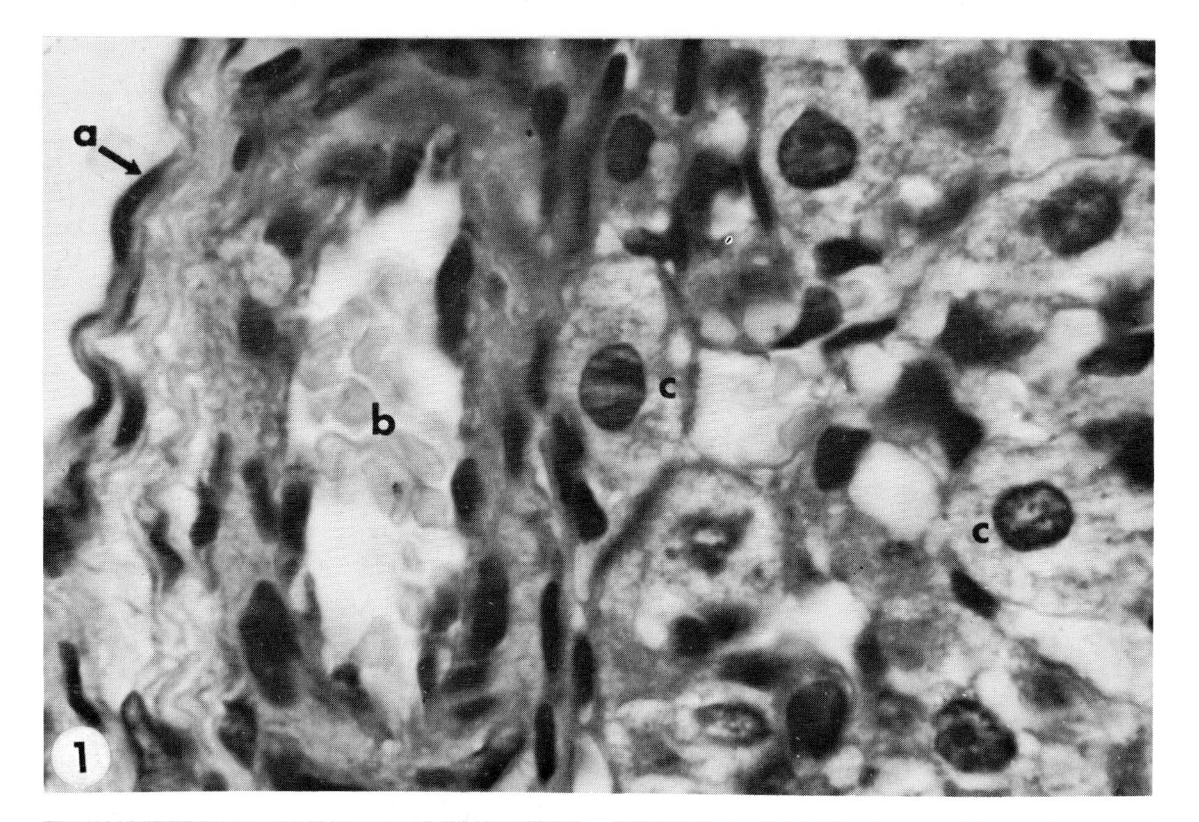

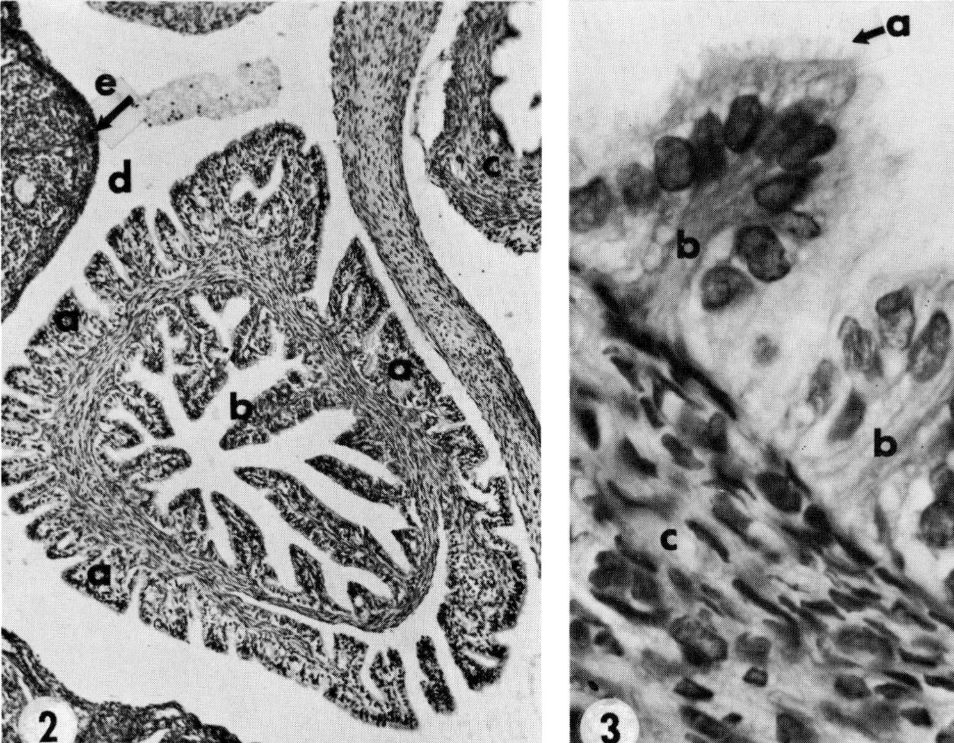

PLATE 63

Female Urogenital System

FIG. 1. Corpus luteum. Cross section. Level 11. (H&E, × 1355)
- a. Epithelial covering of the ovary
- b. Arteriole
- c. Luteal cells

FIG. 2. Fimbriated portion of the oviduct. Cross section. Level 6. (H&E, × 70)
- a. Mucosal folds of the fimbria
- b. Mucosal folds of the infundibulum
- c. Oviduct
- d. Ovarian bursa
- e. Ovary

FIG. 3. Oviduct. Level 6. (H&E, × 1105)
- a. Ciliated columnar epithelial cells
- b. Epithelial folds of the oviduct
- c. Fibro-muscular wall of the oviduct

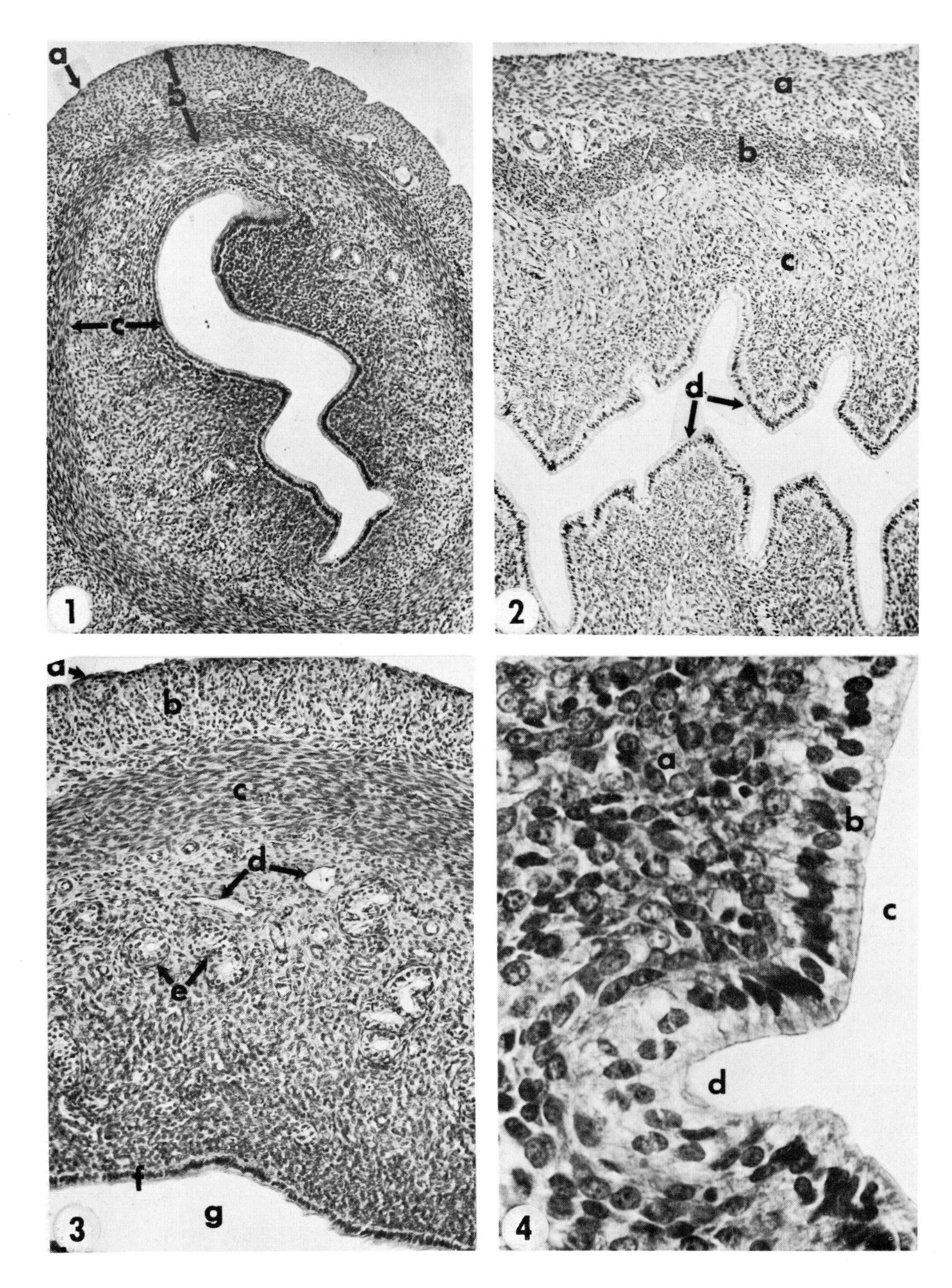

PLATE 64
Female Urogenital System

FIG. 1. Uterine horn. Cross section. Level 9. (H&E, × 60)
a. Perimetrium
b. Myometrium
c. Endometrium

FIG. 2. Uterine horn. Longitudinal section. Level 7. (H&E, × 75)
a. Outer longitudinal smooth muscle layer of the myometrium
b. Inner circular smooth muscle layer of the myometrium
c. Endometrium with small blood vessels
d. Simple columnar epithelium of the endometrium

FIG. 3. Wall of the uterine horn. Cross section, Level 9. (H&E, × 75)
a. Perimetrium
b. Outer longitudinal smooth muscle of the myometrium
c. Inner circular smooth muscle of the myometrium
d. Blood vessels in the endometrium
e. Tubular endometrial glands
f. Simple columnar epithelium of the endometrium
g. Lumen of the uterus

FIG. 4. Mucosa of the uterine horn. Longitudinal section. Level 7. (H&E, × 690)
a. Lamina propria
b. Simple columnar epithelium
c. Lumen of the uterus
d. Intra-epithelial gland

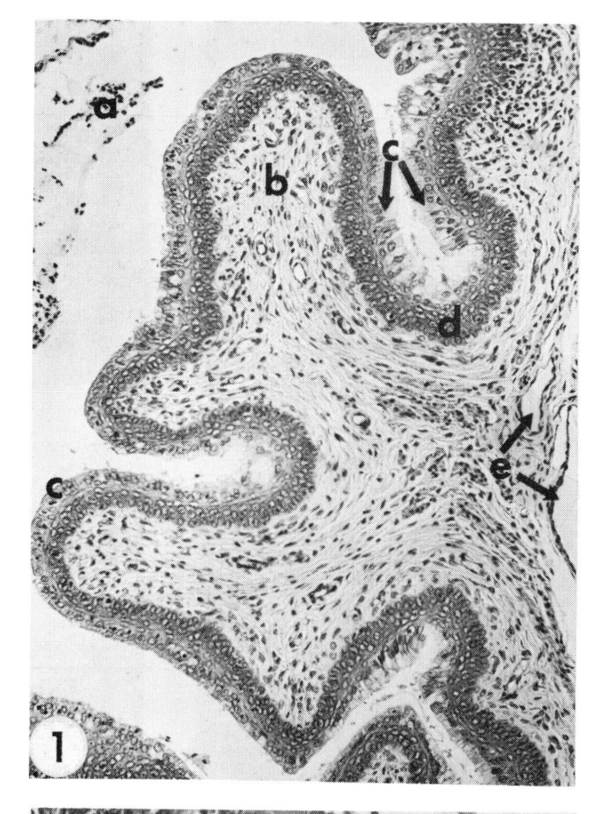

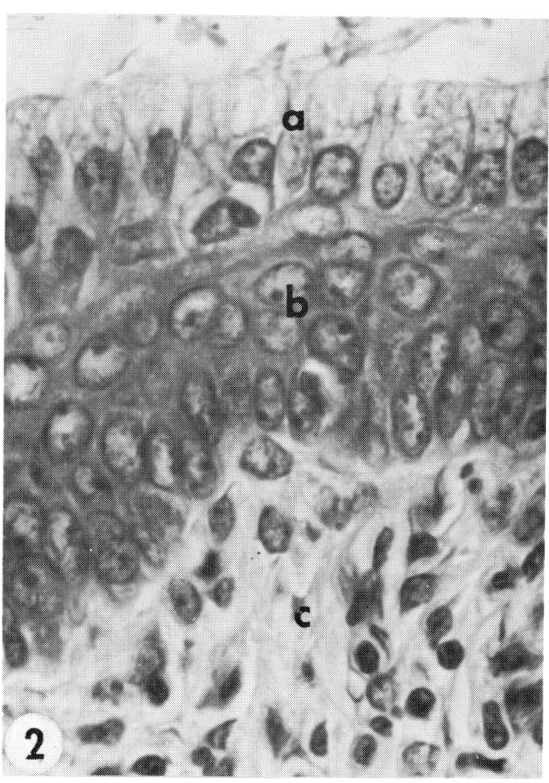

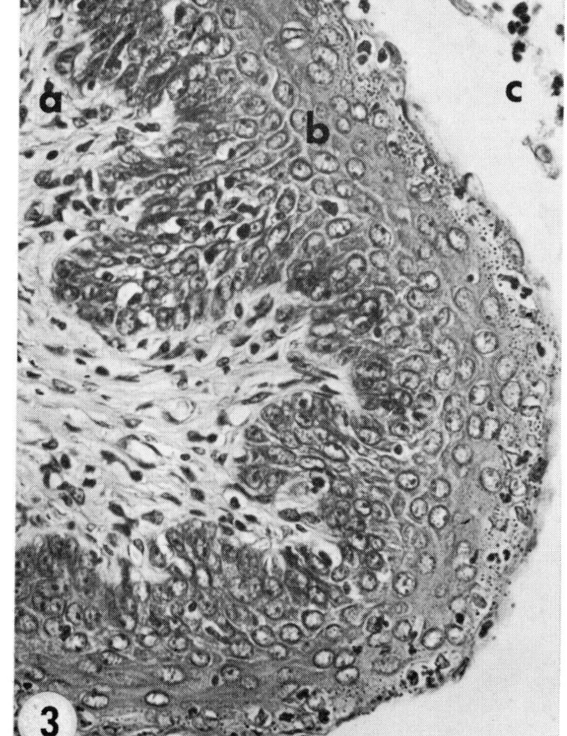

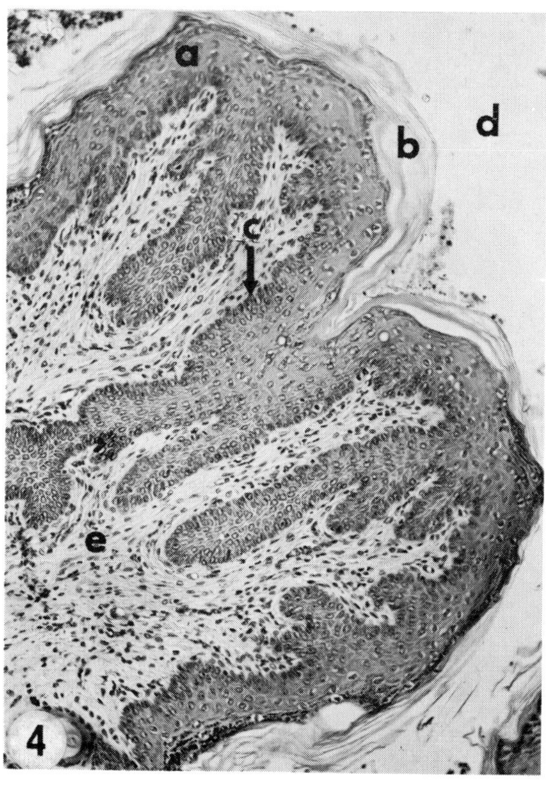

PLATE 65
Female Urogenital System

FIG. 1. Vagina—proximal portion. Cross section. Level 4. (H&E, × 130)
- a. Cellular debris in the lumen
- b. Lamina propria
- c. Stratified squamous epithelium with tall columnar surface cells
- d. Stratified squamous epithelium
- e. Blood vessels

FIG. 2. Vagina—proximal portion. Cross section. Level 4. (H&E, × 935)
- a. Tall columnar mucus-secreting surface cells
- b. Stratified squamous epithelium beneath columnar surface cells
- c. Lamina propria

FIG. 3. Vagina—middle portion. Cross section. Level 3. (H&E, × 345)
- a. Lamina propria
- b. Noncornified stratified squamous epithelium
- c. Vaginal lumen

FIG. 4. Vagina—distal portion. Cross section. Level 2. (H&E, × 130)
- a. Cornified stratified squamous epithelium
- b. Stratum corneum
- c. Vaginal lumen
- d. Basal layer of the epithelium
- e. Lamina propria

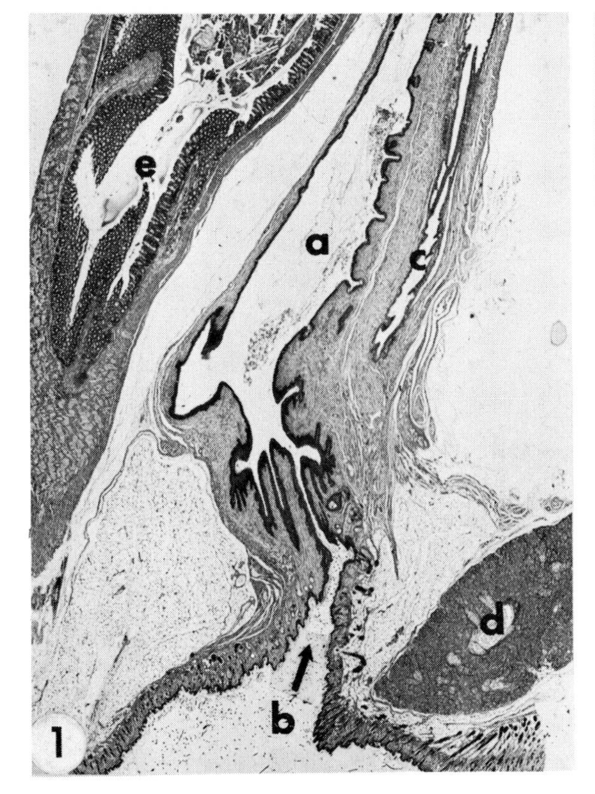

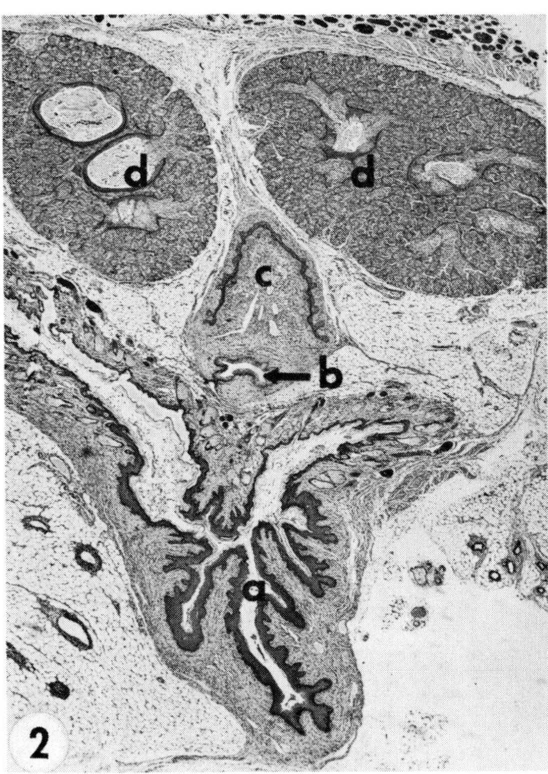

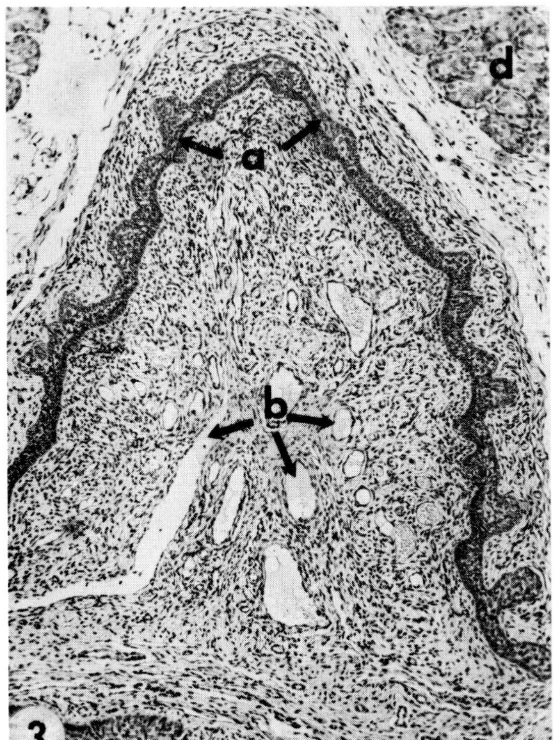

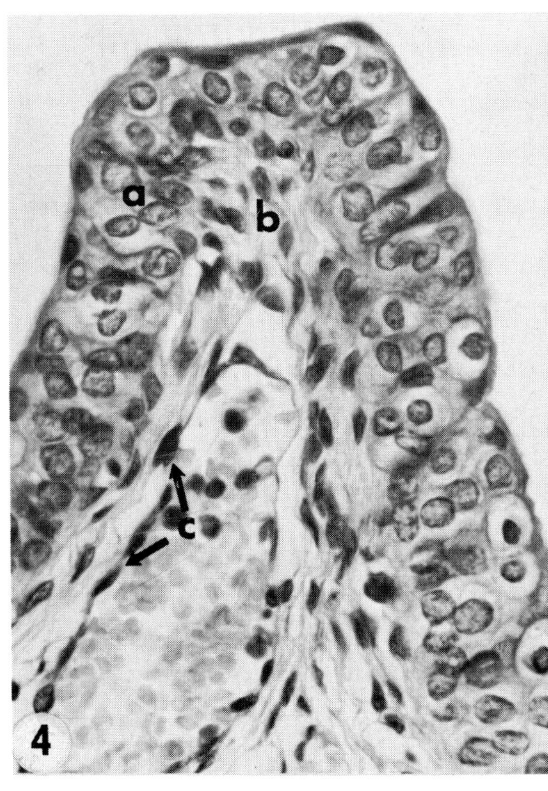

PLATE 66
Female Urogenital System

FIG. 1. Junction of the vestibule and the vagina. Longitudinal section. Level 1. (H&E, × 7)
- a. Lumen of the vagina
- b. Vaginal orifice at the vestibule
- c. Lumen of the urethra
- d. Preputial gland
- e. Lumen of the large intestine

FIG. 2. Vaginal orifice. Cross section. Level 2. (H&E, × 10)
- a. Vagina near the vaginal orifice
- b. Urethra
- c. Clitoris (see enlargement in Fig. 3)
- d. Preputial glands and ducts

FIG. 3. Clitoris. Cross section. Level 2. (H&E, × 50)
- a. Solid epithelial fold prior to the separation of the corpus clitoris
- b. Cavernous spaces of the corpus cavernosum clitoridis
- c. Urethra
- d. Preputial gland

FIG. 4. Mucosa of the female urethra. Cross section. Level 4. (H&E, × 750)
- a. Transitional epithelium
- b. Lamina propria containing prominent capillaries
- c. Endothelium

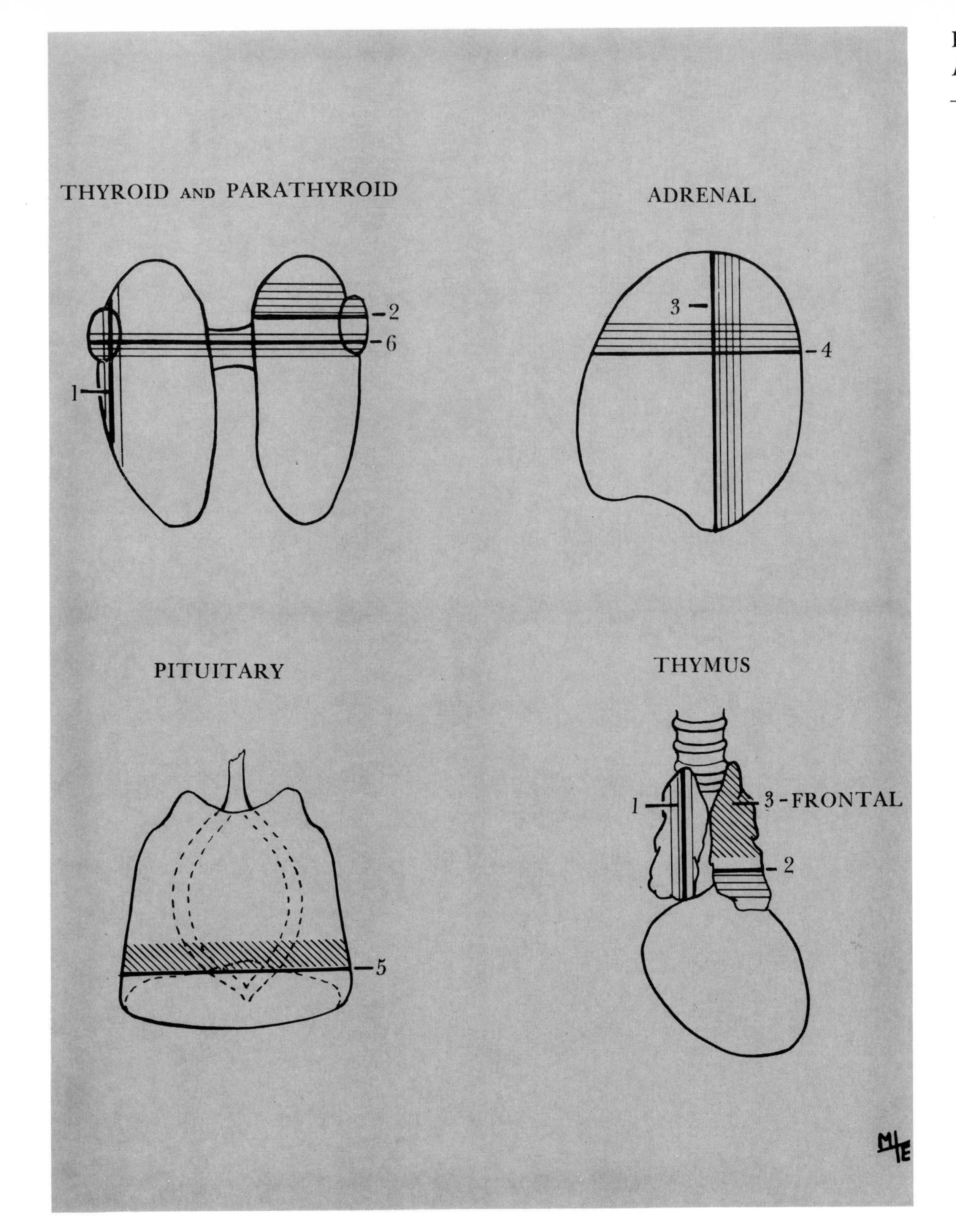

PLATE 67
Endocrine System

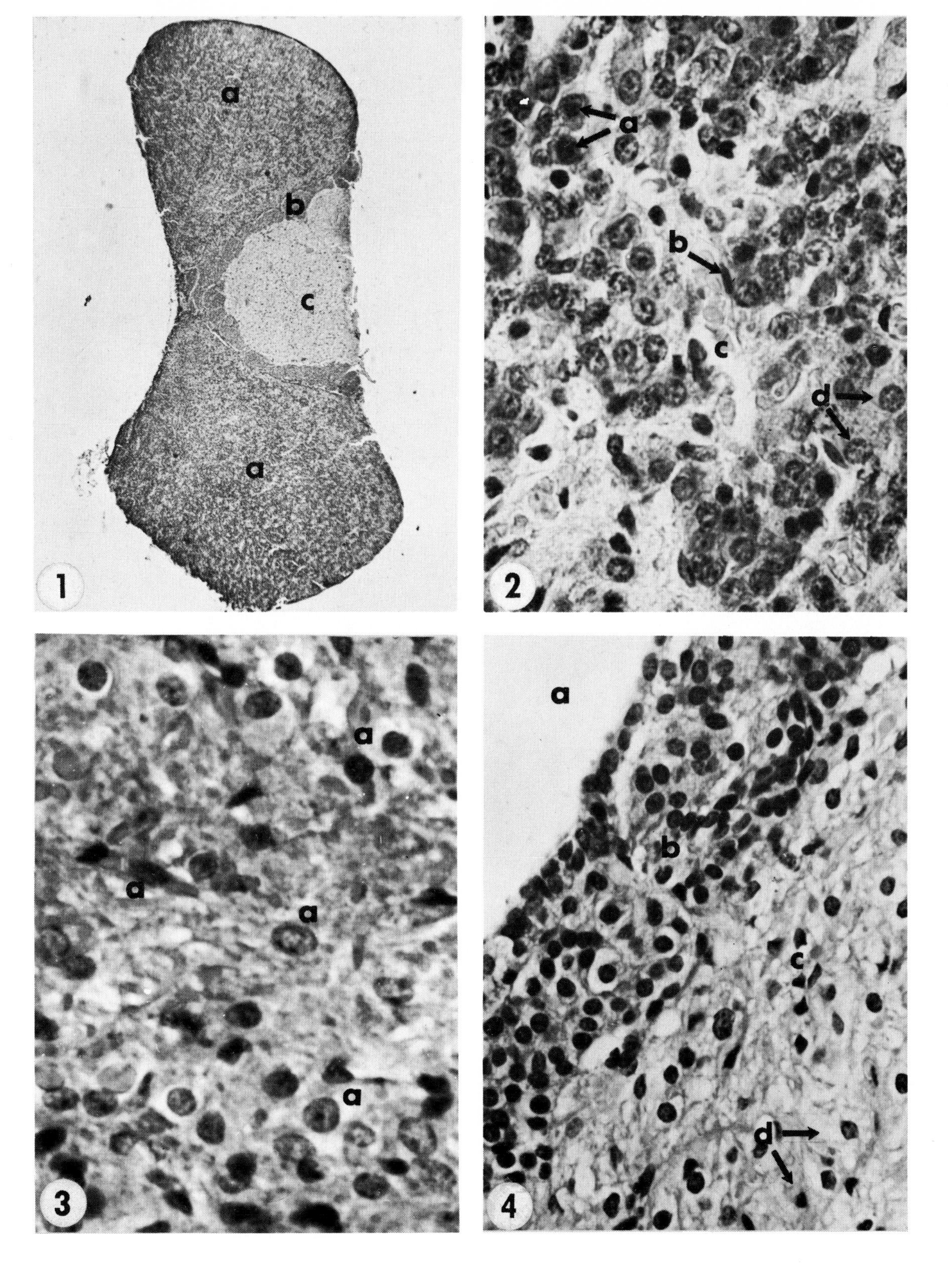

PLATE 68
Endocrine System

FIG. 1 Pituitary gland (hypophysis). Level 5. (H&E, × 25)
- a. Pars anterior (Pars distalis)
- b. Pars intermedia
- c. Pars nervosa

FIG. 2. Pars anterior of the pituitary gland. Level 5. (H&E, × 880)
- a. Basophils
- b. Endothelial cell of a sinusoid
- c. Sinusoid wtih red blood cells
- d. Acidophils

FIG. 3. Pars nervosa. Level 5. (H&E, × 900)
- a. Pituicytes

FIG. 4. Pars intermedia and pars nervosa of the pituitary gland. Level 5. (H&E, × 625)
- a. Vestigial lumen
- b. Pars intermedia
- c. Pars nervosa
- d. Pituicytes

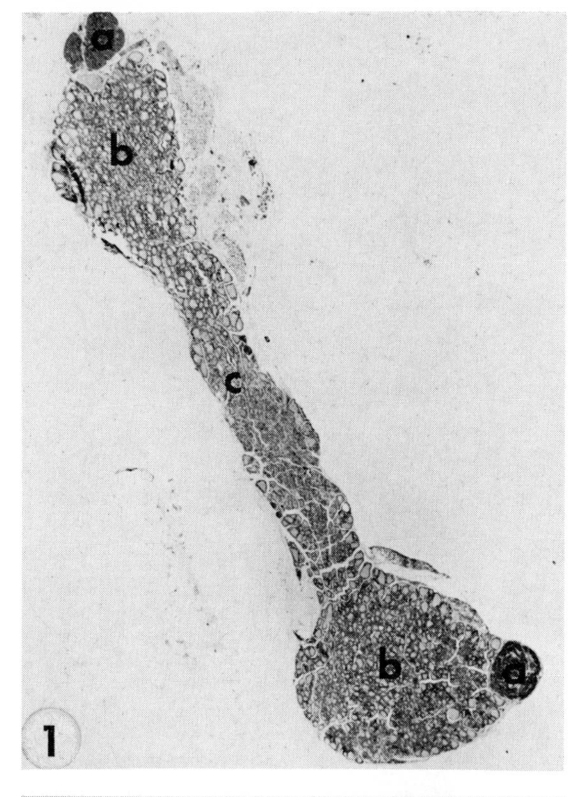

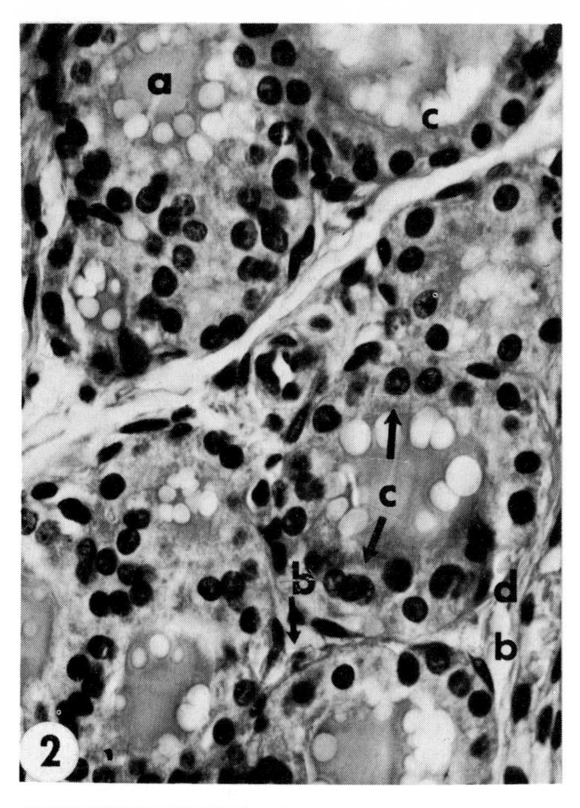

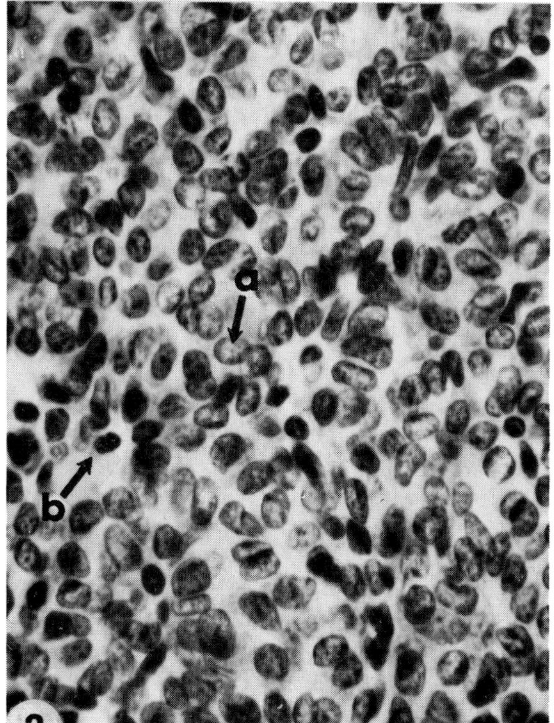

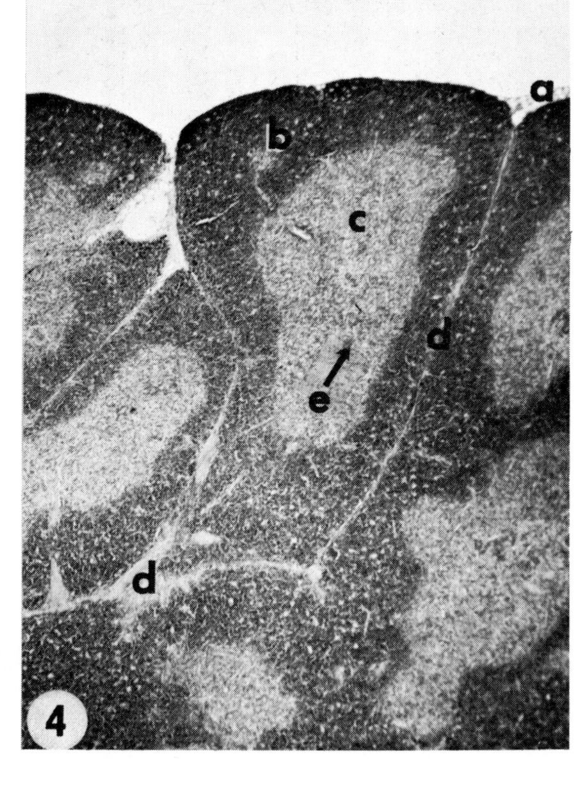

Plate 69
Endocrine System

Fig. 1. Thyroid and parathyroid glands. Cross section. Level 6. (H&E, × 15)
- a. Parathyroid glands
- b. Laterial lobes of the thyroid gland
- c. Isthmus

Fig. 2. Thyroid gland. Cross section. Level 6. (H&E, × 600)
- a. Colloid in the lumen of a follicle
- b. Capillaries
- c. Follicular epithelium (cuboidal)
- d. Connective tissue

Fig. 3. Parathyroid gland. Cross section. (Level 6. (H&E, × 700)
- a. Clear chief cell
- b. Dark chief cell

Fig. 4. Thymus. Longitudinal section. Level 1. (H&E, × 28)
- a. Capsule
- b. Cortex
- c. Medulla
- d. Connective tissue septa
- e. Thymic corpuscle (Hassall)

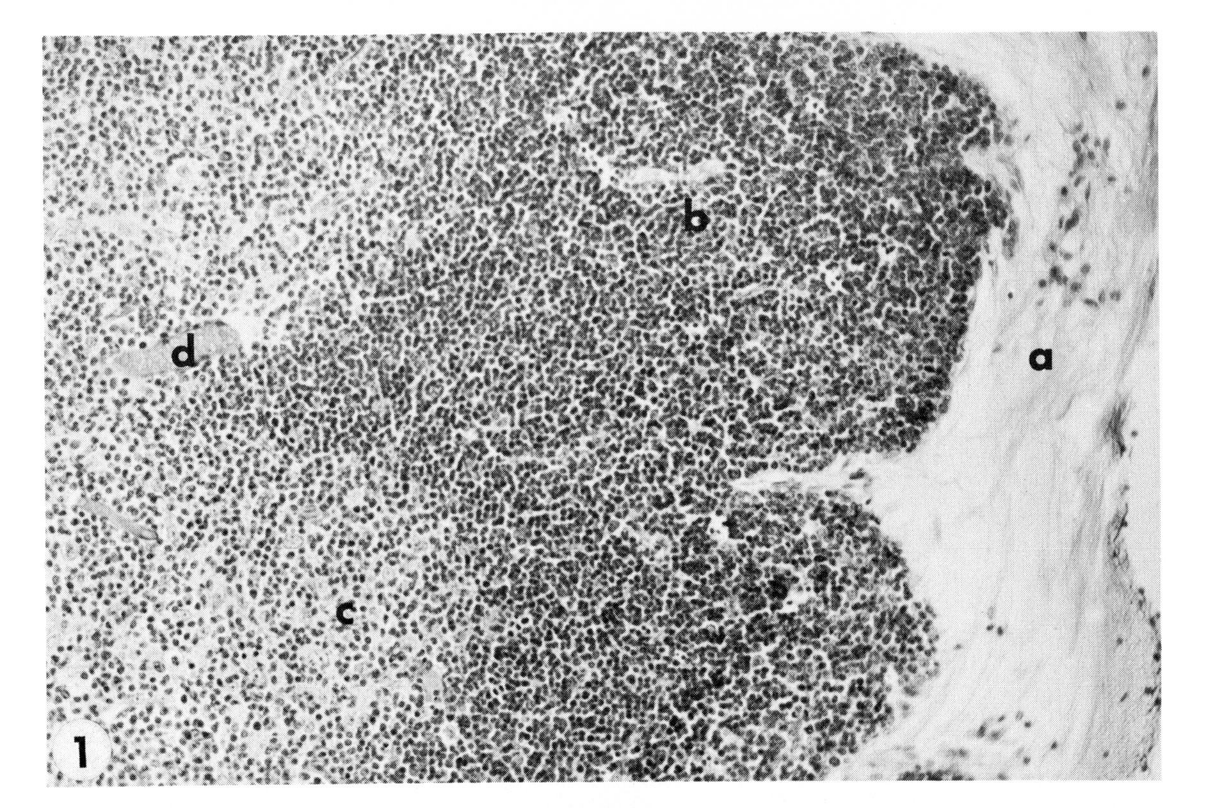

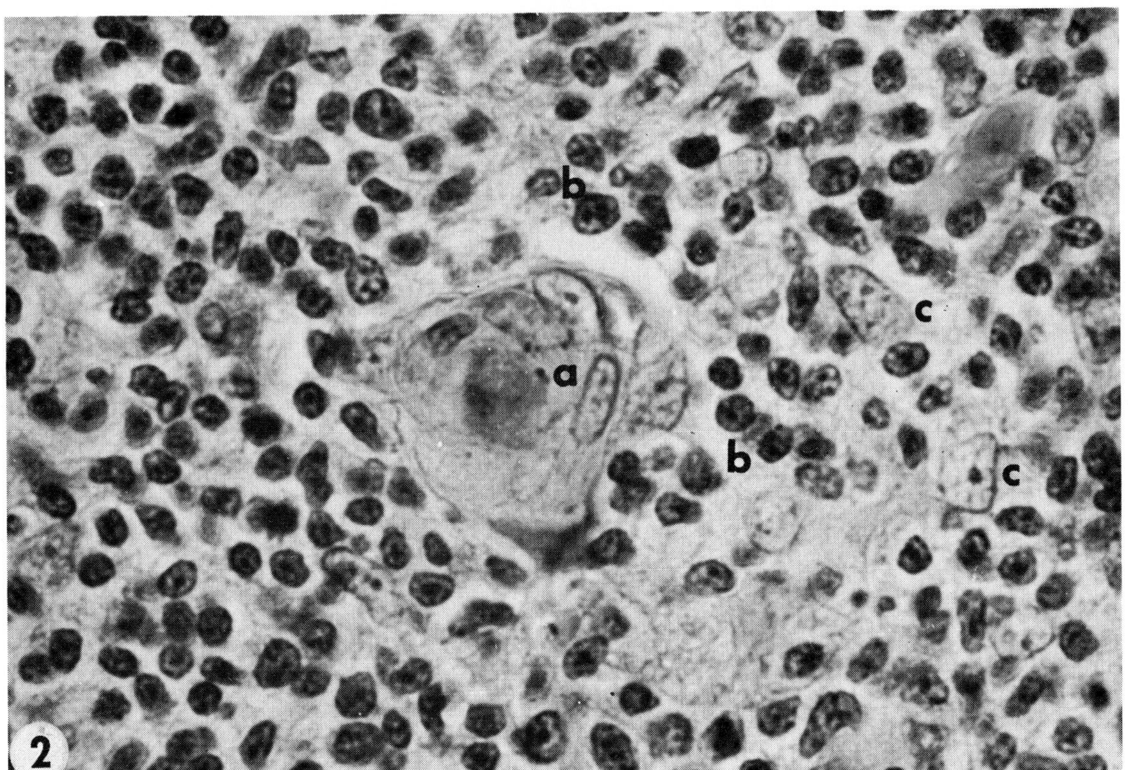

PLATE 70
Endocrine System

FIG. 1. Thymus. Level 1. (H&E, × 255)
a. Capsule
b. Cortex
c. Medulla
d. Blood vessel

FIG. 2. Thymus. Level 1. (H&E, × 2125)
a. Thymic corpuscle
b. Lymphocytes
c. Epithelial cells

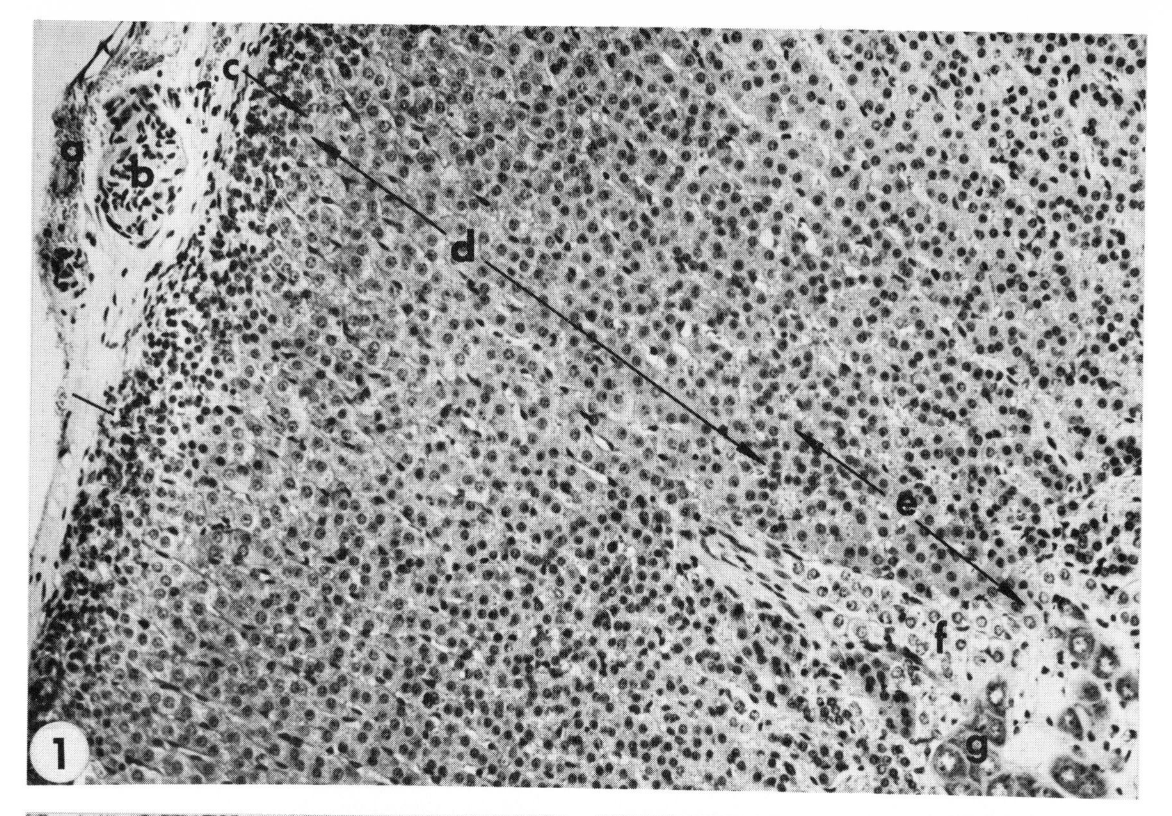

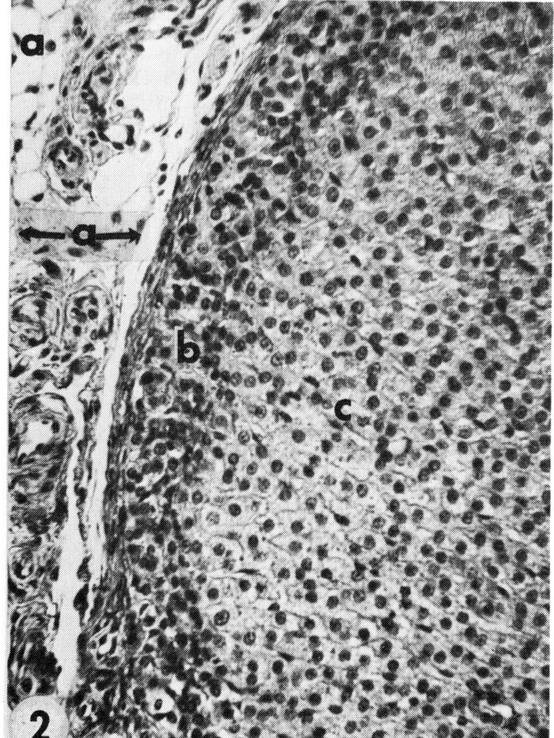

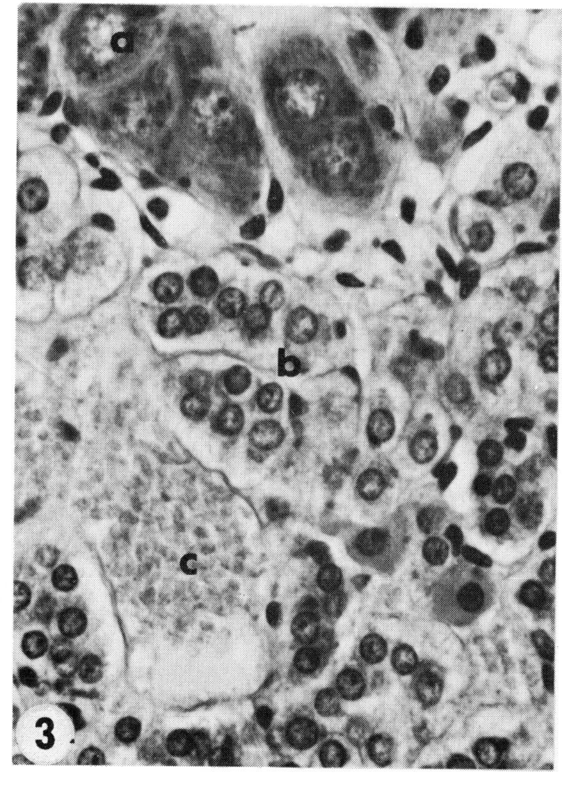

Plate 71
Endocrine System

Fig. 1. Adrenal gland. Longitudinal section. Level 3. (H&E, × 200)
- a. Connective tissue capsule
- b. Nerve trunk
- c. Zona glomerulosa of the adrenal cortex
- d. Zona fasciculata of the adrenal cortex
- e. Zona reticularis of the adrenal cortex
- f. Chromaffin cells of the adrenal medulla
- g. Sympathetic ganglion cells in the adrenal medulla

Fig. 2. Adrenal cortex. Level 3. (H&E, × 260)
- a. Capsule of the adrenal gland
- b. Zona glomerulosa
- c. Zona fasciculata

Fig. 3. Adrenal medulla. Level 3. (H&E, × 630)
- a. Sympathetic ganglion cells
- b. Chromaffin cells
- c. Sinusoid

Plate 72
Nervous System

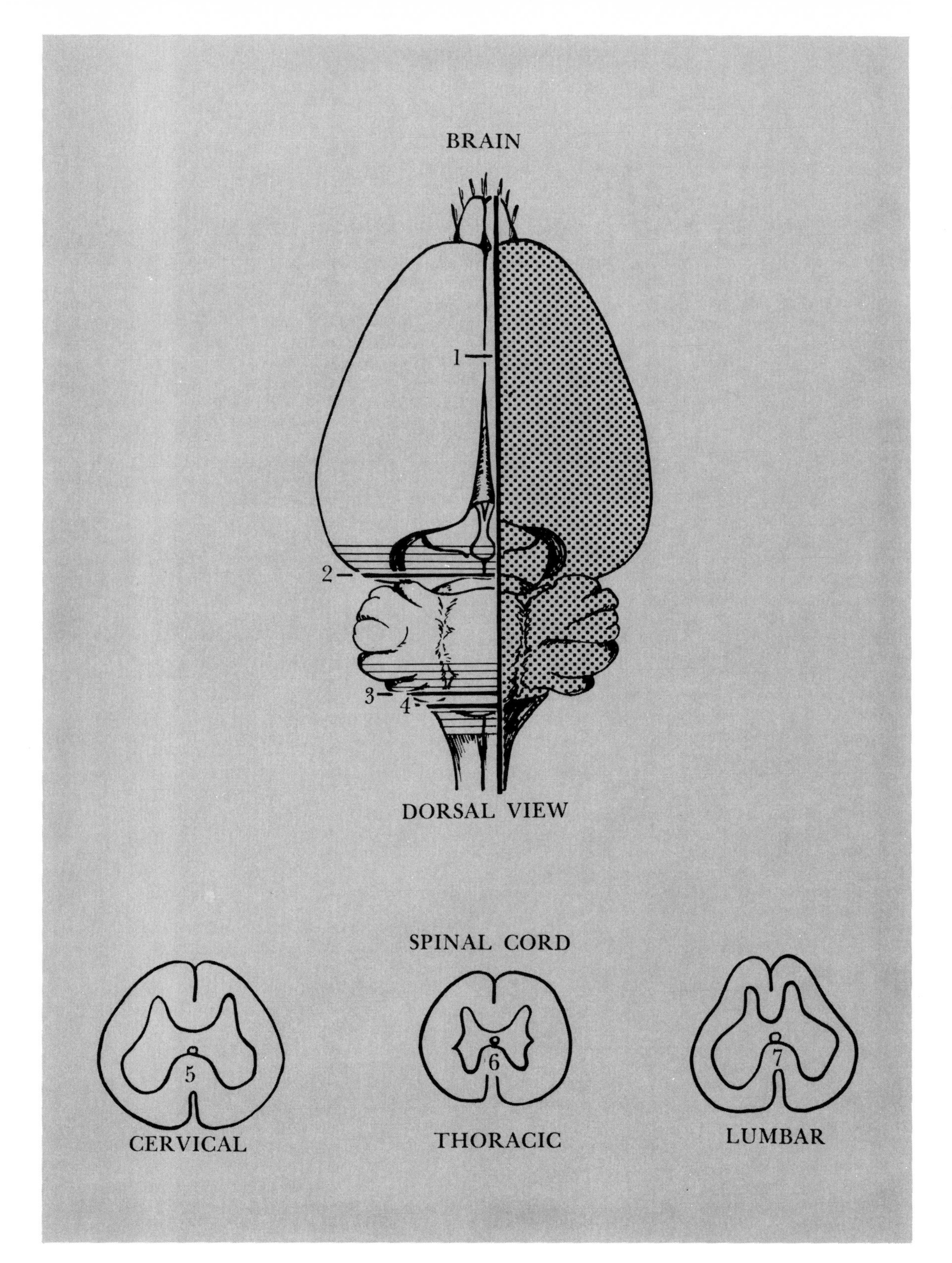

PLATE 73
Nervous System

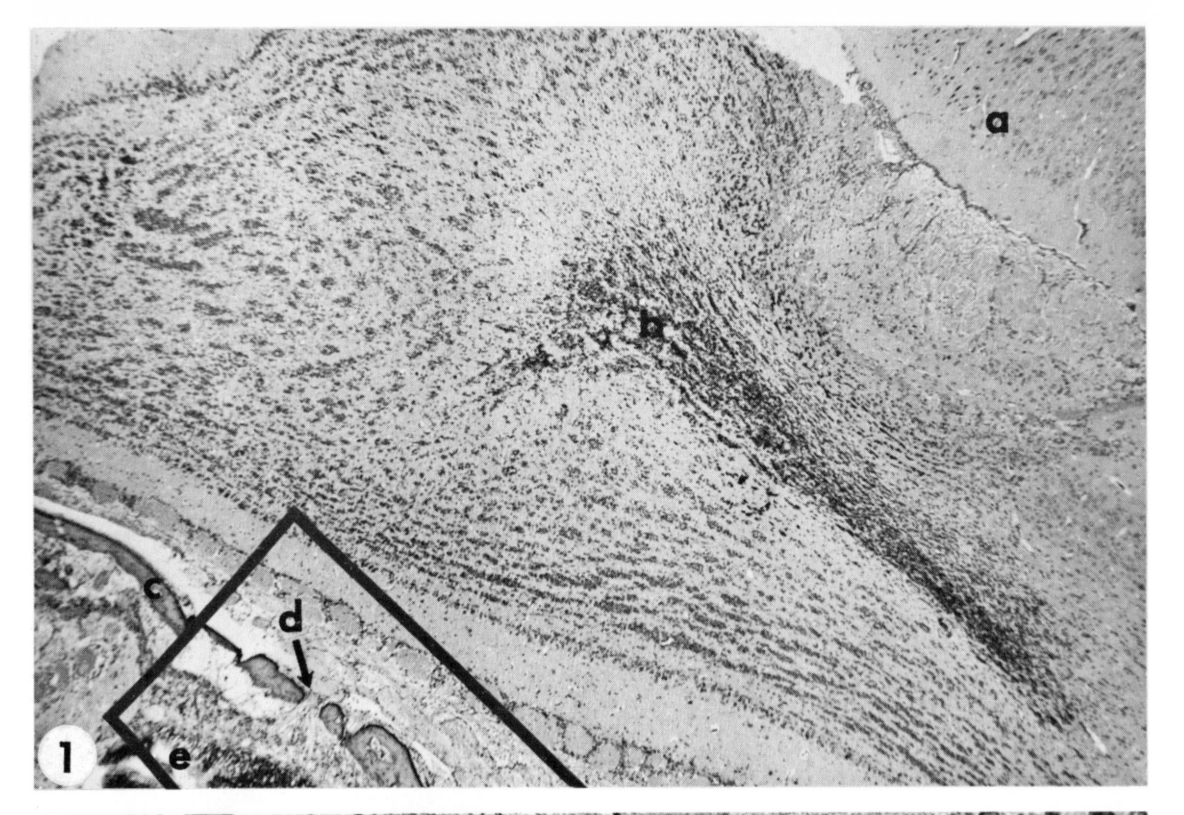

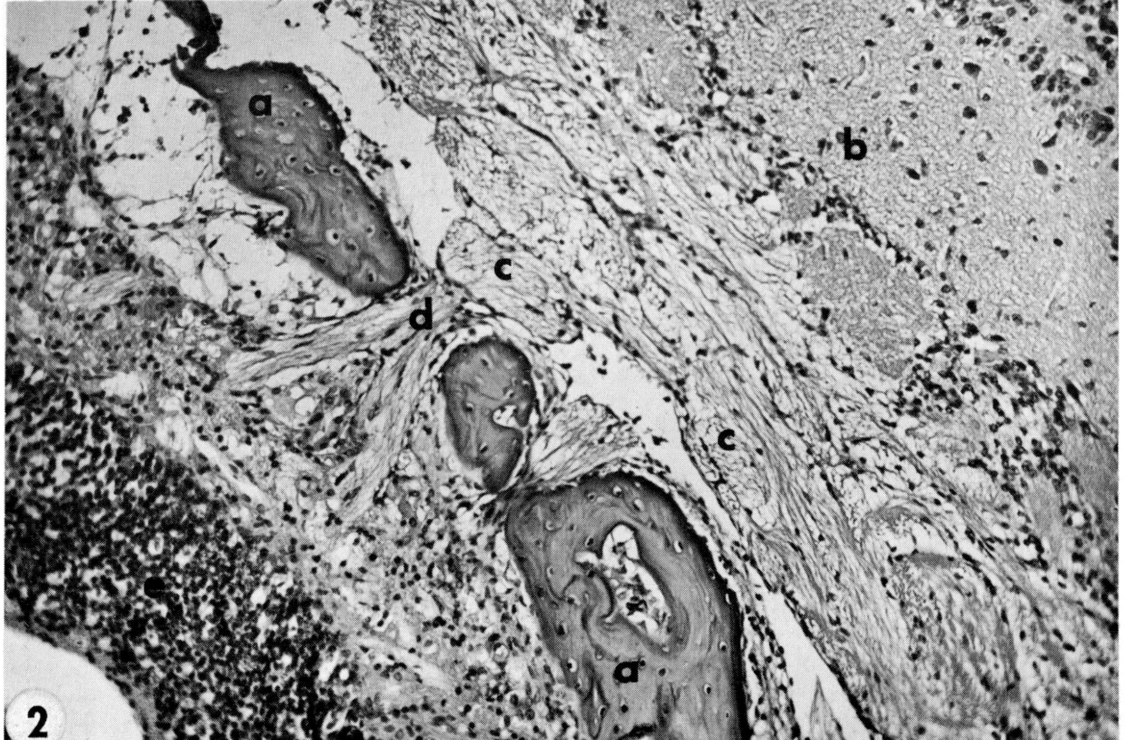

FIG. 1. Olfactory bulb. Longitudinal section. Level 1. (H&E, × 40)
- a. Cerebrum
- b. Olfactory bulb
- c. Cribriform plate of the ethmoid bone
- d. Olfactory nerve
- e. Olfactory mucosa

FIG. 2. Detail of the area marked in Fig. 1. Level 1. (H&E, × 185)
- a. Cribriform plate of the ethmoid bone
- b. Olfactory bulb
- c. Olfactory nerve fibers in cross section
- d. Olfactory nerve fibers penetrating the cribriform plate
- e. Olfactory mucosa

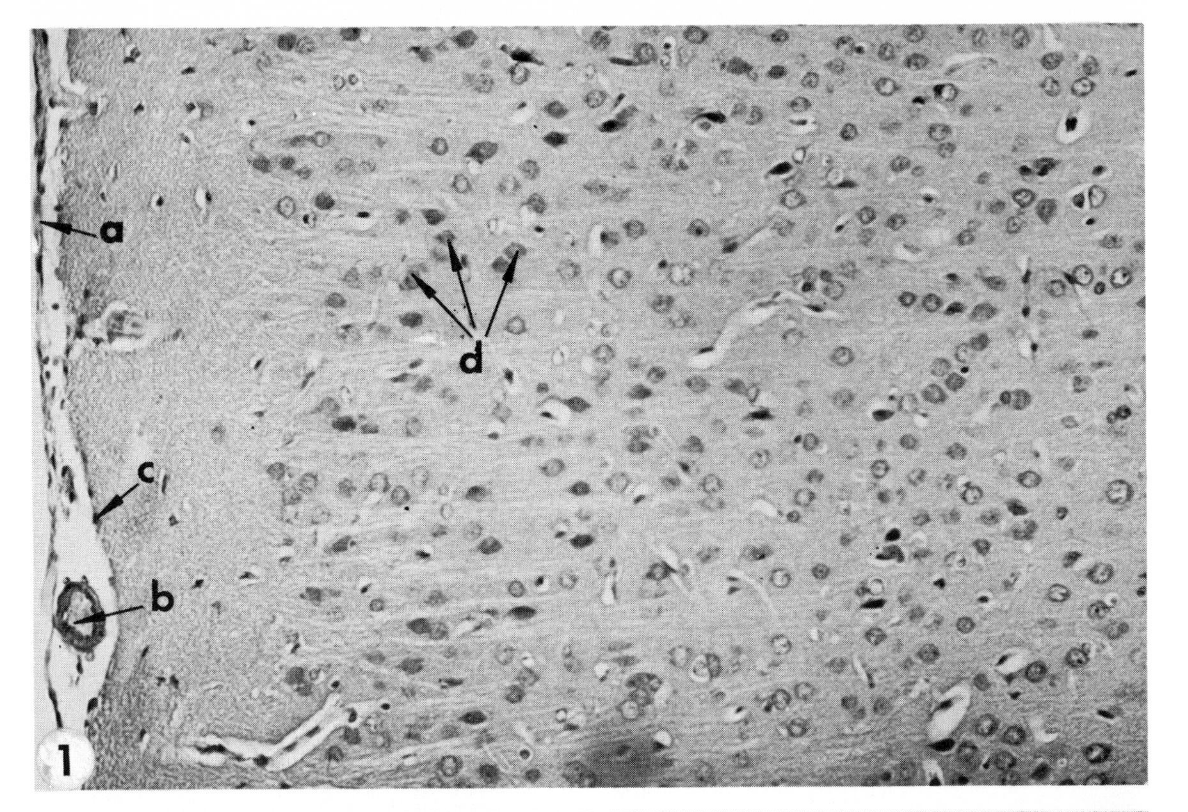

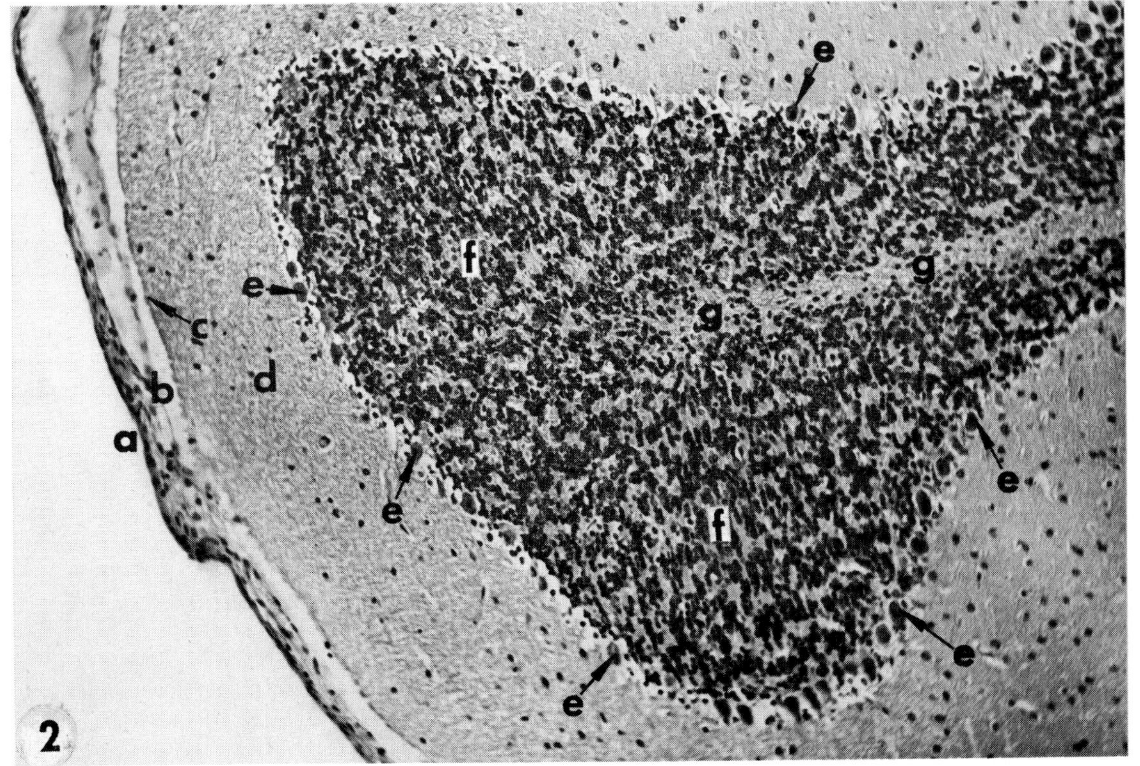

PLATE 74
Nervous System

FIG. 1. Cerebral cortex. Cross section. Level 1. (H&E, × 250)
- a. Dura mater
- b. Meningeal blood vessel
- c. Pia mater
- d. Pyramidal cells

FIG. 2. Cerebellar cortex. Cross section. Level 3. (H&E, × 160)
- a. Dura mater
- b. Arachnoid
- c. Pia mater
- d. Molecular layer of the cortex
- e. Purkinje cell layer of the cortex
- f. Granular cell layer of the cortex
- g. White matter

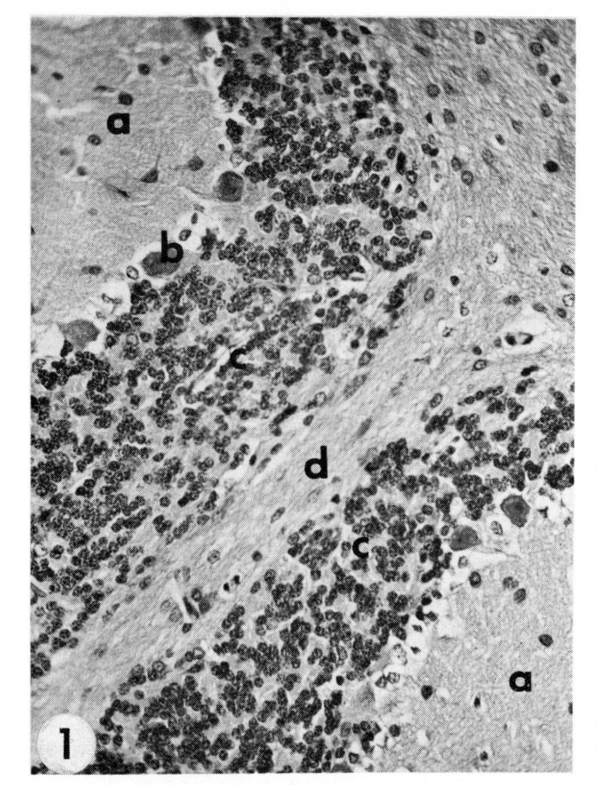

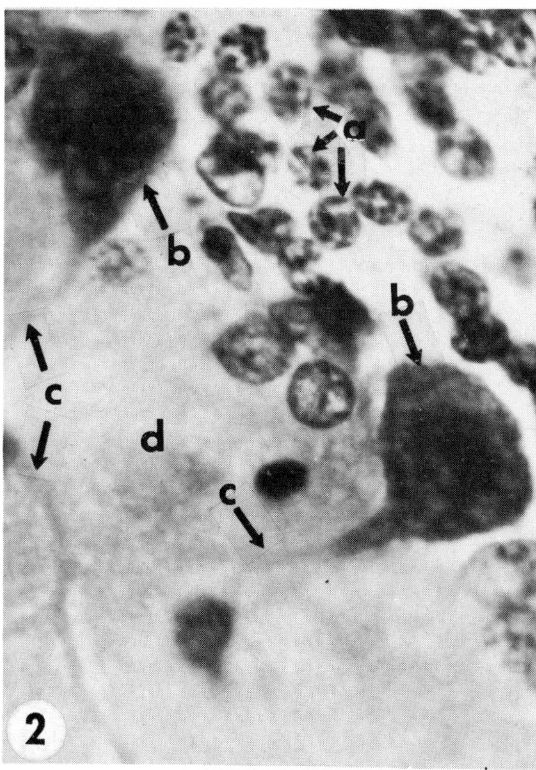

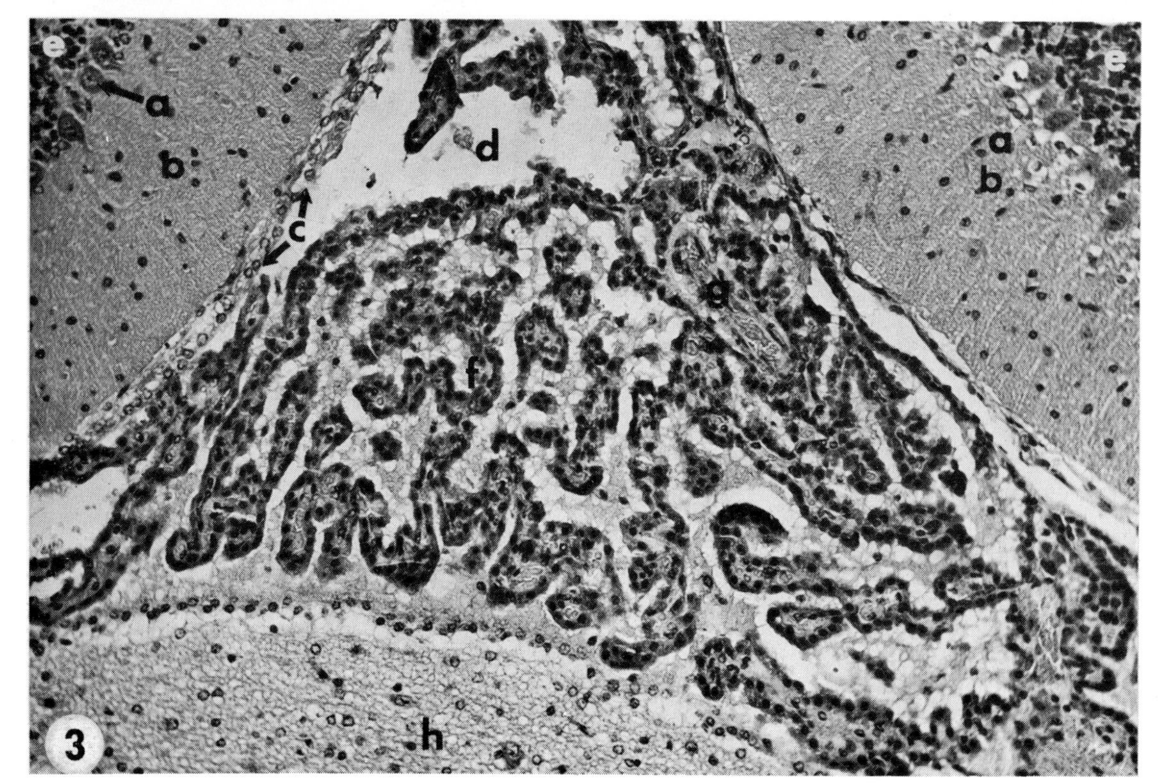

PLATE 75

Nervous System

FIG. 1. Cerebellum. Cross section. Level 3. (H&E, × 240)

a. Molecular layer of the cerebellar cortex
b. Purkinje cell layer of the cerebellar cortex
c. Granular layer of the cerebellar cortex
d. White matter

FIG. 2. Cerebellar cortex. Level 3. (H&E, × 1400)

a. Granule cells of the granular layer
b. Purkinje cells
c. Dendrites of the Purkinje cells in the molecular layer
d. Molecular layer of the cortex

FIG. 3. Choroid plexus projecting into the fourth ventricle of the brain. Longitudinal section. Level 1. (H&E, × 180)

a. Purkinje cell layer of the cerebellar cortex
b. Molecular layer of the cerebellar cortex
c. Simple cuboidal epithelial cells of the ependyma
d. Fourth ventricle
e. Granular layer of the cerebellar cortex
f. Choroid plexus
g. Blood vessel
h. Brain stem

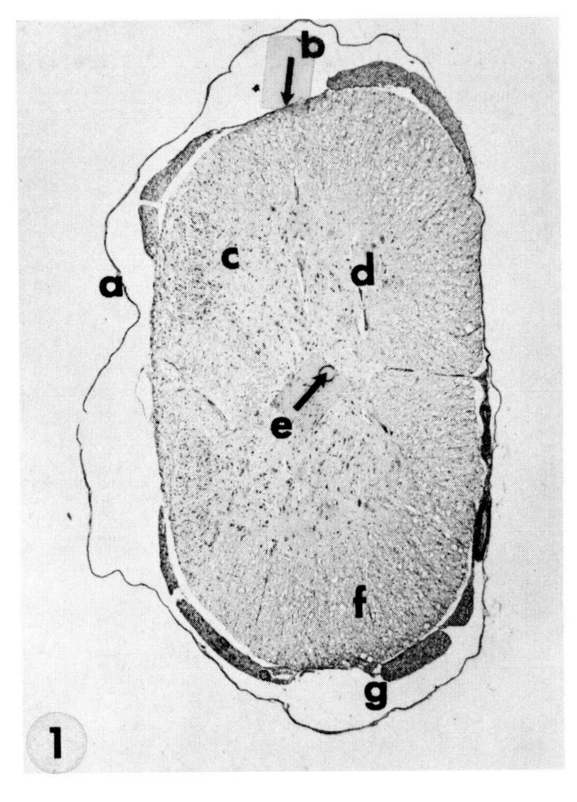

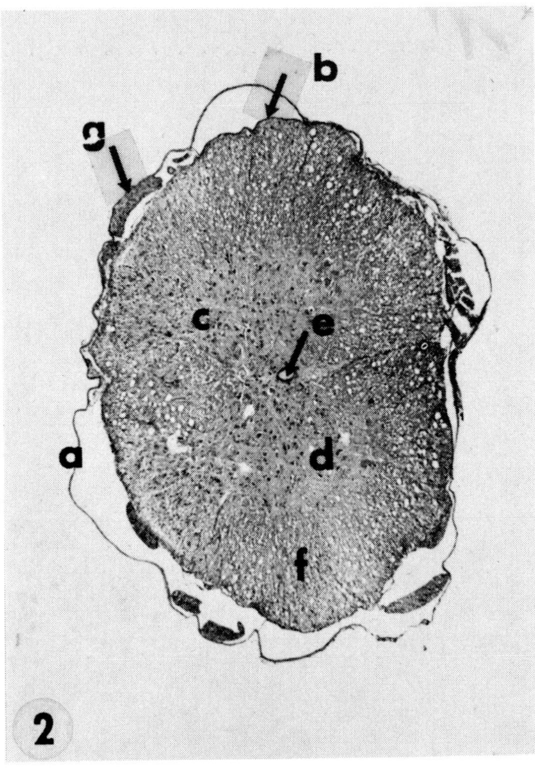

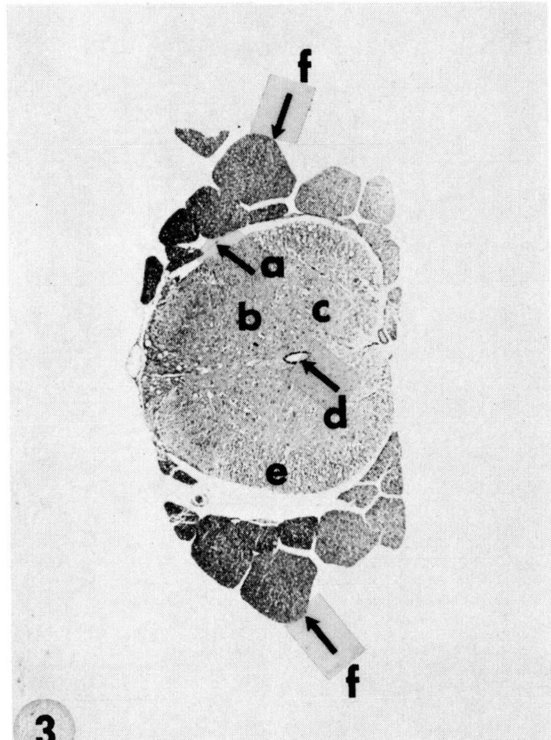

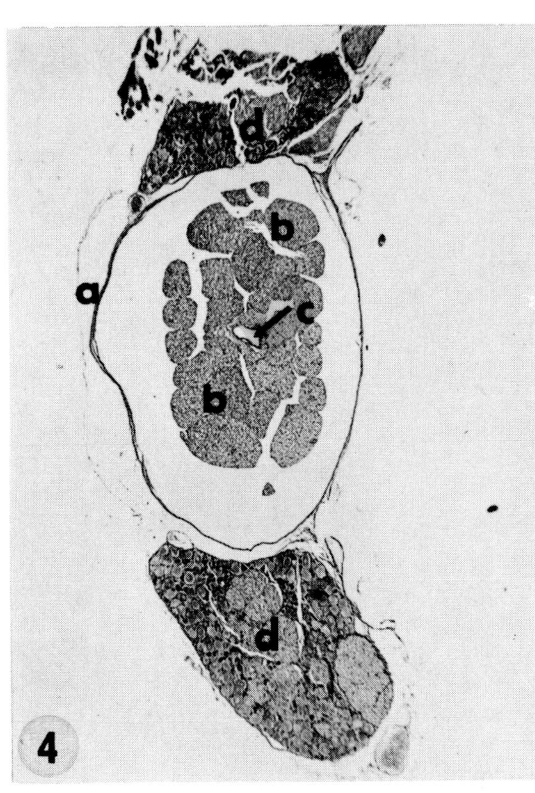

PLATE 76
Nervous System

FIG. 1. Cervical level of the spinal cord. Cross section. Level 5. (H&E, × 36)
- a. Dura mater
- b. Pia mater
- c. Dorsal horn gray
- d. Ventral horn gray
- e. Central canal
- f. White matter
- g. Roots of the spinal nerves

FIG. 2. Thoracic level of the spinal cord. Cross section. Level 6. (H&E, × 36)
- a. Dura mater
- b. Pia mater
- c. Dorsal horn gray
- d. Ventral horn gray
- e. Central canal
- f. White matter
- g. Roots of the spinal nerves

FIG. 3. Lumbar level of the spinal cord. Cross section. Level 7. (H&E, × 36)
- a. Pia mater
- b. Dorsal horn gray
- c. Ventral horn gray
- d. Central canal
- e. White matter
- f. Roots of the spinal nerves

FIG. 4. Cauda equina. Cross sction. (H&E, × 36)
- a. Dura mater
- b. Roots of the spinal nerves
- c. Central canal
- d. Dorsal root ganglion

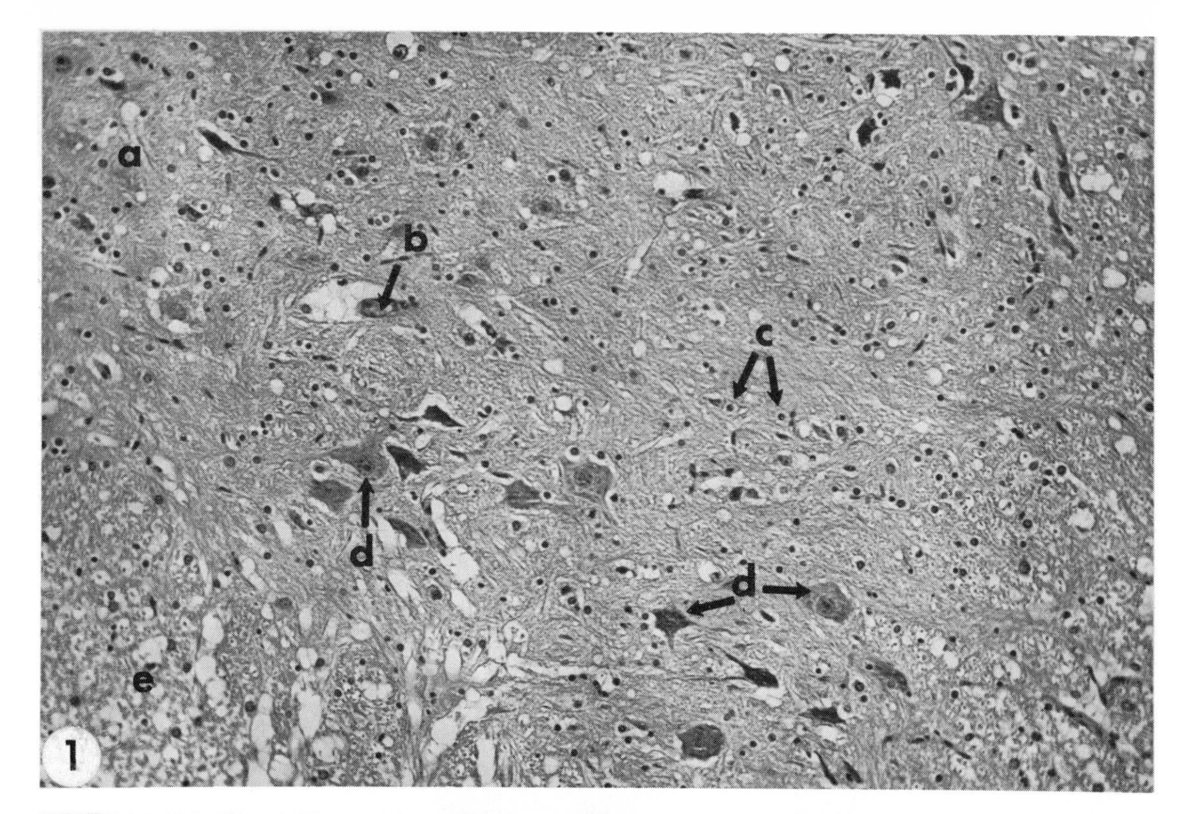

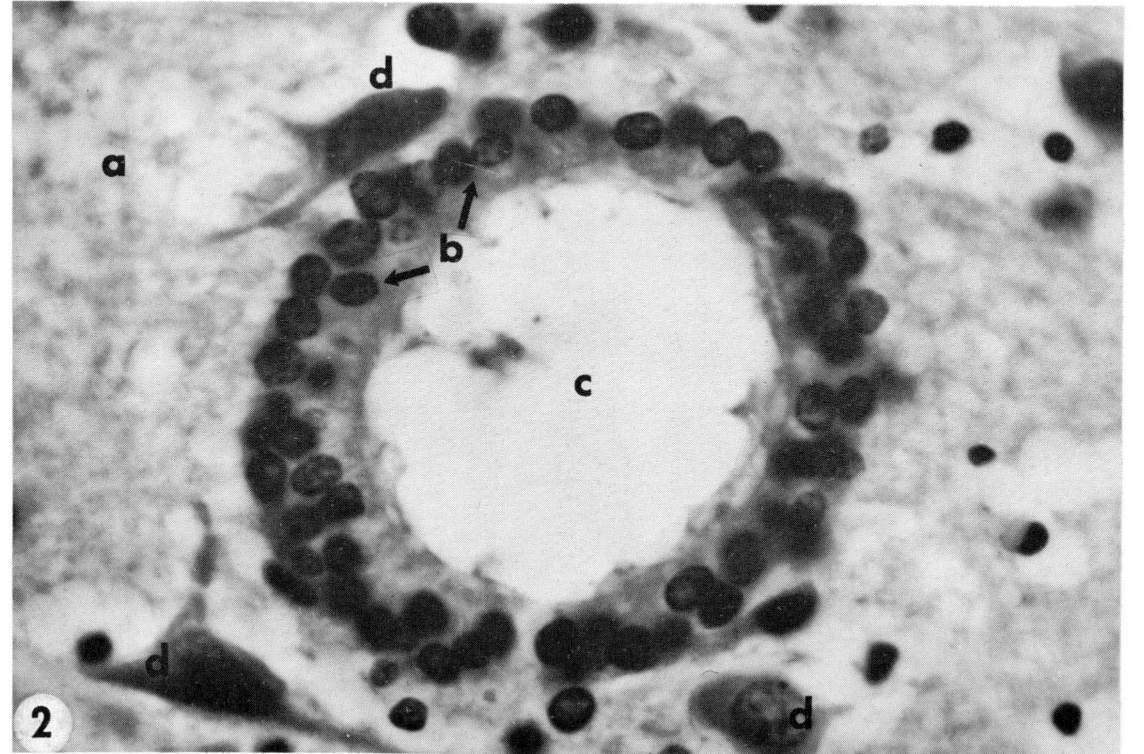

PLATE 77
Nervous System

FIG. 1. Ventral horn of the cervical spinal cord. Cross section. Level 5. (H&E, × 180)
a. Gray matter
b. Blood vessel
c. Neuroglial cell nuclei
d. Neuroglial multipolar neuron cell bodies
e. White matter

FIG. 2. Central canal of the spinal cord. Cross section. Level 5. (H&E, × 1340)
a. Area of gray commissure
b. Ependymal cells
c. Central canal
d. Multipolar neuron cell bodies

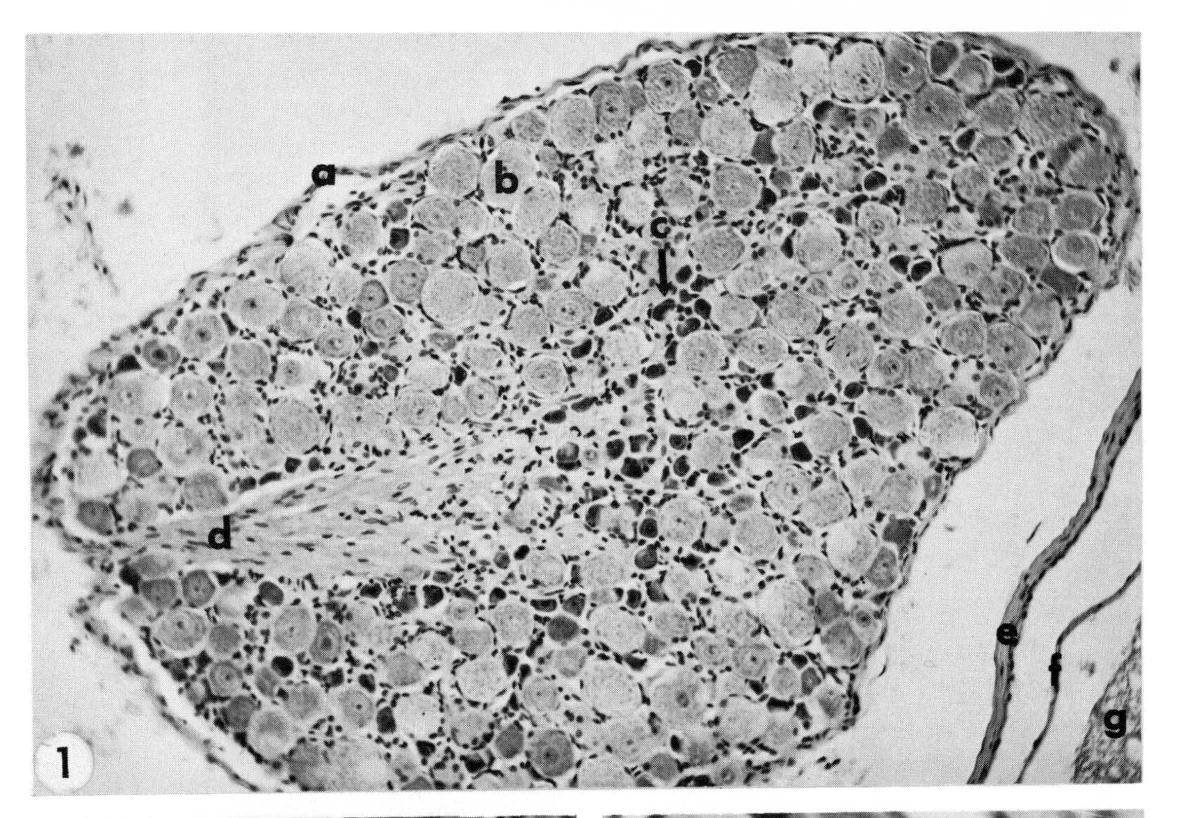

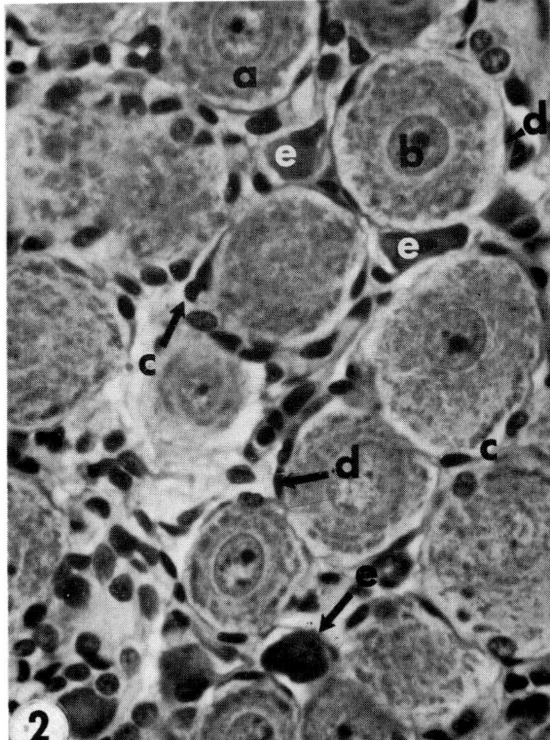

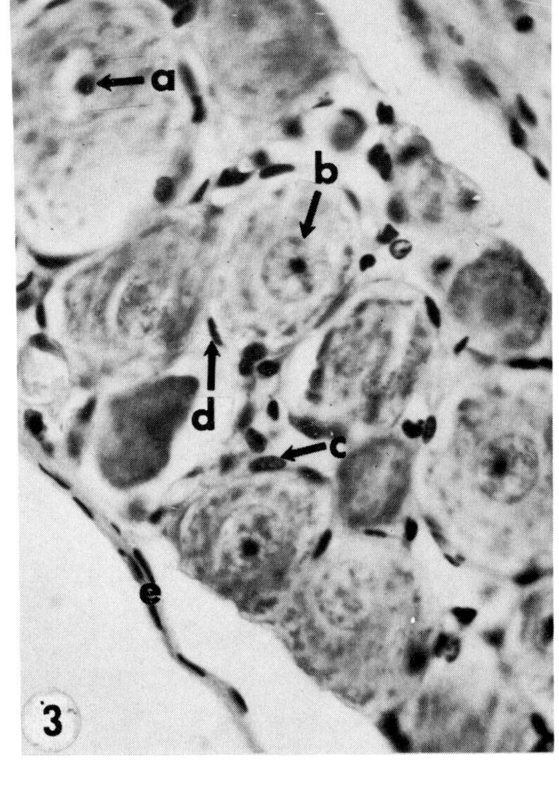

PLATE 78
Nervous System

FIG. 1. Spinal ganglion. Cross section. Level 5. (H&E, × 45)
- a. Connective tissue capsule
- b. Large clear ganglion cell body
- c. Small dark-staining ganglion cell bodies
- d. Nerve fibers
- e. Dura mater
- f. Arachnoid
- g. White matter

FIG. 2. Spinal ganglion. Cross section. Level 5. (H&E, × 380)
- a. Ganglion cell body with Nissl substance
- b. Nucleus of a ganglion cell body with prominent nucleolus
- c. Nucleus of a satellite cell
- d. Nucleus of a fibroblast
- e. Dark-staining ganglion cell bodies

FIG. 3. Autonomic ganglion of the sympathetic chain. Cross section. (H&E, × 430)
- a. Nucleolus of a ganglion cell body
- b. Nucleus of a ganglion cell body
- c. Satellite cells forming an incomplete cellular capsule
- d. Fibroblast
- e. Connective tissue capsule of the ganglion

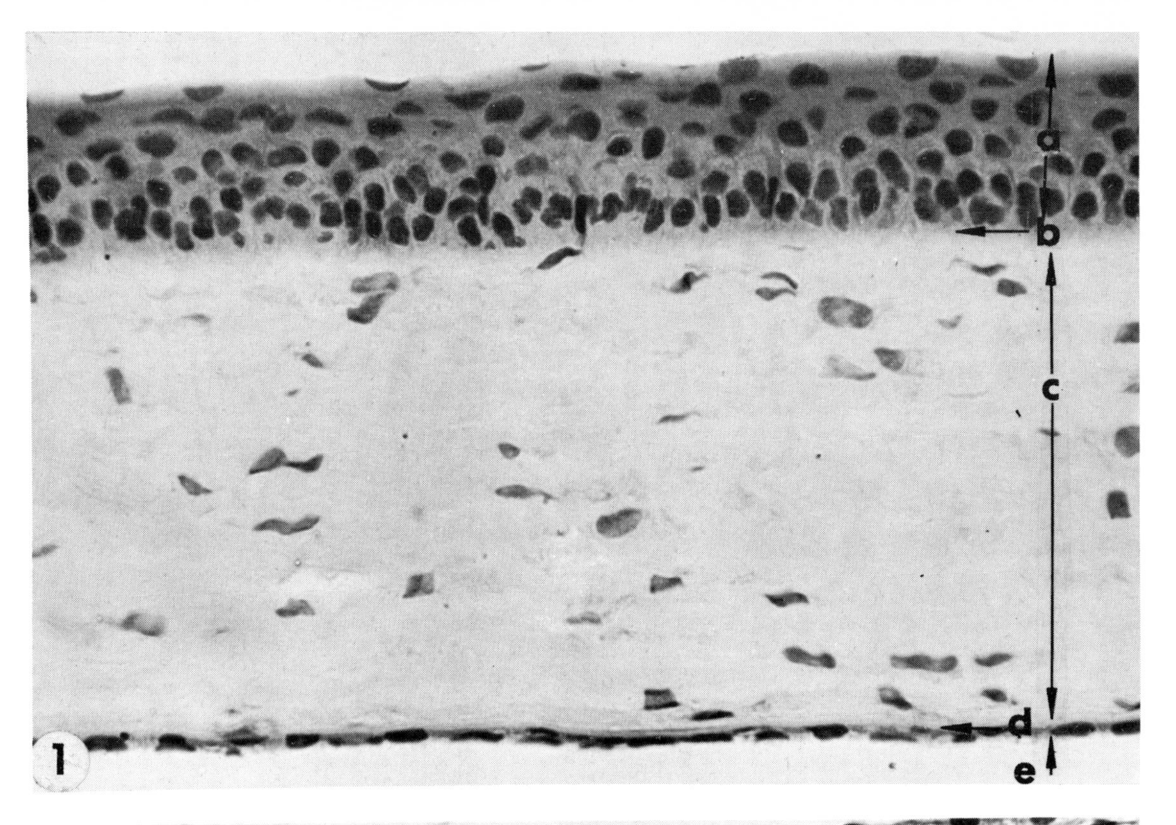

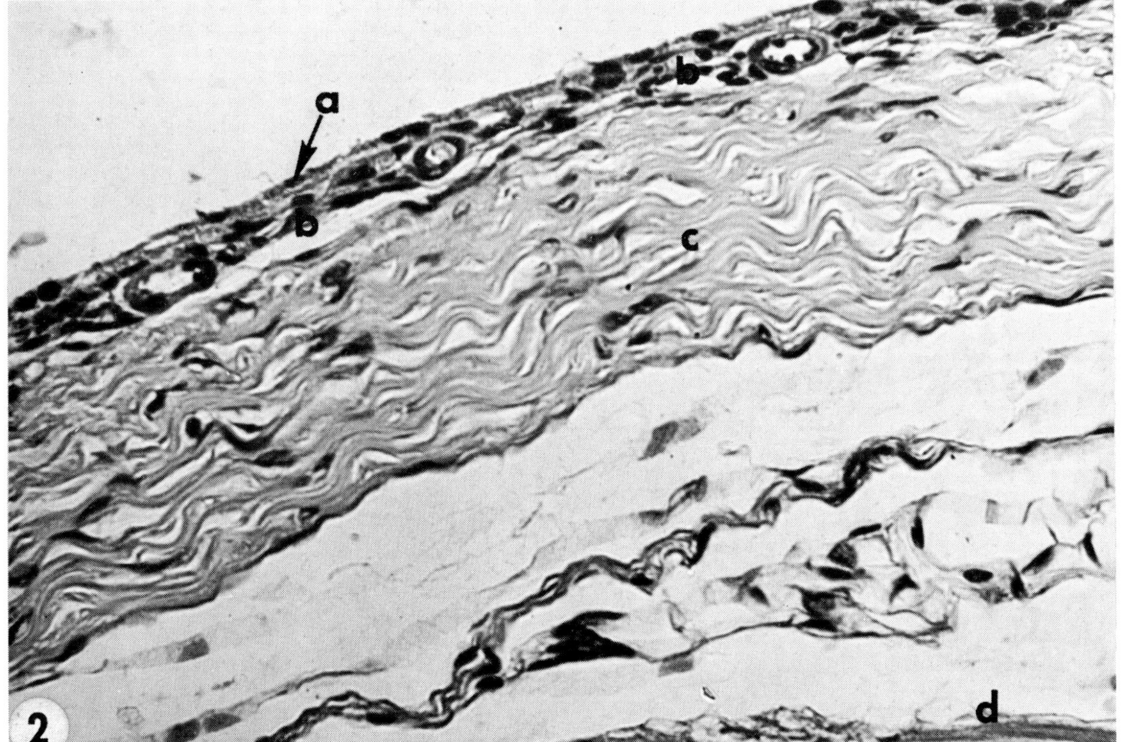

PLATE 79
Eye

FIG. 1. Cornea. (H&E, × 532)
- a. Stratified squamous epithelium
- b. Anterior limiting membrane (Bowman's membrane)
- c. Substantia propria (collagenic fibers)
- d. Posterior limiting membrane (Descemet's membrane)
- e. Mesenchymal epithelium (Descemet's endothelium)

FIG. 2. Sclera and associated structures. (H&E, × 532)
- a. Pigment epithelium
- b. Vascular choroid
- c. Sclera
- d. Intrinsic eye muscles

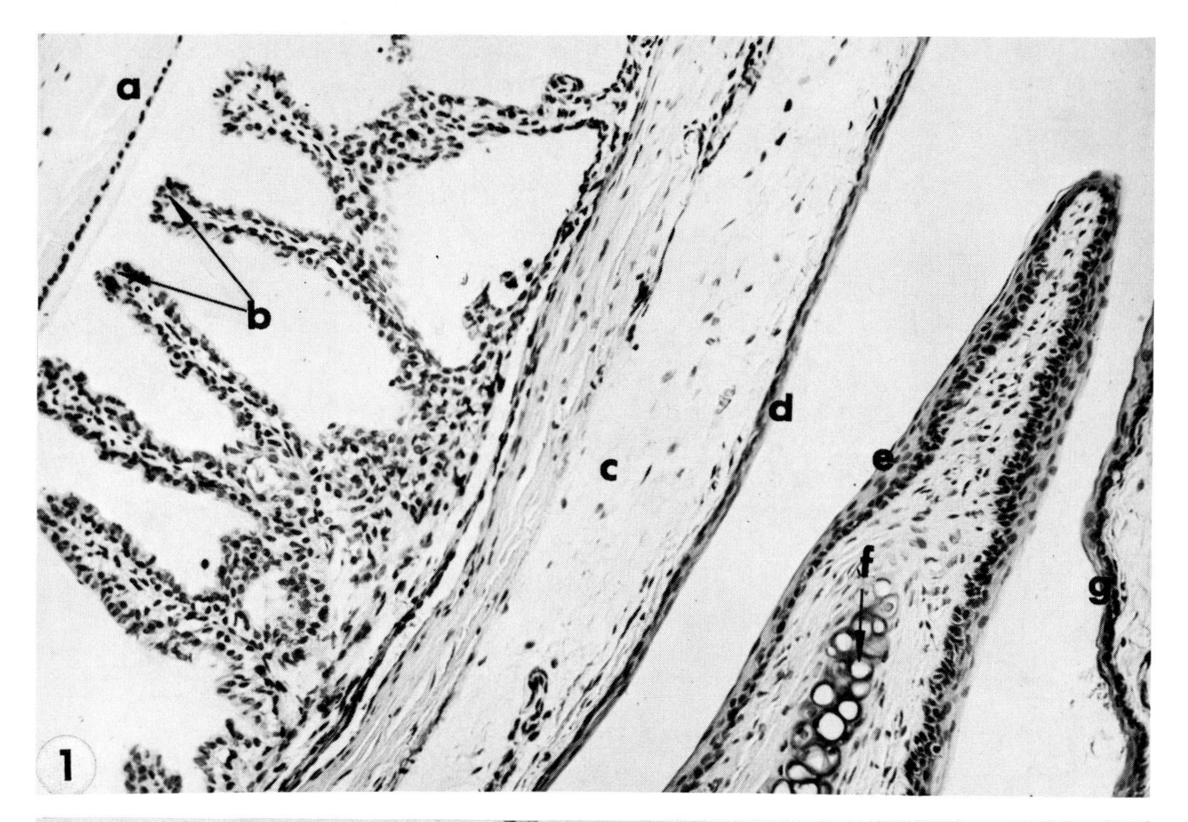

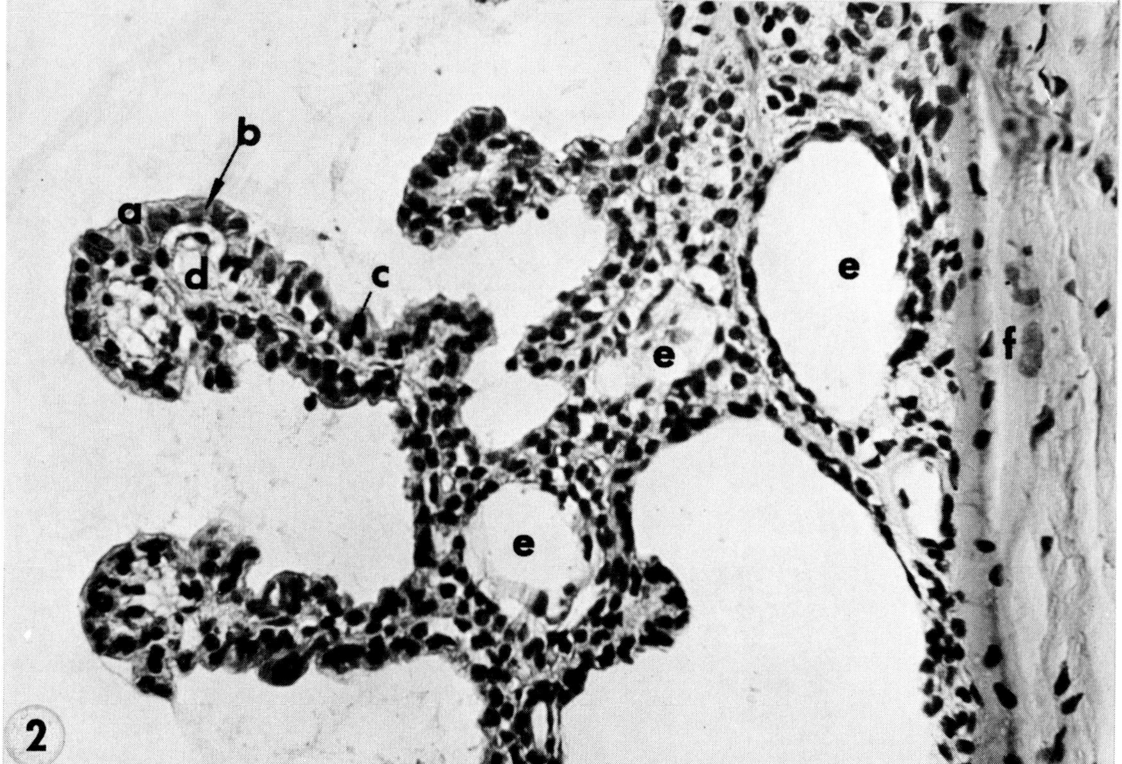

Plate 80
Eye

Fig. 1. Relation of the nictitating membrane to the cornea. Sagittal section. (H&E, × 120)
- a. Lens
- b. Ciliary processes
- c. Cornea
- d. Anterior surface of the cornea
- e. Stratified squamous epithelium of the nictitating membrane
- f. Hyaline cartilage core of the nictitating membrane
- g. Epithelium of the eyelid

Fig. 2. Ciliary processes. Sagittal section. (H&E, × 575)
- a. Two-layered epithelial covering
- b. Outer ciliary epithelium
- c. Inner nonpigmented epithelium
- d. Vascular stroma
- e. Blood vessels
- f. Collagenous tissue of the ciliary body

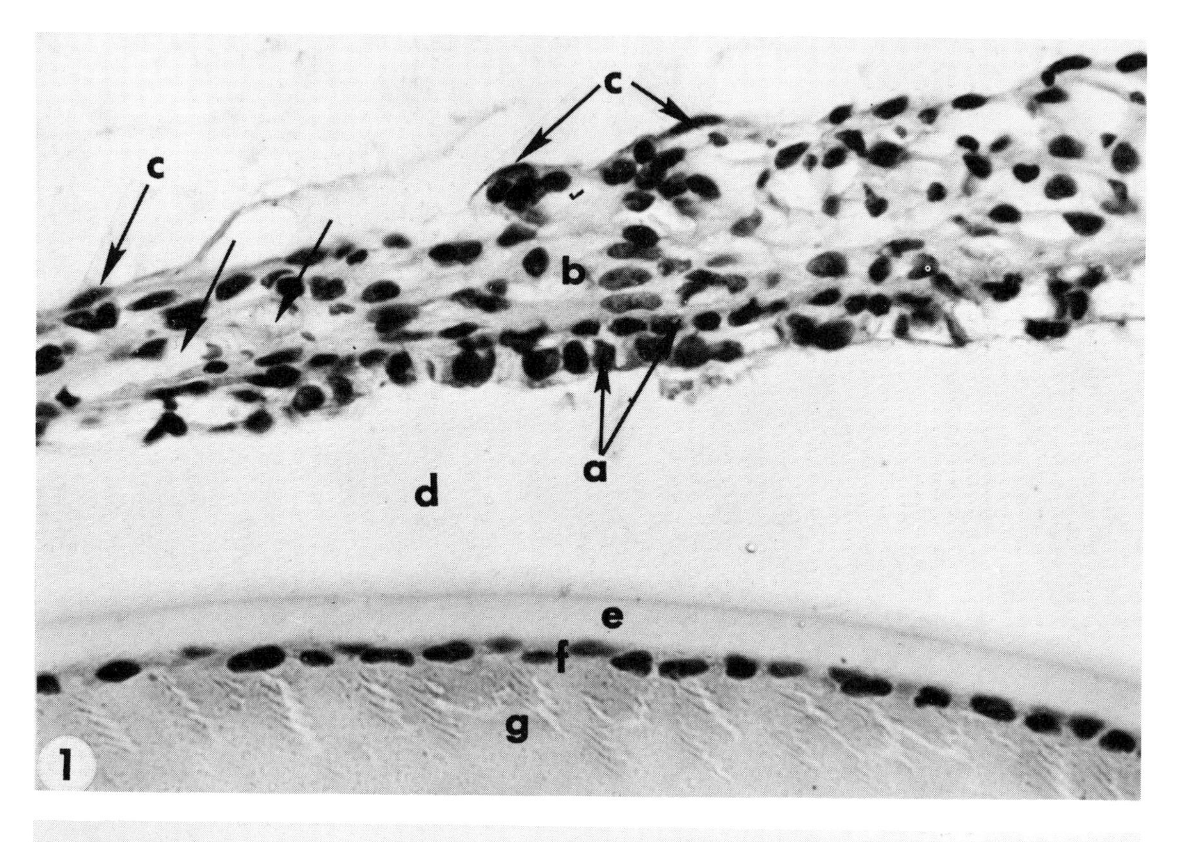

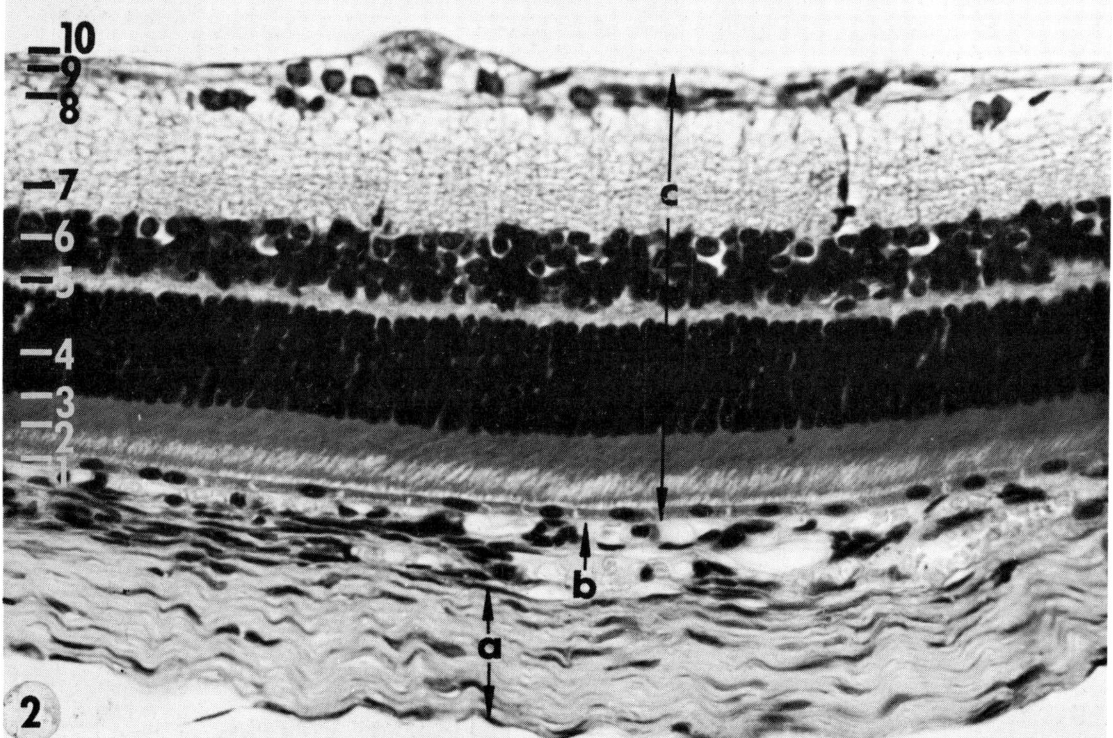

PLATE 81
Eye

FIG. 1. Iris and lens. Sagittal section. (H&E, × 613)

- a. Posterior covering composed of 2 layers of epithelium
- b. Stroma of the iris containing connective tissue and blood vessels (arrow)
- c. Anterior covering of mesenchymal epithelium continuous with Descemet's endothelium of the cornea
- d. Posterior chamber
- e. Homogenous elastic capsule of the lens
- f. Lens epithelium
- g. Lens fibers

FIG. 2. Retina. Sagittal section. (H&E, × 453)

- a. Sclera
- b. Choroid
- c. Retina
  1. Pigment epithelium (nonpigmented in albino rats)
  2. Layer of rods and cones
  3. Outer limiting membrane (not well delineated here)
  4. Outer nuclear layer
  5. Outer plexiform layer
  6. Inner nuclear layer
  7. Inner plexiform layer
  8. Ganglion cell layer
  9. Layer of nerve fibers
  10. Inner limiting membrane

SELECTED REFERENCES

SINCE LITERATURE relative to the microscopic anatomy of the white rat is so voluminous, the authors felt a complete bibliography would be too extensive to undertake. We have chosen references, for the most part, on general and systemic bases.

In a few instances, where systemic references were lacking or we wished to point out something peculiar to the rat, we have included specific organ citations.

GENERAL

BARNETT, S. A.: 1963. *The Rat, a Study in Behaviour.* Aldine Publishing Co., Chicago, Ill.

BARROWS, C. H. Jr.: 1960. Age and cellular metabolism of tissues. Publ. Amer. Inst. Biol. Sci. 6:116.

BOYCOTT, A. E., and DAMANT, G. C. C.: 1908. A note on the total fat of rats, guinea pigs and mice. *J. Physiol.* 37:25.

BRUES, A. M., SACHER, G. A., and FRANCE, H. O.: 1956. Effects of total-body x irradiation on weights of organs in the rat. Biological Effects of External X and Gamma Radiation. Pt. 2. Edited by R. E. Zirkle. Atomic Energy Commission. TID–5220, p. 217.

BUCKNER, G. D., and PETER, A. M.: 1922. The mineral content of the normal white rat during growth. *J. Biol. Chem.* 54:5.

CASTER, W. O., PONCELET, J., SIMON, A. B., and ARMSTRONG, W. D.: 1956. Tissue weights of the rat. I. Normal values determined by dissection and chemical methods. *Proc. Soc. Exp. Biol. and Med.* 91:122.

D'AMOUR, F. E., and BLOOD, F. R.: 1954. *Manual for Laboratory Work in Mammalian Physiology.* University of Chicago Press, Chicago, Ill.

DONALDSON, H. H.: 1906. A comparison of the white rat with man in respect to the growth of the entire body. Boas Anniversary Volume, pp. 5–26. G. E. Stechert & Co., New York.

———: 1912. The history and zoological position of the albino rat. *J. Acad. Nat. Sci.* 15:365.

———: 1923. On changes in the relative weights of the viscera and other organs from birth to maturity—albino rat. *Am. J. Physiol.* 67:1.

———: 1924. *The Rat: Data and Reference Tables for the Albino Rat* (Mus norvegicus albinus) *and the Norway Rat* (Mus norvegicus). Memoirs of the Wistar Institute of Anatomy and Biology—No. 6. The Wistar Institute of Anatomy and Biology, Philadelphia, Pa.

DUNN, M. S., MURPHY, E. A., and ROCKLAND, L. B.: 1947. Optimal growth of the rat. *Physiol. Rev.* 27:72.

EVERITT, A. V.: 1959. The aging process in the laboratory rat. *Excerpta Medica* Sec. 20. 2:135.

FARRIS, E. J., and GRIFFITH, J. Q., Editors: 1949. *The Rat in Laboratory Investigation.* J. B. Lippincott Co., Philadelphia, Pa.

GREENMAN, M. J., and Duhring, F. L.: 1931. *Breeding and Care of the Albino Rat for Research Purposes.* The Wistar Institute of Anatomy and Biology, Philadelphia, Pa.

HATAI, S.: 1913. On the weights of the abdominal and thoracic viscera, the sex glands, ductless glands and the eyeballs of the albino rat *(Mus norvegicus albinus)* according to body weight. *Am. J. Anat.* 15:87.

———: 1915. On the influence of exercise on the growth of organs in the albino rat. *Anat. Rec.* 9:647.

KING, H. D.: 1915. On the weight of the albino rat at birth and the factors that influence it. *Anat. Rec.* 9:213.

LEE, M. O.: 1929. Determination of the surface area of the white rat with its application to the expression of metabolic results. *Am. J. Physiol.* 89:24.

GROSS ANATOMY

CHIASSON, R. B.: 1958. *Laboratory Anatomy of the White Rat.* William C. Brown, Dubuque, Iowa.

GORDON, H. A., and WOSTMANN, B. S.: 1960. Morphological studies on the germfree albino rat. *Anat. Rec.* 137:65.

GREENE, E. C.: 1935. *Anatomy of the Rat.* Trans. Amer. Phil. Soc. No. 27, Philadephia. Reprinted 1959, Hafner Publishing Co., New York.

———: 1949. Gross Anatomy. In: *The Rat in Laboratory Investigation,* E. J. Farris and J. Q. Griffith, Editors, p. 3. J. B. Lippincott Co., Philadelphia, Pa.

HEWETT, G. M. A.: 1904. *The Rat.* Adam and Charles Black, London.

HUNT, H. R.: 1924. *A Laboratory Manual of the Anatomy of the Rat.* Macmillan Co., New York.

ROWETT, H. G. Q.: 1957. *Dissection Guides.* III. The Rat, With Notes on the Mouse. Rinehart, New York.

———: 1957. *The Rat as a Small Mammal.* J. Murray, London.

STUART, R. R.: 1947. *The Anatomy of the White Rat.* Denoyer-Geppert Co., Chicago, Ill.

MICROSCOPIC ANATOMY

BLATTEIS, C. M., and LUTHERER, L. O.: 1965. Fatty-tissue changes in rats with acclimatization to altitude. *Science* 149:1383.

DURAND, A. M. A., FISHER, M., and ADAMS, M.: 1964. Histology in rats as influenced by age and diet. I. Renal and cardiovascular systems. *Arch. Path.* 77:268.

JUNQUERIA, L. C. U., and MARTINS, E. O.: 1947. *Atlas de Anatomia Micróscopica do Rato.* Universidade de São Paulo, Brazil.

KAO, K-Y, T., and MCGAVACK, T. H.: 1959. Connective tissue: I. Age and sex influence on protein composition of rat tissues. *Proc. Soc. Exp. Biol. and Med.* 101:153.

———, SCHWARTZ, J. H., TREADWELL, C. R., and MCGAVACK, T. H.: 1960. Connective tissue: II. Effect of age and sex upon lipid composition of tissue of rat. *Proc. Soc. Exp. Biol. and Med.* 103:666.

———, HILKER, D. M., and MCGAVACK, T. H.: 1960, 1961. Connective tissue: III. Collagen and hexosamine content of tissues of rats of different ages. IV. Synthesis and turnover of proteins in tissues of rats. V. Comparison of synthesis and turnover of collagen and elastin in tissues of rat at several ages. *Proc. Soc. Exp. Biol. and Med.* 104:359; 106:121 and 335.

OMORI, Y.: 1954. Cytological studies on reticuloendothelial system. *Acta Med. et Biol.* 2:439.

RICE, H. G., and JACKSON, C. M.: 1934. The histological distribution of fats in the liver, kidney, trachea, lung, and skin of the rat at various postnatal stages. *Anat. Rec.* 59:135.

SAINTE-MARIE, G.: 1965. The distribution of the autofluorescent cells and of the yellow autofluorescent granules in the rat tissues. *Anat. Rec.* 153:71.

EMBRYOLOGY

ANGULO Y GONZALEZ, A. W.: 1932. The prenatal growth of the albino rat. *Anat. Rec.* 52:117.

AUSTIN, C. R., and SMILES, J.: 1948. III. Phase-contrast microscopy in the study of fertilization and early development of the rat egg. *J. Roy. Micro. Soc.* 68:13.

BLANDAU, R. J.: 1945. The first maturation division of the rat ovum. *Anat. Rec.* 92:449.

BLOOM, W., and BLOOM, M. A.: 1940. Calcification and ossification. Calcification of developing bone in embryonic and newborn rats. *Anat. Rec.* 78:497.

BØE, F.: 1950. Studies on placental circulation in rats. I. Vascular pattern illustrated by experiments with indian ink. II. Vascular pattern illustrated by corrosion preparations. *Acta Endocrinol.* 5:356, 369.

Butcher, E. O.: 1929. The development of the somites in the white rat *(Mus norvegicus albinus)* and the fate of the myotomes, neural tube, and gut in the tail. *Am. J. Anat.* 44:381.

———: 1933. The development of striated muscle and tendon from the caudal myotomes in the albino rat, and the significance of myotomic-cell arrangement. *Am. J. Anat.* 53:177.

Canivenc, R.: 1956. Le placenta de rat et son activité endocrine. *Arch. D'Anat., D'Histol. et D'Embryol.* 39:1.

Dalcq, A. M.: 1951. New descriptive and experimental data concerning the mammalian egg, principally of the rat. IIA. The development of the rat from fertilization to the fifth day. K. Nederland Akad. Wetenschap. Amsterdam 54:364.

Frazer, J. F. D.: 1955. The site of implantation of ova in the rat. *J. Embryol. and Exp. Morphol.* 3:332.

Henneberg, B.: 1899. Die erste Entwickelung der Mammarorgane bei der Ratee. *Anat. Hefte* 13:1.

Huber, G. C.: 1915. *The Development of the Albino Rat, Mus norvegicus albinus.* Amer. Anat. Memoirs, No. 5. The Wistar Institute of Anatomy and Biology, Philadelphia, Pa.

———: 1915. The development of the albino rat from the end of the first to the tenth day after insemination. *Anat. Rec.* 9:84.

———: 1915. The development of the albino rat *(Mus norvegicus albinus).* I. From the pronuclear state to the stage of mesoderm anlage; end of the first to the end of the ninth day. II. Abnormal ova; end of the first to the end of the ninth day. *J. Morphol.* 26:247, 359.

Izquierda, L., and Vial, J. D.: 1962. Electron microscopic observations on the early development of the rat. *Zeitscht. f. Zellforschung* 56:157.

Kammeraad, A.: 1942. The development of the gastro-intestinal tract of the rat. I. Histogenesis of the epithelium of the stomach, small intestine and pancreas. *J. Morphol.* 70:323.

Odor, D. L., and Blandau, R. J.: 1951. Observations on fertilization and the first segmentation division in rat ova. *Am. J. Anat.* 89:29.

Stotsenburg, J. M.: 1915. The growth of the fetus of the albino rat from the thirteenth to the twenty-second day of gestation. *Anat. Rec.* 9:667.

Torrey, T. W.: 1943–1947. The development of the urinogenital system of the albino rat. I. The kidney and its ducts. II. The gonads. III. The urinogenital union. *Am. J. Anat.* 72:113, 1943; 76:375, 1945; 81:139, 1947.

Walander, A.: 1950. Prenatal development of the epithelial primordium of the larynx in rat. *Acta Anat.* Suppl. 13, 1.

GROWTH

Berg, B. N. and Harmison, C. R.: 1957. Growth, disease, and aging in the rat. *J. Gerontol.* 12:370.

Dunn, M. S., Murphy, E. A., and Rockland, L. B.: 1947. Optimal growth of the rat. *Physiol. Rev.* 27:72.

Ferry, E. L.: 1913. The rate of growth of the albino rat. *Anat. Rec.* 7:433.

Hanson, F. B., and Heys, F.: 1927. Differences in the growth curves of albino rats born during the four seasons of the year under uniform laboratory conditions. *Anat. Rec.* 35:83.

Jackson, C. M.: 1913. Postnatal growth and variability of the body and of the various organs in the albino rat. *Am. J. Anat.* 15:1.

———, and Lowery, L. G.: 1912. On the relative growth of the component parts (head, trunk, and extremities) and systems (skins, skeleton, musculature, and viscera) of the albino rat. *Anat. Rec.* 6:449.

King, H. D.: 1915. The growth and variability in the body weight of the albino rat. *Anat. Rec.* 9:751.

Lowery, L. G.: 1913. The growth of the dry substance in the albino rat. *Anat. Rec.* 7:143.

Slonaker, J. R.: 1912. The normal activity of the albino rat from birth to natural death, its rate of growth and the duration of life. *J. Anim. Behavior.* 2:20.

Stotsenburg, J. M.: 1913. The effect of spaying and semi-spaying young albino rats *(Mus norvegicus albinus)* on the growth in body weight and body length. *Anat. Rec.* 7:183.

Zucker, L., Hall, L., Young, M., and Zucker, T. F.: 1941. Animal growth and nutrition, with special reference to the rat. *Growth* 5:399.

BLOOD AND BONE MARROW

Aschkenasy, A.: 1946. La myélogramme du rat blanc adulte. *Le Sang Biologie et Pathologie.* 17:399.

Bruner, H. D., Van de Erve, J., and Carlson, A. J.: 1938. The blood picture of rats from birth to twenty-four days of age. *Am. J. Physiol.* 124:620.

Cameron, D. G., and Watson, G. M.: 1949. The blood counts of the adult albino rat. *Blood. J. Hematol.* 4:816.

Creskoff, A. J., Fitz-Hugh, T. Jr., and Farris, E. J.: 1949. Hematology of the Rat—Methods and Standards. In: *The Rat in Laboratory Investigation,* E. J. Farris and J. Q. Griffith, Editors, p. 406. J. B. Lippincott Co., Philadelphia, Pa.

Endicott, K. M., and Ott, M.: 1945. The normal myelogram in albino rats. *Anat. Rec.* 92:61.

Everitt, A. V., and Webb, C.: 1958. The blood picture of the aging male rat. *J. Gerontol.* 13:255.

Gardner, M. V.: 1947. The blood picture of normal laboratory animals. A review of the literature, 1936–1946. Notes from the Biochemical Research Foundation: Franklin Inst. 243:77.

Godwin, K. O., Fraser, F. J., and Ibbotson, R. N.: 1964. Haematological observations on healthy (SPF) rats. *Brit. J. Exp. Path.* 45:514.

Guzḿan, G.: 1946. Estudios sobre la medula huesosa. V. Tipos celulares y esquemas evolutivos en la medula de la rata blanca. *Bol. Inst. Estud. Med. y Biol.* 4:45.

Harris, C., and Burke, W. T.: 1957. The changing cellular distribution in bone marrow of the normal albino rat between one and fifty weeks of age. *Am. J. Path.* 33:931.

Jacobsen, E., and Plum, C. M.: 1942. Über die embryonale Produktion roter Blutkörperchen bei der Ratte. *Folia Haemat.* 66:164.

Kindred, J. E.: 1942. A quantitative study of the hemopoietic organs of young adult albino rats. *Am. J. Anat.* 71:207.

Kvetová, K.: 1959. Blood picture in rats during post-natal development. *Vet. Čas.* 8:170.

Lopes Netto, J., Soares de Almeida, S., and Penna de Carvalho Lima, L.: 1947. Mielograma do rato normal. *Riv. Inst. Adolfo Lutz* 7:41.

Ma, W-C.: 1936. Blood changes during intoxication and detoxication in the chronically morphinized rat. III. Changes in the blood forming cells of the bone marrow. *Chinese J. Physiol.* 16:599.

Plum, C. M.: 1943. Zur Granulocytopoiese bie Ratten. *Folia Haemat.* 67:119.

Ramsell, T. G., and Yoffey, J. M.: 1961. The bone marrow of the adult male rat. *Acta Anat.* 47:55.

Reich, C., and Dunning, W. F.: 1943. Studies on the morphology of the peripheral blood of rats. I. Normal rats. *Cancer Res.* 3:248.

Roux, M. G., Dessens, Mlle, and Dumas, J-C.: 1963. Sur la cytologie sanguine du rat blanc. *Ann. Pharmaceut. Franc.* 21:83.

Sacchetti, C., and Bianchini, E.: 1953. Ematologia del ratto bianco *Epymis norvegicus. Haemat. Arch.* 37:499.

Sbitneva, M. F., Kaliayeva, T. V. and Rudakov, I. A.: 1964. Pokazateli krovi, otpechatkov kostnoga mozga i selexenki belykh krys v norme. [Normal indices of the blood and of bone marrow and splenic imprints in albino rats.] [Biol. Abs. 46, 38105, 1964.] *Byul. Eksp. Biol. Med.* 57:112.

Scarborough, R. A.: 1930–1931. The blood picture of normal laboratory animals. The rat. *Yale J. Biol. and Med.* 3:267.

Schmidt-Reuter, F.: 1936. Cytologische Studien über die Susammensetzung des normalen Rattenblutes in verschieden Lebensaltern. *Folia Haemat.* 55:368.

Stasney, J., and Higgins, G. M.: 1935. A quantitative cytologic study of the bone marrow of the adult albino rat. *Anat. Rec.* 63:77.

Thewlis, E. W., and Meyer, O. O.: 1942. The blood count of normal white rats. *Anat. Rec.* 82:115.

Töppner, R.: 1942. Das Myelogramm der weissen Laboratoriums Ratte. *Folia Haemat.* 66:48.

Vogel, M.: 1947. The femoral bone marrow cells of the albino rat. *Am. J. Med. Sci.* 213:456.

CIRCULATORY SYSTEM

Braithwaite, J. L.: 1954. The morphology of the collateral circulation following complete interruption of the abdominal aorta in the rat. *J. Anat.* 88:204.

Franklin, K. J.: 1937. *A Monograph on Veins.* Charles C Thomas, Springfield, Ill.

Greene, E. C.: 1949. Circulatory System. In: *The Rat in Laboratory Investigation,* E. J. Farris and J. Q. Griffith, Editors, p. 41. J. B. Lippincott Co., Philadelphia, Pa.

Krames, B. B. and Van Liere, E. J.: 1966. The heart weight and ventricular weights of normal adult albino rats. *Anat. Rec.* 156:461.

Moore, D. H., and Ruska, H.: 1957. Electron microscope study of mammalian cardiac muscle cells. *J. Biophys. and Biochem. Cytol.* 3:261.

———, and Ruska, H.: 1957. The fine structure of capillaries and small arteries. *J. Biophys. and Biochem. Cytol.* 3:457.

Prakash, R.: 1954. The heart of the rat with special reference to the conducting system. *Am. Heart J.* 47:241.

———: 1956. The heart and its conducting system in albino rats. *Agra Univ. J. Research* 5:443.

Shanklin, W. M., and Azzam, N. A.: 1963. A study of valves in the arteries of the rodent brain. *Anat. Rec.* 147:407.

DIGESTIVE SYSTEM

Bertalanffy, F. D.: 1960. Mitotic rates and renewal times of the digestive tract epithelia in the rat. *Acta Anat.* 40:130.

Brogi, G., and Marini, G.: 1960. The daily karyokinetic biorhythm in the sheathing and glandular epithelia of various segments of the digestive tract in the albino rat. *Atti. Acad. Fisiocr. Siena [Medicofis]* 8:980.

Debeyre, A.: 1904. Développement du pancrèas chez le rat: bibliographie. Lille, Masson (in his *Les bourgeous pancreatiques accessories tardiffs),* p.15.

Fish, H. S., Malone, P. D., and Richter, C. P.: 1944. The anatomy of the tongue of the domestic Norway rat. I. The skin of the tongue; the various papillae; their number and distribution. *Anat. Rec.* 89:429.

———, and Richter, C. P.: 1946. Comparative numbers of fungiform and foliate papillae on tongues of domestic and wild Norway rats. *Proc. Soc. Exp. Biol. and Med.* 63:352.

Gadzhiyeva, Z. M.: 1957. Functional and morphological characteristics in the structure of the intestinal mucous membrane in rats. *Byul. Eksp. Biol. i Med.* 11:100.

Kent, J. F.: 1966. Distribution and fine structure of globule leucocytes in respiratory and digestive tracts of the laboratory rat. *Anat. Rec.* 156:439.

Kurtz, S. M.: 1954. Cytologic studies on the salivary glands of the rat in reference to the aging process. *J. Gerontol.* 9:421.

Lindholm, S.: 1960. The occurrence of connective tissue mast cells in the alimentary canal wall of hamster and rat. *Acta Path. Microbiol. Scand.* 48:328.

Martin, B. F.: 1956. The histochemical distribution of "lipase" in the alimentary tract and associated glands of laboratory animals. *J. Anat.* 90:440.

Nordberg, B. K.: 1946. Rotan ruoanswlatuksen tarkastelua. [Studies on the digestive system of the rat.] *Finsk Veterinärtidskrift* 52:173.

Zimmerman, G.: 1955. The omentum of the guinea pig and the rat. *Acta Vet. Hung.* 5:367.

ENDOCRINE SYSTEM

Borghese, E.: 1958. Histological investigations on some endocrine glands of the rat treated with 1-cycloesyl-3-tolylsulphyonylurea. *Monitore Zool. Ital.* 66:256.

Desclin, L.: 1952. Structure hypophysaire et activité thyroïdienne chez le rat. *Ann. D'Endocrinol.* 13:433.

Eisenberg, E., and Gordan, G. S.: 1950. The levator ani muscle of the rat as an index of myotrophic activity of steroidal hormones. *J. Pharm. and Exp. Therap.* 99:38.

Hall, A. R., and Kaan, H. W.: 1942. Anatomical and physiological studies on the thyroid gland of the albino rat. *Anat. Rec.* 84:221.

Hatai, S.: 1914. On the weight of some of the ductless glands of the Norway and of the albino rat according to sex and variety. *Anat. Rec.* 8:511.

Hayes, K. J.: 1965. The so-called "levator ani" of the rat. *Acta Endocrinol.* 48:337.

Hoskins, M. M., and Chandler, S. B.: 1925. Accessory parathyroids in the rat. *Anat. Rec.* 30:95.

Jayne, E. P.: 1953. Cytology of the adrenal gland of the rat at different ages. *Anat. Rec.* 115:459.

Libman, E.: 1953. Recherches histologiques et biometriques sur l'hypophyse de castration du rat male au cours du développement. *Arch. D'Anat. Microsc.* 42:281.

Meyer, R. K. and Hershberger, L. G.: 1957. Effects of testosterone administration on acid soluble and insoluble glycogen in the levator ani muscle. *Endocrinol.* 60:397.

Pauly, J. E.: 1957. Morphological observations on the adrenal cortex of the laboratory rat. *Endocrinol.* 60:247.

Phillips, J. B., and Püp, L. K.: 1957. A cytochemical study of pituitary glands of 1- to 15-day-old rats utilizing the aldehyde-fuchsin staining technique. *Anat. Rec.* 129:415.

Rosof, J. A.: 1934. An experimental study of the histology and cytology of the parathyroid glands in the albino rat. *J. Exp. Zool.* 68:121.

SANTUCCI, A.: 1955. Modifications histologiques des glandes endocrines par suite de l'administration d'histamine et extracts thyroidiens. *Compt. Rend. Assoc. Anat.* 41:1055.

VENABLE, J. H.: 1966. Morphology of the cells of normal, testosterone-deprived and testosterone-stimulated levator ani muscles. *Am. J. Anat.* 119:271.

FEMALE GENITAL SYSTEM

BOURG, R.: 1931. Recherches sur l'histophysiologie de l'ovaire, du testicule et des tractus genitaux du rat et de la souris. Folliculine et gravidine. *Arch. de Biol.* 41:245.

BURACK, E., WOLFE, J. M., LANSING, W., and WRIGHT, A. W.: 1941. The effect of age upon the connective tissue of the uterus, cervix, and vagina of the rat. *Cancer Res.* 1:227.

DEANE, H. W.: 1952. Histochemical observations on the ovary and oviduct of the albino rat during the estrous cycle. *Am. J. Anat.* 91:363.

DRAHN, F.: 1924. Der Weibliche Geschlechtsapparat von Kanninchen, Meerschweinchen, Ratte und Maus. In: *Biologie und Pathologie des Weiber.* I. Band, J. Halban, und L. Seitz, Editors. Urban und Schwarzenberger, Berlin.

KIRKHAM, W. B.: 1910. Ovulation in mammals, with special reference to the mouse and rat. *Biol. Bull.* 18:245.

———, and BURR, H. S.: 1913. The breeding habits, maturation of eggs and ovulation of albino rat. *Am. J. Anat.* 15:291.

MAHONEY, J. J.: 1940. The embryology and postnatal development of the prostate gland in the female rat. *Anat. Rec.* 77:375.

MYERS, J. A.: 1916–1919. Studies on the mammary gland. I. The growth and distribution of the milk ducts and the development of the nipple in the albino rat from birth to ten weeks of age. *Am. J. Anat.* 19:353, 1916; II. The fetal development of the mammary gland in the female albino rat. *Am. J. Anat.* 22:195, 1917; III. A comparison of the developing mammary glands in male and female albino rats from the late fetal stages to ten weeks of age. *Anat. Rec.* 13:205, 1917; IV. The histology of the mammary gland in the male and female albino rat from birth to ten weeks of age. *Am. J. Anat.* 25:395, 1919; V. The effects of inanition on the mammary gland in male and female albino rats from birth to ten weeks of age. *Am. J. Dis. Child.* 17:311, 1919; VI. The development of the mammary gland from its earliest appearance until the period of pregnancy. *Am. J. Dis. Child.* 18:4, 1919.

———, and MYERS, F. J.: 1921. Studies on the mammary gland. VII. The distribution of the subcutaneous fat and its relation to the developing mammary glands in male and female albino rats from birth to ten weeks of age. *Anat. Rec.* 22:353.

MYERS, F. J., and MEYERS, J. A.: 1921. Studies on the mammary gland. VIII. Gross changes in the mammary gland in the female albino rat during the period of involution (Abstract). *Anat. Rec.* 21:74.

PRICE, D.: 1939. Normal development and regression of the prostate gland of the female rat. *Proc. Soc. Exp. Biol. and Med.* 41:580.

ROBBOY, S. J., and KAHN, R. H.: 1962. A histochemical study of the rat reproductive system during the estrous cycle by starch gel zone electrophoresis. *Anat. Rec.* 142:272.

SOUDERS, H. J., and MORGAN, A. F.: 1957. Weight and composition of organs during the reproductive cycle in the rat. *Am. J. Physiol.* 191:1.

WOLFE, J. M., BURACK, E., LANSING, W., and WRIGHT, A. W.: 1942. The effects of advancing age on the connective tissue of the uterus, cervix and vagina of the rat. *Am. J. Anat.* 70:135.

MALE GENITAL SYSTEM

BEAUMONT, M., and MANDL, A. M.: 1963. A quantitative study of primordial germ cells in the male rat. *J. Embryol. and Exp. Morphol.* 11:715.

BROWN, H.: 1885. On spermatogenesis in the rat. *Quart. J. Micr. Sci.* 25:343.

BRANDES, D., GYORKEY, F., and GROTH, D.: 1962. Fine structural and histochemical study of the effect of castration on the rat prostatic complex. I. The coagulating gland. *Lab. Invest.* 11:339.

CLEGG, E. J.: 1959. Postnatal changes in the histology of the seminal vesicle and coagulating gland in the rat. *J. Anat.* 93:361.

———: 1966. Prepubertal growth in the Leydig cells and accessory reproductive organs of the rat. *J. Anat.* 100: 369.

DANGELO, J. G., and MUNGER, B. L.: 1964. The ultrastructure of the rat preputial gland. *J. Ultrastruct. Res.* 11:230.

DUESBERG, J.: 1909. La spermiogénèse chez le rat (*Mus decumanus* Pall., variété albinos). *Arch. f. Zellforschung* 2:137.

———: 1909. Note complémentaire sur la spermatogénèse du rat. *Arch. f. Zellforschung* 3:553.

HARKIN, J. C.: 1961. Ultrastructural alterations with age in prostatic epithelial cells of the rat. *Lab. Invest.* 10:696.

HUCKINS, C.: 1962. The formation and early development of the sex cords in the male albino rat (Abstract). *Anat. Rec.* 142:242.

LOEWENTHAL, N.: 1897. Note sur la structure fine des glandes de Cowper du rat blanc. *Bibliog. Anat.* 4:168.

MOORE, C. R., PRICE, D., and GALLAGHER, T. F.: 1930. Rat-prostate cytology as a testis-hormone indicator and the prevention of castration changes by testis-extract injections. *Am. J. Anat.* 45:71.

REID, B. L., and CLELAND, K. W.: 1957, 1959. The structure and function of the rat epididymis. I. The histology of the rat epididymis. II. The histogenesis of the rat epididymis. *Austral. J. Zool.* 5:223 and 7:22.

RISLEY, P. L., and SKREPETOS, C. N.: 1964. Histochemical distribution of cholinesterases in the testis, epididymis and vas deferens of the rat. *Anat. Rec.* 148:231.

ZAGARESE, R.: 1948. Considerazioni su alcuni rilievi istologici ed istochimici nell'apparato genitale maschile del ratto adulto normale. *Riv. Anat. Patol. e. Oncol.* 14:839.

INTEGUMENTARY SYSTEM

ABERCROMBIE, M., and JAMES, D. W.: 1957. Long-term changes in the size and collagen content of scars in the skin of rats. *J. Embryol. and Exp. Morphol.* 5:171.

ADDISON, W. H. F., and HOW, H. W.: 1921. The development of the eyelids of the albino rat, until the completion of disjunction. *Am. J. Anat.* 29:1.

ANDREW, W.: 1951. Age changes in the skin of Wistar Institute rats with particular reference to the epidermis. *Am. J. Anat.* 89:283.

BUTCHER, E. O:. 1934. The hair cycles in the albino rat. *Anat Rec.* 61:5.

CHASE, H. B.: 1954. Growth of hair. *Physiol. Rev.* 34:113.

DURWARD, A., and RUDALL, K. M.: 1949. Studies on hair growth in the rat. *J. Anat.* 83:325.

EBLING, F. J.: 1954. Changes in the sebaceous glands and epidermis during the estrous cycle of the albino rat. *J. Endocrin.* 10:147.

———, and HALE, P. A.: 1966. The composition of female rat skin in relation to region, age, hair growth cycle and hormones. *J. Endocrin.* 36:177.

ERICKSON, T. C.: 1931. The postnatal development of the caudal integument in the rat. *Am. J. Anat.* 47:173.

FRASER, D. A.: 1931. The winter pelage of the adult albino rat. *Am. J. Anat.* 47:55.

HASHIMOTO, K., and OGAWA, K.: 1963. Histochemical studies on the skin. I. The activity of phosphatases during the histogenesis of the skin in the rat. *Am. J. Anat.* 113:35.

———, OGAWA, K., and LEVER, W. F.: 1962. Histochemical studies on the skin. II. The activity of succinic, malic, and lactic dehydrogenase systems during the embryonic development of the skin in the rat. *J. Invest. Dermatol.* 39:21.

———, OGAWA, K., and LEVER, W. F.: 1963. Histochemical studies of the skin. III. The activity of the cholinesterases during the embryonic development of the skin in the rat. *J. Invest. Dermatol.* 40:15.

HAYASHI, H., and NAKAGAWA, T.: 1963. Functional activity of the sweat glands of the albino rat. *J. Invest. Dermatol.* 41:365.

HELLINGA, G.: 1946. Hair growth in rats. *Acta Brevia Neerland.* 14:83.

HOLMES, R. A.: 1960. The microscopic anatomy of the skin of *Mus norvegicus albinus.* M.S. thesis, Michigan State University, East Lansing.

JOHNSON, E.: 1958. Quantitative studies of hair growth in the albino rat. I. Normal males and females. *J. Endocrin.* 16:337.

MORETTI, G., GIACOMETTI, C., BOIDO, V., and REBORA, A.: 1963. Histamine, serotonin and mast cells in the skin of the rat during the hair cycle. *J. Invest. Dermatol.* 40:205.

RAEKALLIO, J., LINDFORS, R., ELFVING, G., HÄSTBACKA, J., and PUITTINEN, J.: 1964. Histochemical observations on wound healing in denervated and healthy rat skin. *Acta Path. et Micr. Scand.* 62:53.

RANDALL, P., and DUSHOFF, I. M.: 1956. Skin cycles in rodents. *Transplant. Bull.* 3:47.

SWEENY, P. R., PEARCE, R. H., and VANCE, H. G.: 1963. The chemical anatomy of rat skin. *Canad. J. Biochem. and Physiol.* 41:2307.

LYMPHATIC SYSTEM

ANDREW, W.: 1946. Age changes in the vascular architecture and cell content in the spleens of 100 Wistar Institute rats, including comparison with human material. *Am. J. Anat.* 79:1.

Braithwaite, J. L., and Adams, D. J.: 1956. Vascular compartments in the rat spleen. *Nature* 178:1178.

Higgins, G. M.: 1925. On the lymphatic system of the newborn rat *(Mus norvegicus albinus). Anat. Rec.* 30:243.

Hummel, K. P.: 1935. The structure and development of the lymphatic tissue in the intestine of the albino rat. *Am. J. Anat.* 57:351.

Job, T. T.: 1915. The adult anatomy of the lymphatic system in the common rat *(Epimys norvegicus). Anat. Rec.* 9:447.

———: 1918. Lymphatico-venous communications in the common rat and their significance. *Am. J. Anat.* 24:467.

Kindred, J. E.: 1938. A quantitative study of the lymphoid organs of the albino rat. *Am. J. Anat.* 62:453.

MUSCULAR SYSTEM

Long, M. E.: 1947. The development of the muscle-tendon attachment in the rat. *Am. J. Anat.* 81:159.

Lowry, O. H., and Hastings, A. B.: 1942. Histochemical changes associated with aging. I. Methods and calculations. *J. Biol. Chem.* 143:257.

———, Hastings, A. B., Hull, T. Z., and Brown, A. N.: 1942. Histochemical changes associated with aging. II. Skeletal and cardiac muscle in the rat. *J. Biol. Chem.* 143:271.

———, McCay, C. M., Hastings, A. B., and Brown, A. N.: 1942. Histochemical changes associated with aging. III. The effects of retardation of growth on skeletal muscle. *J. Biol. Chem.* 143:281.

NERVOUS SYSTEM

Andrew, W.: 1965. Structural alterations with aging in the nervous system. In: The Neurologic and Psychiatric Aspects of the Disorders of aging. *Res. Publ. Ass. Res. Nerv. Mental Dis.* 35:129.

Bosque, P. G.: 1955. Anatomia comparada del sistema nervioso vegetativo. El "truncus sympathicus" y los ganglios prevertebrales de los mamiferos roedores. *Arch. Español Morfol.* 12:131.

Craigie, E. H.: 1920. On the relative vascularity of various parts of the central nervous system of the albino rat. *J. Comp Neurol.* 31:429.

———: 1925. *An Introduction to the Finer Anatomy of the Central Nervous System Based Upon That of Albino Rat.* Blakiston's Son and Co., Philadelphia, Pa.

Donaldson, H. H.: 1908. A comparison of the albino rat with man in respect to the growth of the brain and of the spinal cord. *J. Comp. Neurol. and Psychol.* 18:345.

———: 1909. On the relation of the body length to the body weight and to the weight of the brain and of the spinal cord in the albino rat *(Mus norvegicus* var. *albus). J. Comp. Neurol. and Psychol.* 19:155.

———: 1910. On the percentage of water in the brain and in the spinal cord of the albino rat. *J. Comp. Neurol. and Psychol.* 20:119.

———: 1911. On the influence of exercise on the weight of the central nervous system of the albino rat. *J. Comp. Neurol.* 21:129.

———: 1912. A comparison of the European Norway and Albino rats *(Mus norvegicus* and *Mus norvegicus albinus)* with those of North America in respect to the weight of the central nervous system and to cranial capacity. *J. Comp. Neurol.* 22:71.

———: 1918. A comparison of growth changes in the nervous system of the rat with corresponding changes in the nervous system of man. *Proc. Nat. Acad. Sci.,* U.S. 4:280.

———, and Hatai, S.: 1911. A comparison of the Norway rat with the albino rat in respect to body length, brain weight, spinal cord weight and the percentage of water in both the brain and the spinal cord. *J. Comp. Neurol.* 21:417.

Hatai, S.: 1909. A comparison of the albino with the gray rats in respect to the weight of the brain and spinal cord. *Anat. Rec.* 3:245.

Hamilton, A.: 1901. The division of differentiated cells in the central nervous system of the white rat. *J. Comp. Neurol.* 11:297.

Hammett, F. S.: 1926. Correlations and variability of the central nervous system and body size of the albino rat. *Biol. Bull.* 50:509.

Herrick, C. J.: 1926. *Brains of Rats and Men: A Survey of the Original and Biological Significance of the Cerebral Cortex.* University of Chicago Press, Chicago.

Koenig, J. F. R., and Klippel, R. A.: 1963. *The Rat Brain.* Williams & Wilkins, Baltimore, Md.

Krieg, W. J. S.: 1955. *Brain Mechanisms in Diachrome.* Pantagraph Printing Co., Bloomington, Ill.

Kuhlenbeck, H.: 1954. Some histologic age changes in the rat's brain and their relation-

ship to comparable changes in the human brain. *Confin. Neurol.* 14:329.
RILEY, H. A.: 1960. *An Atlas of the Basal Ganglia, Brain Stem and Spinal Cord Based on Myelin-stained Material.* Rev., Hafner Publishing Co., New York.
WINDLE, W. F., and BAXTER, R. E.: 1936. Development of reflex mechanisms in the spinal cord of the albino rat embryos. Correlations between structure and function, and comparisons with the cat and the chick. *J. Comp. Neurol.* 63:189.
ZEMAN, W., and INNES, J. R. M.: 1963. *Craigie's Neuroanatomy of the Rat.* Academic Press, New York.

RESPIRATORY SYSTEM

BANG, B. G., and BANG, F. B.: 1959. A comparative study of the vertebrate nasal chamber in relation to upper respiratory infections. I. Comparative morphology of the nasal chambers of three commonly used laboratory animals: chicken, rat and ferret. II. Adaptive variation in relation to defense against disease. *Bull. Johns Hopkins Hosp.* 104:107,125.
GLAS, E.: 1904. Über die Entwickelung und Morphologie der innern Nase der Ratte. *Anat. Hefte.* 25:275.
KELEMEN, G.: 1947. The junction of the nasal cavity and the pharyngeal tube in the rat. *Arch. Otolaryngol.* 45:159.
———: 1962. Histology of the nasal and paranasal cavities of germfree-reared and ex-germfree rats. *Acta Anat.* 48:108.
KENT, J. F.: 1966. Distribution and fine structure of globule leucocytes in respiratory and digestive tracts of the laboratory rat. *Anat. Rec.* 156:439.
KLAVINS, J. V.: 1963. Demonstration of striated muscle in the pulmonary veins of the rat. *J. Anat.* 97:239.
RHODIN, J.: 1959. Ultrastructure of the tracheal ciliated mucosa in rat and man. *Annals of Otol., Rhin., and Laryng.* 68:964.
———, and DALHMAN, T.: 1955. Electron microscopy of collagen and elastin in the lamina propria of the tracheal mucosa of rat. *Exp. Cell Res.* 9:371.
ROGERS, W. M.: 1929. The development of the pharynx and the pharyngeal derivatives in the white rat *(Mus norvegicus albinus). Am. J. Anat.* 44:283.
TENNEY, S. M., and REMMERS, J. E.: 1963. Comparative quantitative morphology of the mammalian lung; Diffusion area. *Nature* 197:54.

SKELETAL SYSTEM

ACHESON, R. M., MACINTYRE, M. N., and OLDHAM, E.: 1959. Techniques in longitudinal studies of the skeletal development of the rat. *Brit. J. Nutr.* 13:283.
BECKS, H., and EVANS, H. M.: 1953. *Atlas of the Skeletal Development of the Rat (Long-Evans strain), Normal and Hypophysectomized.* Am. Inst. of Dental Med. (now, Am. Inst. of Oral Biology), Berkeley, Calif.
BROOKES, M.: 1958. The vascular architecture of tubular bone in the rat. *Anat. Rec.* 132:25.
DAWSON, A. B.: 1925. The age order of epiphyseal union in the long bones of the albino rat. *Anat. Rec.* 31:1.
DONALDSON, H. H., and CONROW, S. B.: 1919. Quantitative studies on the growth of the skeleton of the albino rat. *Am. J. Anat.* 26:237.
HATAI, S.: 1907. Studies on the variation and correlation of skull measurements in both sexes of mature albino rats *(Mus norvegicus* var. *albus). Am. J. Anat.* 7:423.
HARRISON, T. J.: 1958. The growth of the pelvis in the rat—a mensural and morphological study. *J. Anat.* 92:236.
LEBLOND, C. P., WILKINSON, G. W., BÉLANGER, L. F., and ROBICHON, J.: 1950. Radioautographic visualization of bone formation in the rat. *Am. J. Anat.* 86:289.
MOSS, M. L.: 1954. Growth of the calvaria in the rat: The determination of osseous morphology. *Am. J. Anat.* 94:333.
OUTHOUSE, J., and MENDEL, L. B.: 1933. The rate of growth. I. Its influence on the skeletal development of the albino rat. *J. Exp. Zool.* 64:257.
PRITCHARD, J. J.: 1952. A cytological and histochemical study of bone and cartilage formation in the rat. *J. Anat.* 86:259.
STRONG, R. M.: 1925. The order, time and rate of ossification of the albino rat *(Mus norvegicus albinus)* skeleton. *Am. J. Anat.* 36:313.
WALKER, D. G., and WIRTSCHAFTER, Z. T.: 1957. *The Genesis of the Rat Skeleton: A Laboratory Atlas.* Charles C Thomas, Springfield, Ill.
WARNOCK, G. M., and DUCKWORTH, J.: 1944. Changes in the skeleton during gestation and lactation in the rat. *Biochem. J.* 38:220.
WEIKEL, J. H., BONNER, J. F., and NEUMAN, W. F.:

1955. Skeletal growth of the rat. *Proc. Soc. Exp. Biol. and Med.* 88:122.

ZUCKER, T. F., and ZUCKER, L. M.: 1946. Bone growth in the rat as related to age and body weight. *Am. J. Physiol.* 146: 585.

SPECIAL SENSE ORGANS

LUCAS, D. R., and TROWELL, O. A.: 1958. *In vitro* culture of the eye and the retina of the mouse and rat. *J. Embryol. and Exp. Morphol.* 6:178.

NORRBY, A.: 1958. On the growth of the crystalline lens, the eyeball and the cornea in the rat. *Acta Ophthal. Suppl.* 49:1.

VENABLE, J. H., and GRAFFLIN, A. L.: 1940. Gross anatomy of the orbital glands in the albino rat. *J. Mammalogy* 21:66.

WADA, T.: 1923. *Anatomical and Physiological Studies on the Growth of the Inner Ear of the Albino Rat.* The Wistar Institute of Anatomy and Biology, Philadelphia, Pa.

URINARY SYSTEM

ANDREW, W., and PRUETT, D.: 1957. Senile changes in the kidneys of Wistar Institute rats. *Am. J. Anat.* 100:51.

ARATAKI, M.: 1926. On the postnatal growth of the kidney, with special reference to the number and size of the glomeruli (albino rat). *Am. J. Anat.* 36:399.

BARAJAS, L., and LATTA, H.: 1963. A three-dimensional study of the juxtaglomerular apparatus in the rat—Light and electron microscopic observations. *Lab. Invest.* 12:257.

BAXTER, J. S., and YOFFEY, J. M.: 1948. The postnatal development of renal tubules in the rat. *J. Anat.* 82:189.

KITTELSON, J. A.: 1917. The postnatal growth of the kidney of the albino rat, with observations on an adult kidney. *Anat. Rec.* 13:385.

LATTA, H., MAUNSBACH, A. B., and MADDEN, S. C.: 1961. Cilia in different segments of the rat nephron. *J. Biophys. Biochem. Cytol.* 11:248.

TORREY, T. W.: 1943. The development of the urinogenital system of the albino rat. I. The kidney and its ducts. *Am. J. Anat.* 72:113.

YOUNG, D., and WISSIG, S. L.: 1964. A histologic description of certain epithelial and vascular structures in the kidney of the normal rat. *Am. J. Anat.* 115:43.

INDEX

Acini
  mucous, 89
  serous, 89, 91
Abdominal wall, 55
Adipose tissue, 55, 83
Adrenal gland
  capsule, 153
  cortex, 153
  medulla, 153
Alpha cells, 93
Alveolar bone, 65
Ameloblasts, 65
Anal canal, 87
Anal sphincter, 87
Anorectal junction, 87
Anus
  anal canal, 87
  anorectal junction, 87
  anal sphincter, 87
  circumanal glands, 87
  epithelium, 87
Aorta
  ascending, 35, 39
  descending, 35
Arrector pili muscle, 55
Arteries
  aorta, 35
  arterioles, 47
  brachial, 37
  carotid, 39
  common iliac, 41
  conducting, 35, 39
  distributing, 37, 41, 43
  external elastic membrane, 37, 43
  femoral, 37
  hepatic, 91
  internal elastic membrane, 35, 37, 41
  muscular, 37, 41, 43
  pulmonary, 101
  spermatic, 43
  tunica adventitia, 35, 39, 41, 43
  tunica intima, 35, 37
  tunica media, 35, 37, 39, 41, 43
Arteriole, 47, 137
Articulations, 21

Basement membrane, 53, 123
Beta cells, 93
Blood-vascular system, 27–45
Bone
  alveolar, 65
  calcification, 15
  canaliculi, 21
  cancellous, 23
  cement line, 19, 21
  development, 15, 17, 23
  endosteum, 19
  epiphysis, 15
  Haversian canal, 21
  Haversian system, 21
  lacunae, 17, 21
  lamellar, 17, 21
  marrow, 15, 17, 23
  osteoblasts, 17,
  osteoclasts, 17
  osteocytes, 17, 21
  perichondrium, 15
  periosteum, 15, 19, 23
  trabecular, 15, 17
Bowman's capsule
  kidney, 105, 107
  parietal layer, 105
  visceral layer, 105
Bowman's membrane, 169
Brain
  cerebellum, 159, 161

Brain *(Continued)*
  cerebrum, 157, 159
  choroid plexuses, 161
  pia-arachnoid, 159
Bronchi
  primary, 101
  secondary, 101
Bronchiole
  respiratory, 101
  terminal, 101
Buccal mucosa, glands, 63
Bulbourethral gland, duct, 117, 119

Canaliculi, 21
Capillaries, 21, 39
Cardiac muscle, fibers, 29, 31
Carotid artery, body, 39
Cartilage
  elastic, 55, 71
  hyaline, 15, 31, 91, 97, 99
Cauda equina, 163
Cecum, 83, 85
Cells
  alpha, 93
  basal, 99
  beta, 93
  blood, 45
  centro-acinar, 93
  chief, parathyroid, 149
  chief, stomach, 77
  ganglion, 153, 165, 167
  goblet, 79, 81, 83, 85
  granule, zymogen, 93
  granulosa, 135
  Küpffer, 91
  of Leydig, 123
  neuroepithelial, 67
  neuroglial, 165
  Paneth, 79, 81
  parietal, 77
  Purkinje, 159, 161
  pyramidal, 159
  reticulo-endothelial, 47, 49, 91
  Sertoli, 123
  theca, 135
Cementum, tooth, 65
  cementocytes, 65
Centro-acinar cells, 93
Cerebellum
  cortex, 159, 161
  granular layer, 159, 161
  gray matter, 159, 161
  molecular layer, 159, 161
  pia mater, 159
  Purkinje cell layer, 159, 161
  white matter, 159, 161
Cerebrum
  cortex, 157, 159
  pia mater, 159
  pyramidal cells, 159
Chief cells
  parathyroid, 149
  stomach, 77
Choroid, eye, 169, 173
Choroid plexuses, 161

Ciliary process, 171
Circulatory system, 27–45
Circumanal glands, 87
Clitoris, 143
Coagulating gland, 113, 117
Colloid, thyroid gland, 149
Colon
  crypt of Lieberkühn, 85
  taenia coli, 85
Connective tissue
  adipose, 55, 83
  elastic, 35, 39
  loose, 91
  reticular, 89, 91
  white fibrous (collagenous), 25, 31, 59
Convoluted tubules, kidney, 105, 107
  distal, 105, 107
  proximal, 105, 107
Cornea
  Bowman's membrane, 169, 171
  Descemet's membrane, 169
  epithelium, 169
  substantia propria, 169
Corona radiata, 133
Coronary vein, 43
Corpus luteum, 137
Crypts of Lieberkühn, 79, 81, 83, 85

Dentin, 65
Dermis, 53, 55
Digestive system, 67–93
Distal convoluted tubules, 105, 107
Ductuli efferentes, testes, 125
Ductus deferens, 113, 121
Duodenum, 79

Enamel, teeth, 65
  ameloblasts, 65
Endocardium, 29, 31
Endocrine system, 145–53
Endometrium, 137
Endosteum, 19
Epidermis
  stratum basale, 53, 55
  stratum corneum, 53
  stratum granulosum, 53
  stratum spinosum, 53
Epididymis, 121, 123, 125
Epiglottis, 71
Epiphysis, 15
Epithelium
  ciliated 99, 121, 137
  columnar, 77, 79, 83, 85, 115, 117, 121, 139
  cuboidal, 89, 91, 115, 135, 149, 161
  endothelium, 35, 37, 39, 41, 49
  glandular, 89, 91
  mesenchymal, 169, 173
  mesothelium, 91
  pseudostratified, 63, 97, 99, 125
  stratified columnar, 109
  stratified squamous, 53, 59, 63, 65, 69, 71, 75, 77, 124, 141, 169
  surface modifications, 99, 107, 125
  transitional, 107, 109, 119, 143
Epoöphoron, 135

Esophagus, 71, 75
Eye, 169–73
Eyelid
  meibomian gland, 59
  nictitating membrane, 59
  orbicularis oculi muscle, 59
  palpebral conjunctiva, 59
External elastic membrane, 37, 43

Fimbria, 131, 137
Follicle
  hair, 55, 57
  ovary, 131, 133
  primary, 133
  secondary, 57, 133, 135
  thyroid, 149
Ganglion cells
  atrial wall, 31
  dorsal root, 163, 167
  sympathetic, 167
Gastric glands, stomach, 77
Gastric pits, stomach, 77
Gingiva, 65
Glands
  adrenal, 153
  buccal, 63
  bulbourethral, 117, 119
  circumanal, 87
  coagulating, 113, 117
  gastric, 77
  lacrimal (exorbital), 91
  parathyroid, 149
  pituitary, 147
  preputial, 127, 143
  pyloric, 77
  salivary, 89, 91
  sebaceous, 55, 57, 63
  sweat, 53
  tarsal, 59
  thymus, 149, 151
  thyroid, 149
  trachea, 97, 99
  urethral, 109
  uterine horn, 139
Glomerular capsule, kidney, 105, 107
Glomerulus, kidney, 105
Gray matter
  cerebellum, 159, 161
  cerebrum, 157, 159
  spinal cord, 163

Hair
  cortex, 57
  cuticle, 57
  follicle, 55, 57, 63
  inner root sheath, 57
  outer root sheath, 57
  sebaceous glands, 55, 57
  shaft, 57
Hard palate, 63
Hassall's corpuscle, 149, 151
Haversian canal, system, 21
Heart
  conduction system, 31
  endocardium, 29, 31
  myocardium, 29, 31, 43
  Purkinje fibers, 31
  trigonum fibrosum, 31
Hyaline cartilage, 15, 31, 97

Ileocecal junction, 83
Ileum
  crypts of Lieberkühn, 81, 83
  epithelium, 81, 83
  ileocecal junction, 83
  Peyer's patches, 81
Infundibulum, 131, 137
Integumentary system, 51–59
Interstitial cells, testis, 123
Iris
  anterior border layer, 173
  epithelium, 173
  vessel layer, 173
Islands of Langerhans, 93

Joints, synovial membrane, 21
Juxta-glomerular apparatus, kidney, 105

Keratohyalin granules, 53
Kidney
  Bowman's capsule, 105, 107
  capsule, 105
  cortex, 105
  distal convoluted tubule, 105, 107
  glomerular capsule, 105
  glomerulus, 105
  junction kidney pelvis and ureter, 107
  juxta-glomerular apparatus, 105
  macula densa, 105
  proximal convoluted tubule, 105, 107
  uriniferous tubules, 105
Küpffer cells, liver, 91

Lacrimal gland (exorbital), 91
Lacunae, bone, 17, 21
Lamellae, bone, 17, 21
Large intestine
  colon, 85
  rectum, 87
  anal canal, 87
Larynx
  cartilages, 70
  epiglottis, 71
Lens
  elastic capsule, 171, 173
  epithelium, 173
  fibers, 173
Leucocytes, granular, 45
  basophil, 45
  eosinophil, 45
  neutrophil, 45
Leucocytes, nongranular, 45
  lymphocytes, 45
  monocytes, 45
Leydig, cells of, 123
Liver
  central vein, 91, 93
  hepatic artery, 91
  hepatic cells, 91, 93
  Küpffer cells, 91

Liver *(Continued)*
lymphatic, 91
parenchyma, 91
portal area, 91
portal vein, 91
reticular fibers, 93
sinusoids, 91
Lungs
alveolar ducts, 101
pulmonary alveoli, 101
visceral pleura, 101
Lymph node
capsule, 47
cords, 47
cortex, 47
cortical nodules, 47
germinal center, 47
hilum, 47
lymphatic vessel, 47
medulla, 47
primary nodules, 47
reticulo-endothelial cells, 47
sinuses, 47
Lymphatic vessels, 37, 43, 47
Lymphoid organs
lymph node, 47
spleen, 49
thymus, 149, 151

Macula densa, kidney, 105
Medulla, adrenal, 153
lymph node, 47
ovary, 137
thymus, 149, 151
Megakaryocytes, spleen, 49
Meibomian gland (tarsal gland), 59
Metacarpal pad
dermis, 53
epidermis, 53
sweat glands, 53
Microvilli, 107
Mouth
glands, 63
hard palate, 63
lips, 63
soft palate, 63, 69, 71
teeth, 65
tongue, 67
Muscle
arrector pili, 55
cardiac, 29, 31
skeletal, 15, 23, 25, 57, 63, 67, 75
smooth, 35, 85
Muscle spindle, 25
Muscular arteries, 37, 41, 43
Musculo-skeletal system, 13–25
Myocardium, 29, 31, 43
Myometrium, 137

Nasal cavity
nasolacrimal duct, 97
olfactory region, 97
respiratory region, 97
turbinates, 97
vestibular region, 69, 97
vomeronasal organ, 97
Nervous system, 155–67
Neuroglia cells, 165
Neurohypophysis, pituicytes, 147
Nictitating membrane, 171

Odontoblasts, 65
Olfactory, 97, 157
bulb, 157
mucosa, 97, 157
nerve, 157
Oöcyte, 133, 135
Oögenesis, 133
Oral cavity, 61, 63, 67, 69, 71
Oropharynx, 71
Os penis, 127
Osseous tissue, 15–23
Osteoblasts, 17
Osteoclasts, 17
Osteocytes, 17
Ovarian bursa, 131, 137
Ovarian follicles, 131, 133
Ovary
antrum, 131, 135
bursa, 131, 137
corpus luteum, 137
cortex, 131
epoöphoron, 135
follicles, 131, 133
medulla, 131
oögenesis, 133
rete ovarii, 131
surface epithelium, 133
theca externa, 135
theca interna, 135
tunica albuginea, 135
vestigial structures, 135
Oviduct
ampulla, 131, 137
epithelium, 137
fimbria, 131, 137
infundibulum, 131, 137
isthmus, 131
muscularis, 137

Palpebral conjunctiva, 59
Pancreas
acini, 93
blood supply, 93
centro-acinar cells, 93
intralobular pancreatic duct, 93
islands of Langerhans, 93
Panniculus adiposus, 55
Papilla, tongue, 67
circumvallate, 67, 69
filiform, 67
foliate, 67
fungiform, 67
Parathyroid gland, chief cells, 149
Parotid gland, 89, 91
Penis
corpus cavernosum, 127
epithelium, 127
os penis, 127
prepuce, 127

Perichondrium, 15, 97, 99
Perimetrium, 139
Periodontal membrane, 65
Periosteum, 15, 19
Peyer's patches, 81
Pharynx, 71
Pia-arachnoid, 159
Pia mater
  cerebellum, 159
  cerebrum, 159
  spinal cord, 163
Pinna
  dermis, 55
  elastic cartilage, 55
  epidermis, 55
Pituitary gland
  pars anterior, 147
  pars intermedia, 147
  pars nervosa, 147
Platelets, 45
Prepuce
  parietal layer, 127
  visceral layer, 127
Preputial gland 127, 143
Primary follicles, 133
Prostate gland, epithelium, 113, 115, 121
Proximal convoluted tubules, 105, 107
Pulmonary alveolae, 101
Pulp
  dental, 65
  splenic, 49
Purkinje
  cells, 159, 161
  fibers, 31
Pyramidal cell, 159

Rectum, 87
Renal pelvis, 107
Reproductive systems, 111–43
Respiratory system, 95–101
Rete ovarii, 131, 135
Reticular fibers
  liver, 93
  sublingual salivary gland, 89
Reticulo-endothelial cells
  lymph node, 47
  spleen, 49
Retina, layers, 173

Salivary gland
  ducts, 89, 91
  parotid, 89, 91
  sublingual, 89
  submaxillary, 89
Sclera, 169, 173
Sebaceous gland, skin, 55, 57, 63
  meibomian, 57
  preputial gland, 127
Sebum, 57
Seminal vesicle, 113, 115
Seminiferous tubule
  primary spermatocytes, 123
  secondary spermatocytes, 123
  Sertoli cells, 123
Sertoli cells, 123
Skeletal muscle, 15, 23, 25, 57, 63, 75
Skin
  dermis, 53, 55, 57
  epidermis, 53, 55
  keratohyalin, 53
  panniculus adiposus, 55
  sebaceous glands, 55, 57, 63
  sweat glands, 53
Small intestine
  crypts of Lieberkühn, 79, 81, 83
  duodenum, 79
  ileum, 81, 83
  jejunum, 81
  villi, 79, 81, 83
Smooth muscle, 35, 85
Soft palate, 63, 69, 71
Spermatogenesis, 123
Spinal cord
  cauda equina, 163
  central canal, 163
  cervical, 163, 165
  dorsal horn, 163
  dura mater, 163
  lumbar, 163
  neuroglial cells, 165
  pia mater, 163
  thoracic, 163
  ventral horn, 163, 165
Spinal nerves, 163
Spleen
  capsule, 49
  germinal center, 49
  megakaryocytes, 49
  pulp, 49
  reticulo-endothelial cells, 49
  sinusoids, 49
  splenic corpuscles, 49
Splenic corpuscles, 49
Stomach
  fundic region, 77
  nonglandular region, 77
  pyloric region, 77, 79
Stratum basale, 53, 141
Stratum corneum, 53, 141
Stratum granulosum, 53
Stratum spinosum, 54
Sublingual gland, 89
Submaxillary gland, 89
Sweat glands, 53
Synovial membrane, 21

Taenia coli, 85
Tail, 53
Taste buds, 67, 69
Teat, 55
Teeth
  ameloblasts, 65
  cementum, 65
  dentin, 65
  enamel, 65
  odontoblasts, 65
  periodontal membrane, 65
  pulp, 65, 97
  root, 65
Tendon-muscle junction, 25

Testis
  interstitial cells (cells of Leydig), 121, 123
  seminiferous tubules, 121
  tunica albuginea, 123, 125
  tunica vaginalis parietalis, 121
Thymus
  capsule, 149, 151
  cortex, 149, 151
  Hassall's corpuscle, 149, 151
  lymphocytes, 149, 151
  medulla, 149, 151
Thyroid gland
  colloid, 149
  follicles, 149
Tongue
  glands, 67, 69
  laminal propria, 67
  muscles, 67
  papillae, 67, 69
  taste buds, 67
Trachea
  cartilage, 97, 99
  epithelium, 97, 99
  glands, 97, 99
  mucosa, 97, 99
  muscle, 97, 99
  perichondrium, 97, 99
Tunica albuginea
  ovary, 135
  testis, 123, 125
  vaginalis parietalis, 121

Ureter
  epithelium, 107, 113
  muscularis, 107
Urethra
  female, 143
  male, 109, 113, 127
Urinary bladder
  epithelium, 109, 113
  lamina propria, 109
  mucosal gland, 109
Urinary system, 103–109
Urogenital system
  female, 129–43
  male, 111–27
Uterine horn
  endometrium, 139
  epithelium, 139
  glands, 139
  myometrium, 139

Vagina
  epithelium, 141
  fibrosa, 141
  mucosa, 141
  orifice, 143
Veins
  central, liver, 91
  common iliac, 41
  coronary, 43
  femoral, 37
  portal, liver, 91
  posterior vena cava, 39
  pulmonary, 101
  spermatic, 43
  tunica adventitia, 37, 39, 41, 43
  tunica media, 37, 39, 41, 43
Vomeronasal organ, 97

White blood cells, 45
White matter
  brain, 157, 159, 161
  spinal cord, 163

Zona fasciculata, 153
Zona glomerulosa, 153
Zona pellucida, 133, 135
Zona reticularis, 153